Year 6 Practice Book 6B

Draw your favourite animal.

How much do you think it weighs in kg?

This book belongs to ______________________________.

My class is ______________________________.

Contents

This looks like a good challenge!

It is time to do some practice!

How to use this book

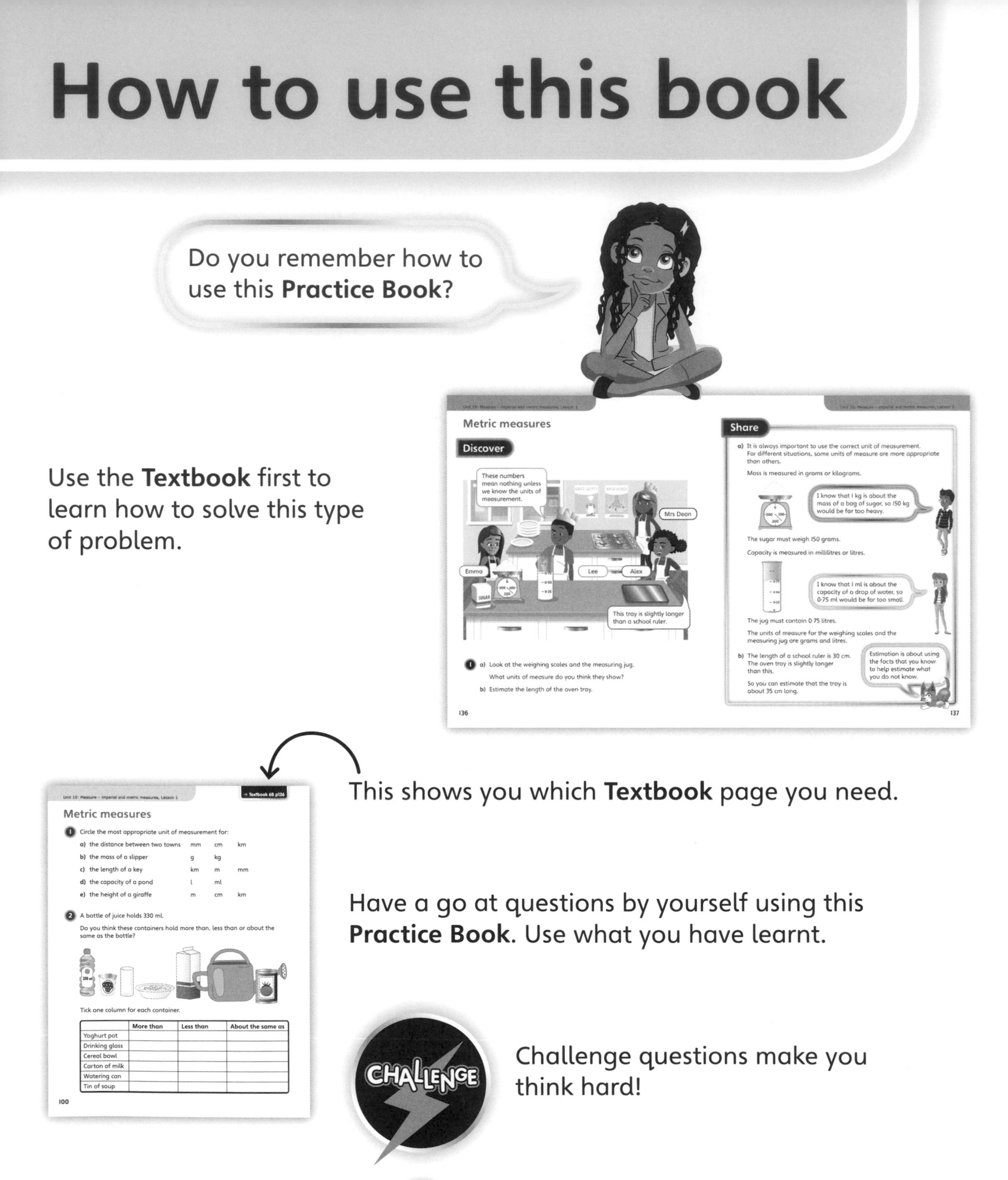

Use the **Textbook** first to learn how to solve this type of problem.

This shows you which **Textbook** page you need.

Have a go at questions by yourself using this **Practice Book**. Use what you have learnt.

Challenge questions make you think hard!

Questions with this light bulb make you think differently.

Reflect

Each lesson ends with a **Reflect** question so you can think about what you have learnt.

Reflect

Look carefully at this shopping list:

1,000 ml milk
0·25 kg flour
$\frac{1}{2}$ m shoelaces

Do you think that the most appropriate units of measurement have been used for each item? Explain your answer.

Use **My power points** at the back of this book to keep track of what you have learnt.

My journal

At the end of a unit your teacher will ask you to fill in **My journal**.

This will help you show how much you can do now that you have finished the unit.

→ Textbook 6B p156

End of unit check

My journal

1. The children have each made a mistake. Find each mistake and then give the correct answer.

a) Lexi: 650 millilitres is the same as 4·5 litres.

The mistake is ______

The correct answer is ______

b) Max: The difference between 250 g and 1 kg is 249 g.

The mistake is ______

The correct answer is ______

c) Kate: 1 mile is about 1·6 km, so 2 miles are about 2·12 km.

The mistake is ______

The correct answer is ______

Power check

How do you feel about your work in this unit?

Power puzzle

The answer to each of these conversions is linked to a letter.

The letters spell out things people can eat. Crack the code to find out what they are. Be careful – the item in part b) is two words!

KEY:

56,000	5,600	470	39	2·1	0·21	0·47
P	L	S	I	E	T	A

a)

	Number	Letter
56 km = ? m		
470 g = ? kg		
47 cm = ? mm		
210 g = ? kg		
390 mm = ? cm		
2,100 ml = ? l		
0·47 l = ? ml		

b)

	Number	Letter
47 cm = ? m		
56 kg = ? g		
560 m = ? cm		
5·6 kg = ? g		
0·21 cm = ? mm		
56 l = ? ml		
3,900 cm = ? m		
2,100 g = ? kg		

Now invent your own conversion code for your partner to crack!

You could use imperial and metric conversions.

→ Textbook 6B p8

Multiplying by 10, 100 and 1,000

1 Draw counters to show each number multiplied by 10.

a)

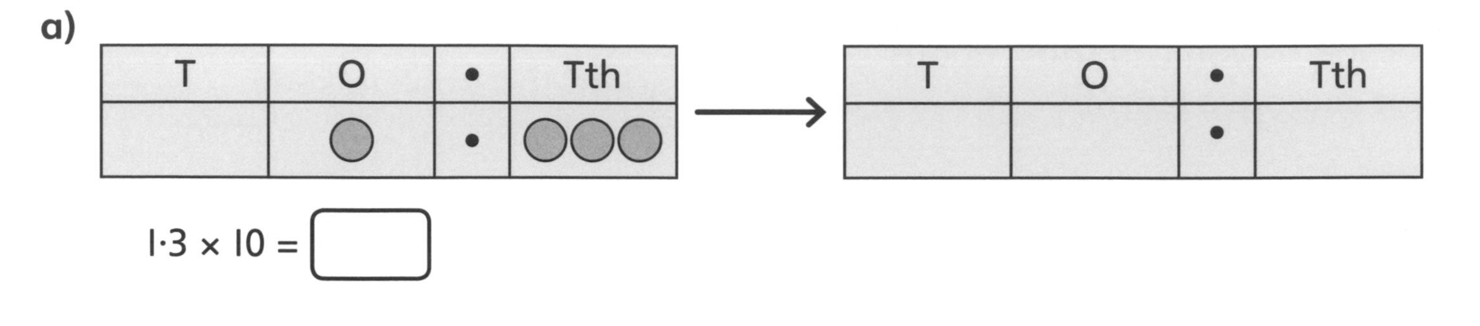

T	O	•	Tth
	●	•	●●●

→

T	O	•	Tth
		•	

$1{\cdot}3 \times 10 =$ ☐

b)

T	O	•	Tth	Hth
	●●●	•		●●●

→

T	O	•	Tth
		•	

$3{\cdot}03 \times 10 =$ ☐

2 a) Which of these represents the answer to 10·08 multiplied by 100? Tick your answer.

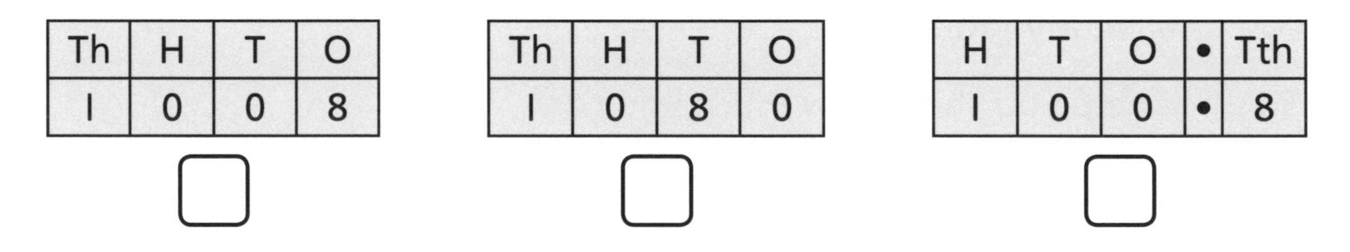

Th	H	T	O
1	0	0	8

☐

Th	H	T	O
1	0	8	0

☐

H	T	O	•	Tth
1	0	0	•	8

☐

b) Which of these represents the answer to 8·103 multiplied by 1,000? Tick your answer.

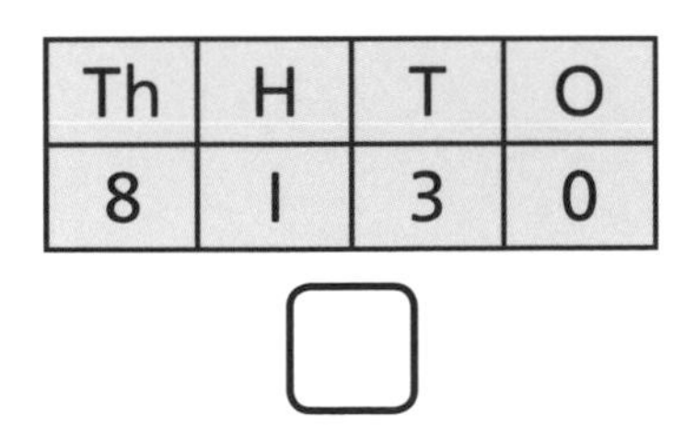

Th	H	T	O
8	1	3	0

☐

Th	H	T	O
8	1	0	3

☐

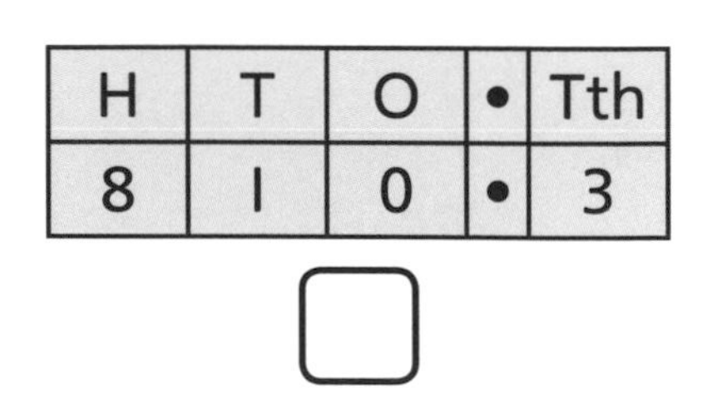

H	T	O	•	Tth
8	1	0	•	3

☐

c) What is 0·012 multiplied by 1,000?

$0{\cdot}012 \times 1{,}000 =$ ☐

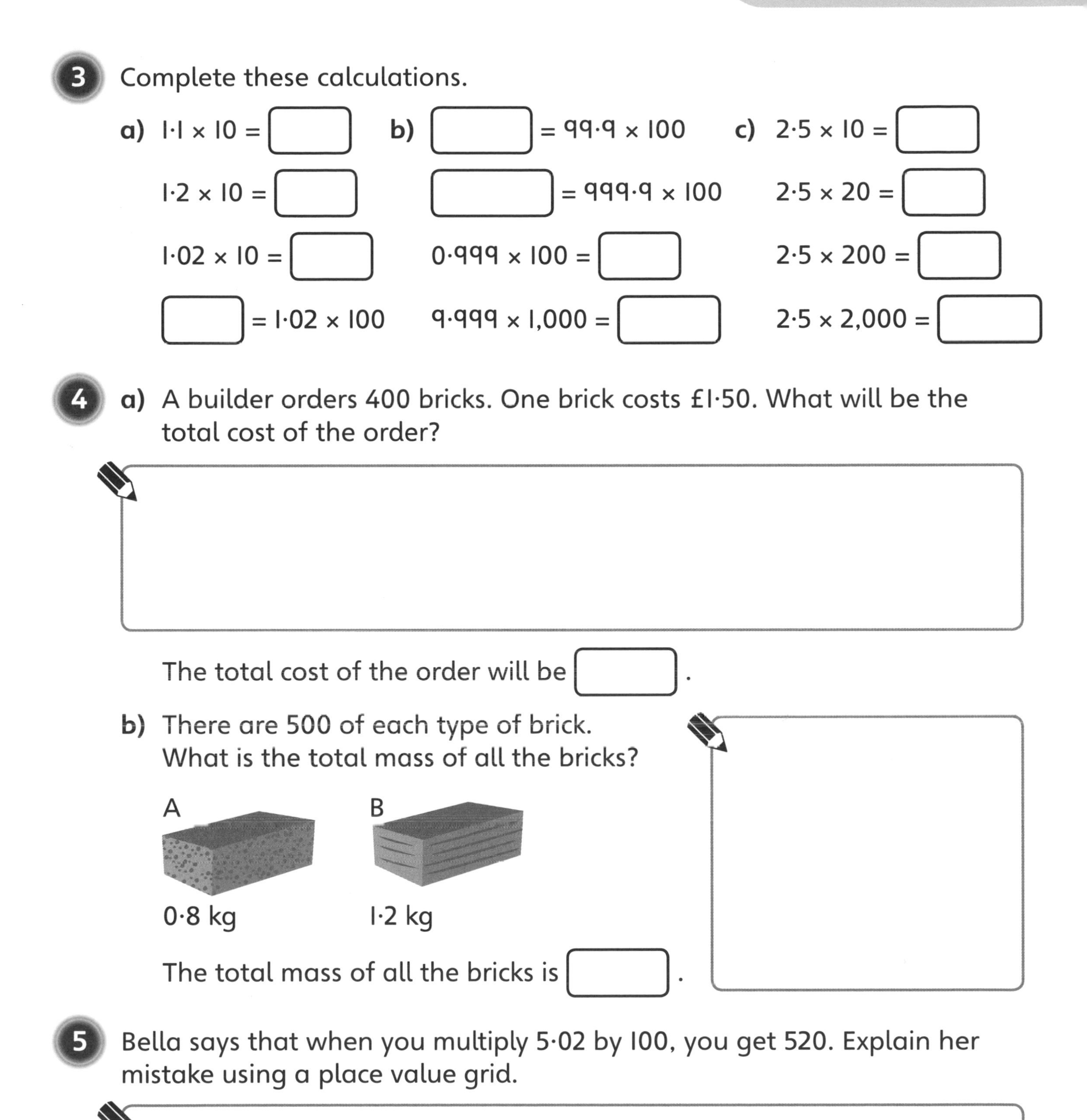

3 Complete these calculations.

a) $1·1 \times 10 = \square$

$1·2 \times 10 = \square$

$1·02 \times 10 = \square$

$\square = 1·02 \times 100$

b) $\square = 99·9 \times 100$

$\square = 999·9 \times 100$

$0·999 \times 100 = \square$

$9·999 \times 1,000 = \square$

c) $2·5 \times 10 = \square$

$2·5 \times 20 = \square$

$2·5 \times 200 = \square$

$2·5 \times 2,000 = \square$

4 a) A builder orders 400 bricks. One brick costs £1·50. What will be the total cost of the order?

The total cost of the order will be $\square$.

b) There are 500 of each type of brick. What is the total mass of all the bricks?

A
0·8 kg

B
1·2 kg

The total mass of all the bricks is $\square$.

5 Bella says that when you multiply 5·02 by 100, you get 520. Explain her mistake using a place value grid.

CHALLENGE

6 Complete each calculation.

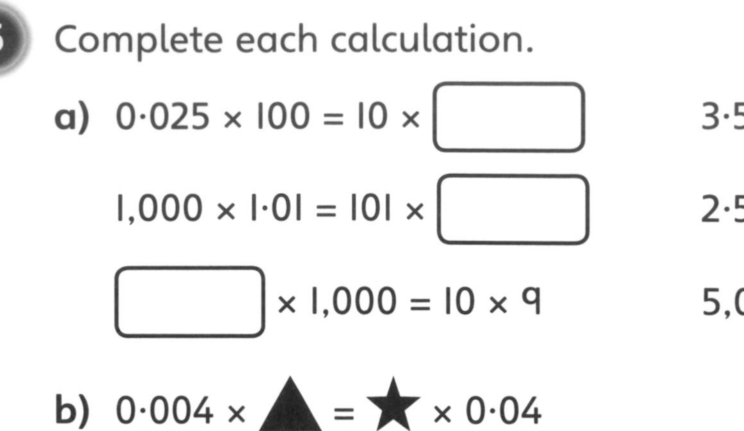

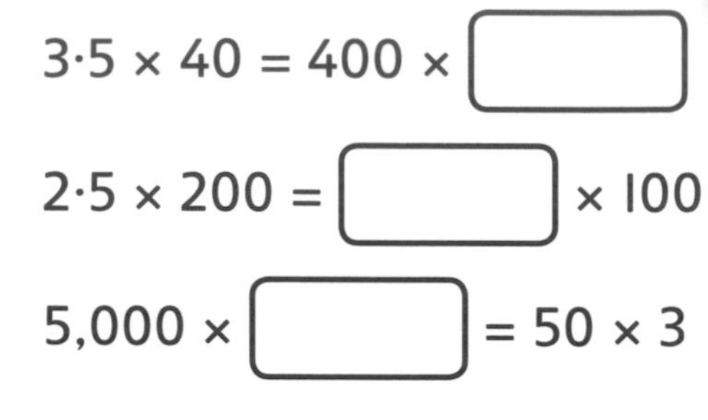

a) $0{\cdot}025 \times 100 = 10 \times$ ☐ $3{\cdot}5 \times 40 = 400 \times$ ☐

$1{,}000 \times 1{\cdot}01 = 101 \times$ ☐ $2{\cdot}5 \times 200 =$ ☐ $\times 100$

☐ $\times 1{,}000 = 10 \times 9$ $5{,}000 \times$ ☐ $= 50 \times 3$

b) $0{\cdot}004 \times$ ▲ $=$ ★ $\times 0{\cdot}04$

How many different solutions can you find?

	Solution 1	Solution 2	Solution 3	Solution 4	Solution 5	Solution 6	Solution 7
▲							
★							

Reflect

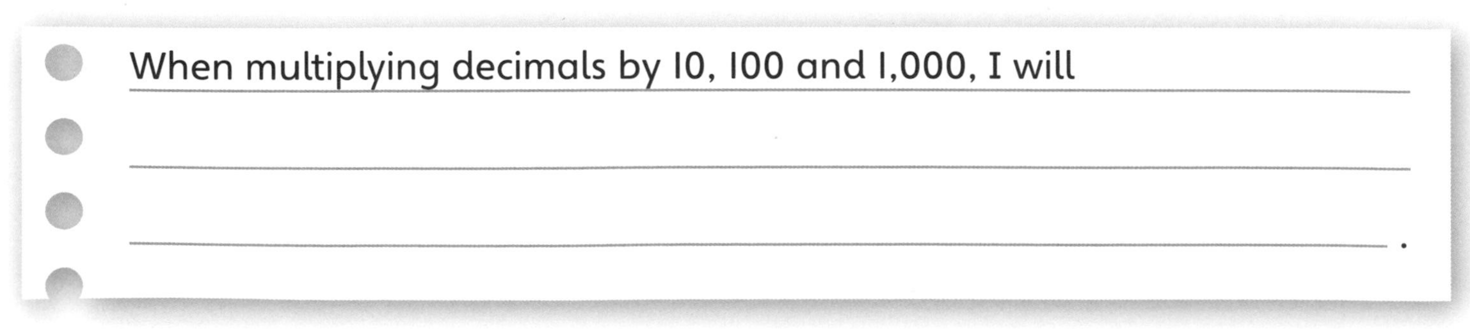

When multiplying decimals by 10, 100 and 1,000, I will

→ Textbook 6B p12

Dividing by multiples of 10, 100 and 1,000

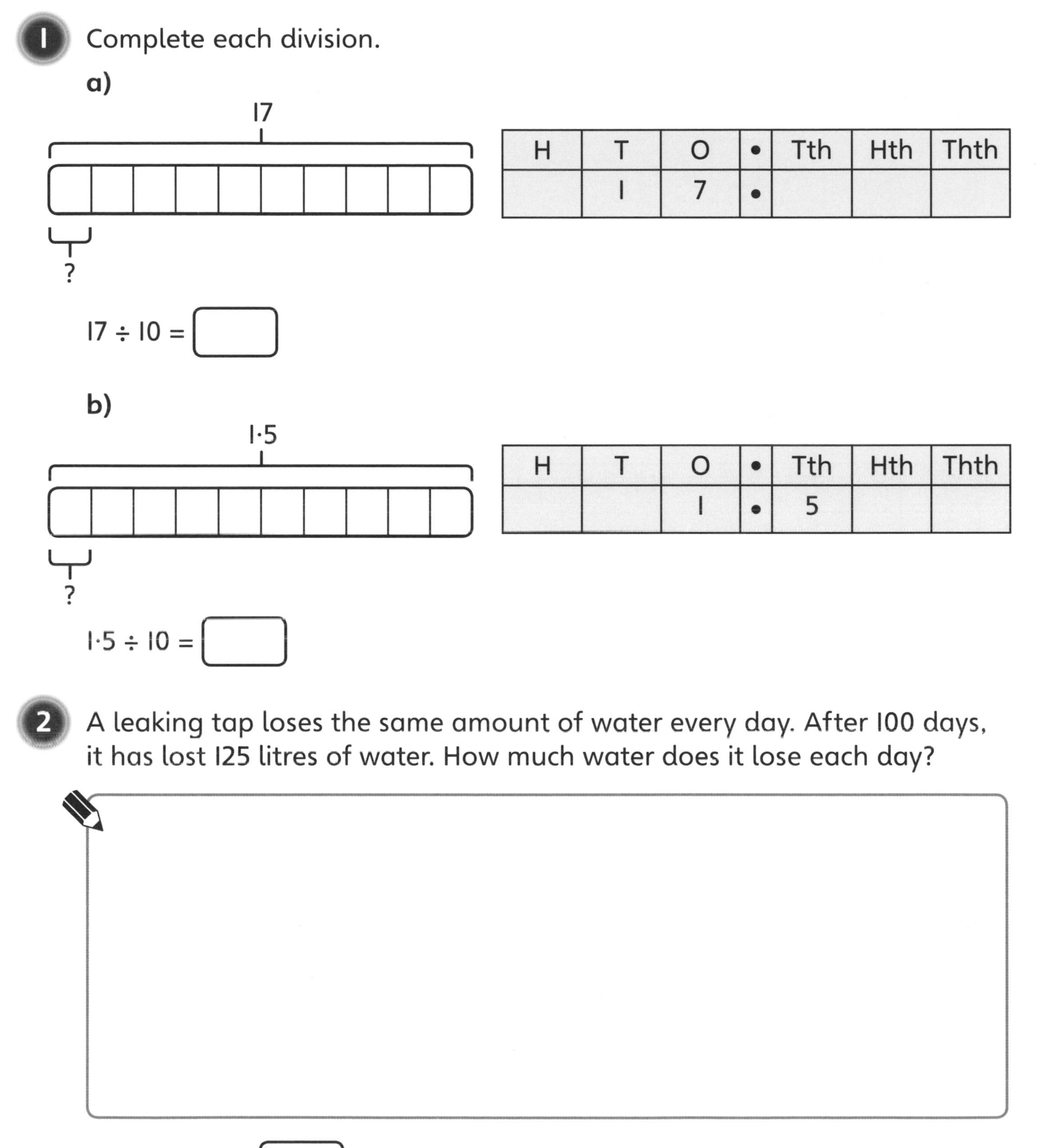

1 Complete each division.

a)

17

?

H	T	O	•	Tth	Hth	Thth
	1	7	•			

17 ÷ 10 = [ ]

b)

1·5

?

H	T	O	•	Tth	Hth	Thth
		1	•	5		

1·5 ÷ 10 = [ ]

2 A leaking tap loses the same amount of water every day. After 100 days, it has lost 125 litres of water. How much water does it lose each day?

The tap loses [ ] litres of water each day.

3 Which of these represents the answer to 2,050 divided by 1,000?
Tick your answer.

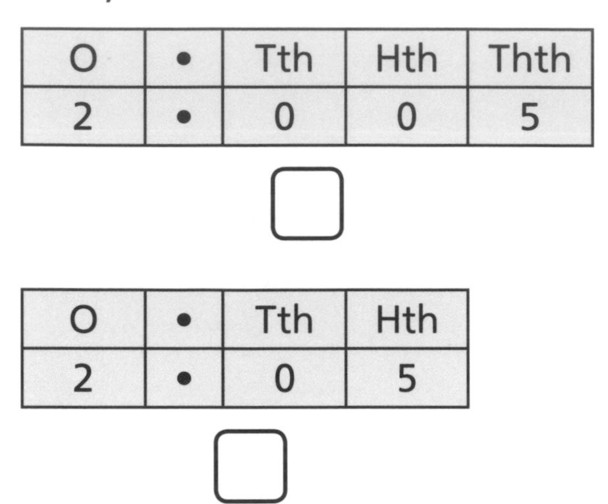

O	•	Tth	Hth	Thth
2	•	0	0	5

☐

O	•	Tth	Hth
2	•	0	5

☐

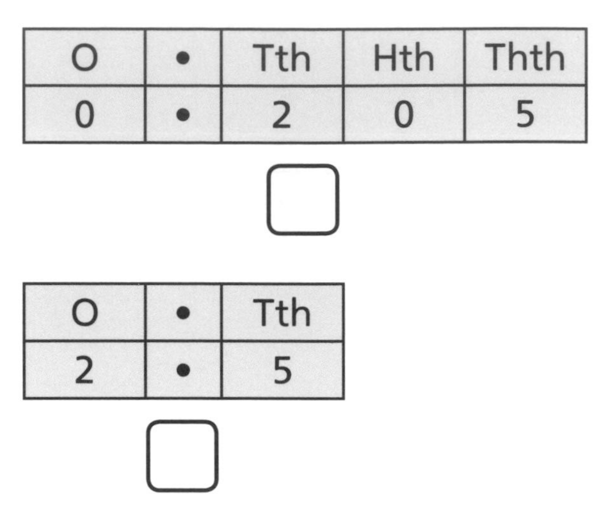

O	•	Tth	Hth	Thth
0	•	2	0	5

☐

O	•	Tth
2	•	5

☐

4 What division calculation does this diagram show?

O	•	Tth	Hth
	•	0·1 0·1 0·1 0·1	0·01 ×40

→

O	•	Tth	Hth
	•		0·01 0·01 0·01 0·01

☐ ÷ ☐ = ☐

5 Each number has been divided by 10, 100 or 1,000.
Complete the calculations.

O	•	Tth	Hth	Thth
0	•	3	0	6

30·6 ÷ ☐ = 0·306

O	•	Tth	Hth
0	•	3	6

3·6 ÷ ☐ = 0·36

O	•	Tth	Hth	Thth
0	•	0	3	6

36 ÷ ☐ = 0·036

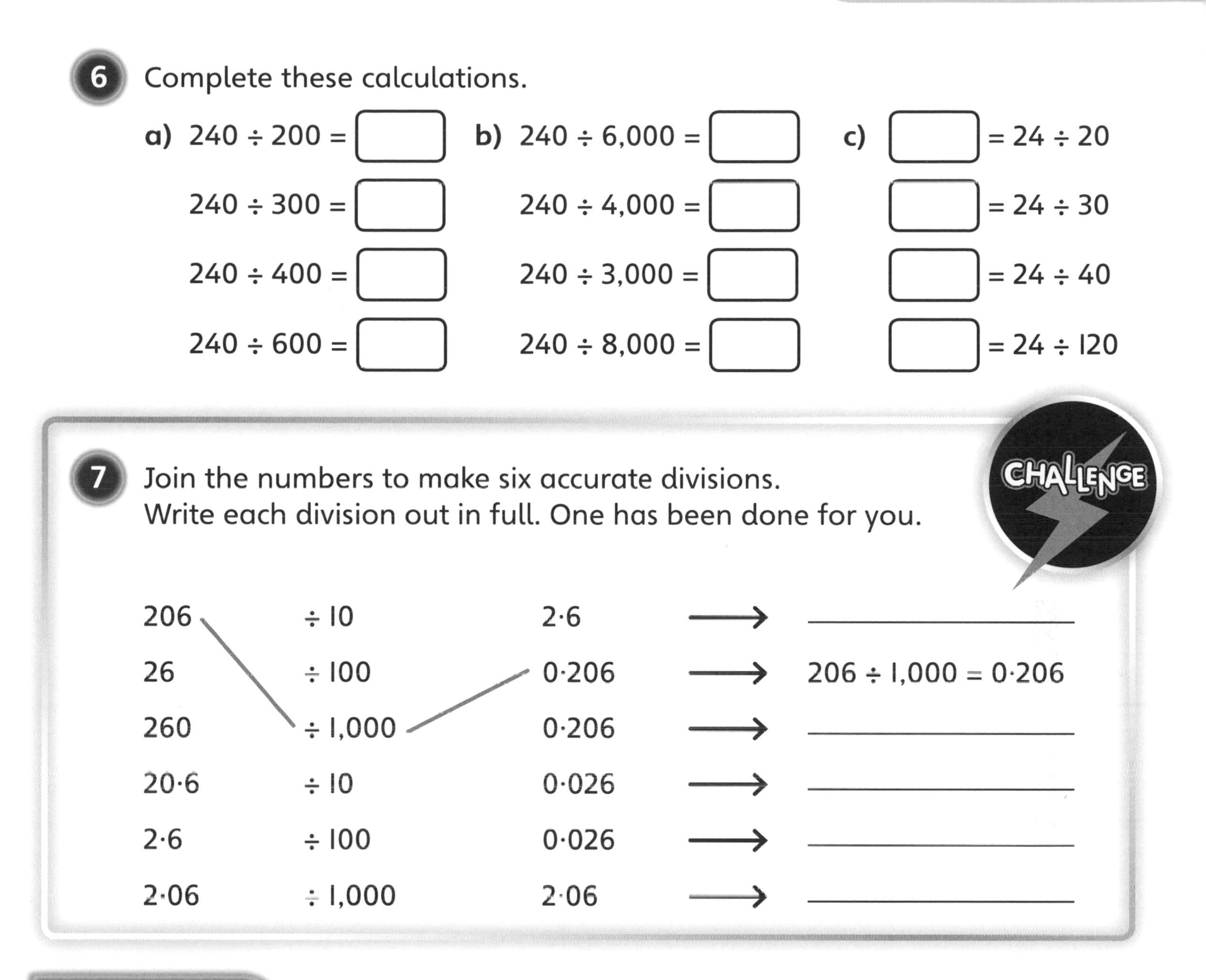

6 Complete these calculations.

a) 240 ÷ 200 = ☐

240 ÷ 300 = ☐

240 ÷ 400 = ☐

240 ÷ 600 = ☐

b) 240 ÷ 6,000 = ☐

240 ÷ 4,000 = ☐

240 ÷ 3,000 = ☐

240 ÷ 8,000 = ☐

c) ☐ = 24 ÷ 20

☐ = 24 ÷ 30

☐ = 24 ÷ 40

☐ = 24 ÷ 120

7 Join the numbers to make six accurate divisions.
Write each division out in full. One has been done for you.

206	÷ 10	2·6	⟶	________
26	÷ 100	0·206	⟶	206 ÷ 1,000 = 0·206
260	÷ 1,000	0·206	⟶	________
20·6	÷ 10	0·026	⟶	________
2·6	÷ 100	0·026	⟶	________
2·06	÷ 1,000	2·06	⟶	________

Reflect

Write a word problem that is solved by dividing by 10, 100 or 1,000 and gives a decimal answer. Find the answer to your word problem.

→ Textbook 6B p16

Decimals as fractions

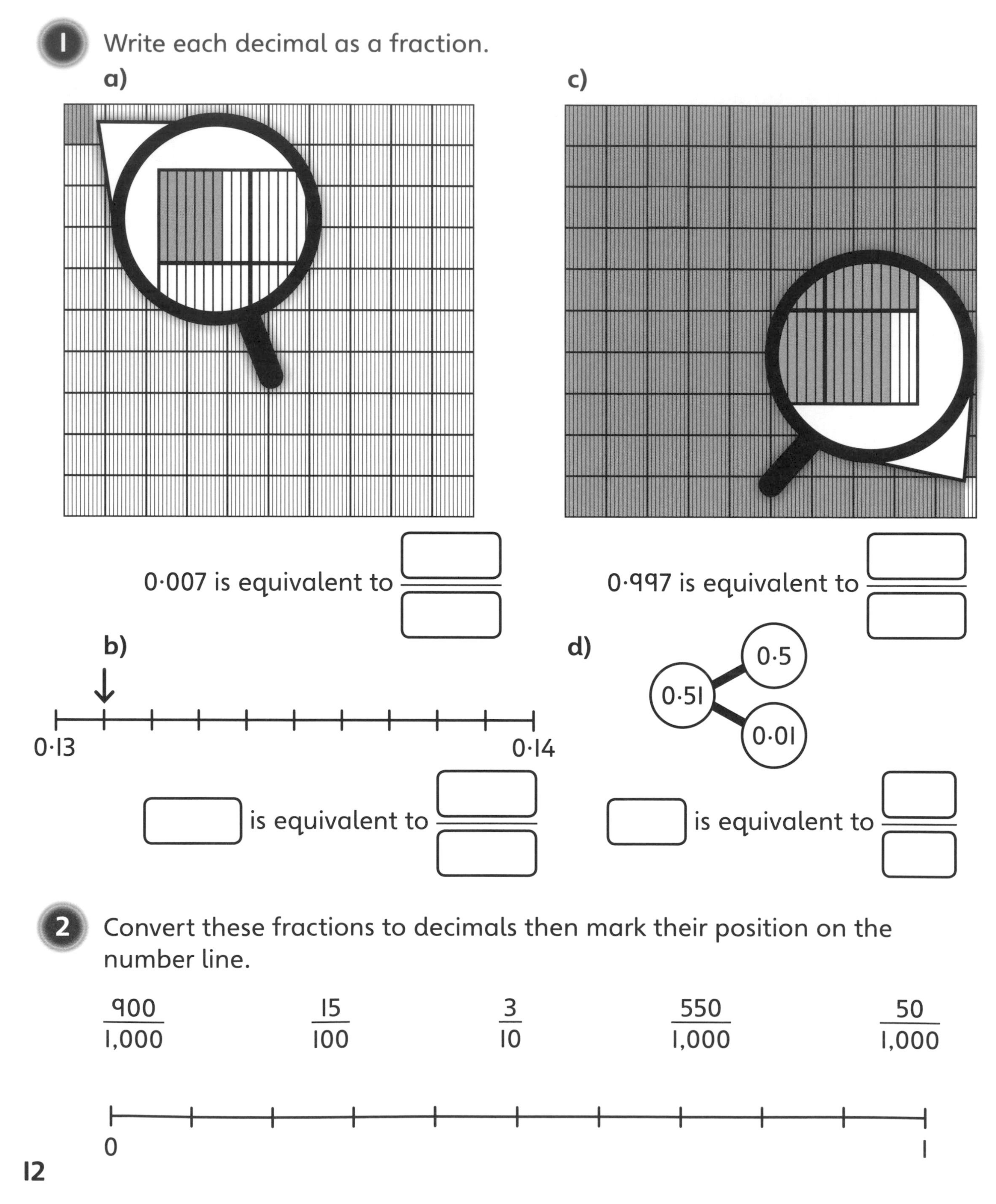

1 Write each decimal as a fraction.

a)

0·007 is equivalent to $\frac{\square}{\square}$

b)

$\square$ is equivalent to $\frac{\square}{\square}$

c)

0·997 is equivalent to $\frac{\square}{\square}$

d)

$\square$ is equivalent to $\frac{\square}{\square}$

2 Convert these fractions to decimals then mark their position on the number line.

$\frac{900}{1,000}$ $\frac{15}{100}$ $\frac{3}{10}$ $\frac{550}{1,000}$ $\frac{50}{1,000}$

3 Match each decimal to the equivalent fraction.

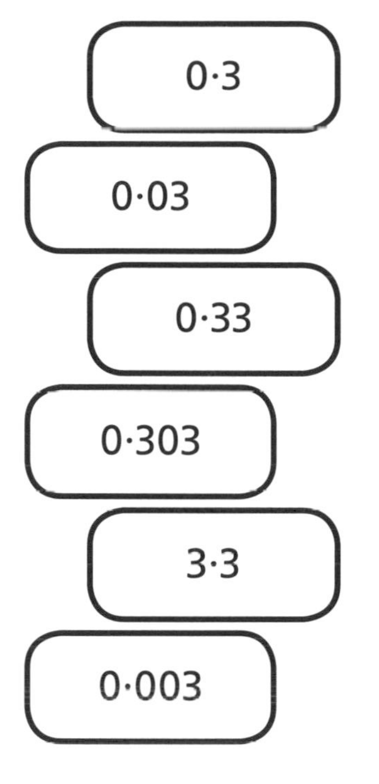

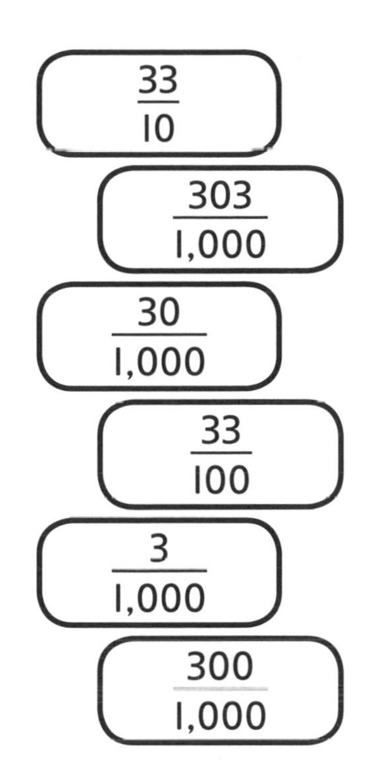

4 Write each decimal as a fraction, then simplify as far as you can.

a) 0·04 ______________________________

b) 0·05 ______________________________

c) 0·004 ______________________________

d) 0·005 ______________________________

5 **a)** Which of these fractions is equivalent to 1·823? Circle your answer.

$1\frac{823}{1,000}$ $\quad$ $1\frac{823}{100}$ $\quad$ $\frac{8}{23}$ $\quad$ $\frac{1,000}{823}$

b) Which of these fractions is equivalent to 0·85? Circle your answer.

$\frac{85}{10}$ $\quad$ $\frac{17}{10}$ $\quad$ $\frac{8}{5}$ $\quad$ $\frac{17}{20}$

CHALLENGE

6 **a)** Which of these decimals add together to make $\frac{3}{25}$?

0·1   0·105   0·02   0·015   0·01   0·2

Is there more than one possibility?

b) Which pairs of decimals have a difference of $\frac{5}{250}$?

0·2   0·04   2   1·02   2·04   1·98   1   2·6   10·4

Reflect

Explain how to write 0·555 as a fraction and how to simplify it as far as you can.

→ Textbook 6B p20

Fractions as decimals 1

1 Write each fraction on a place value grid.

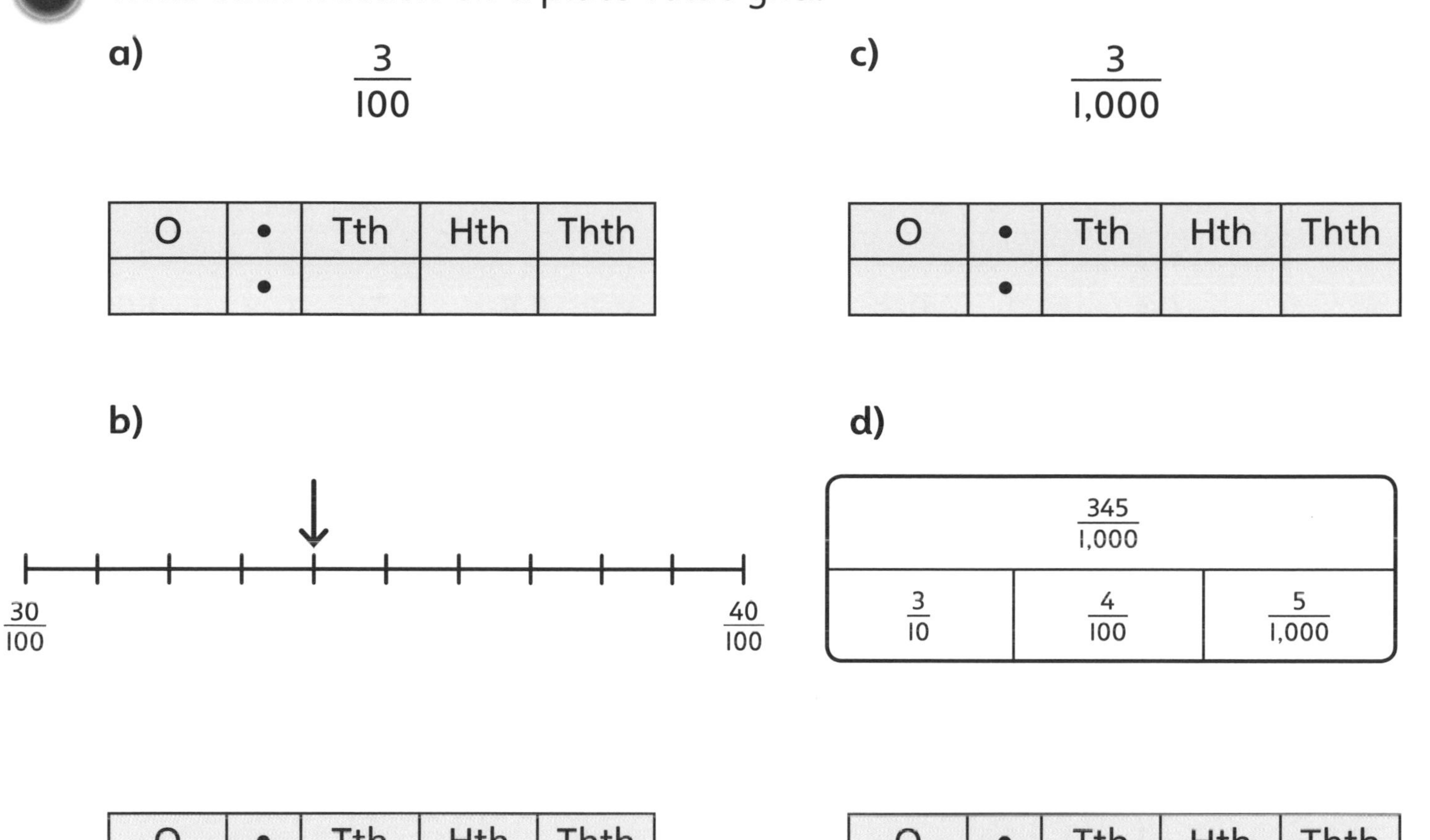

a) $\frac{3}{100}$

O	•	Tth	Hth	Thth
	•			

c) $\frac{3}{1,000}$

O	•	Tth	Hth	Thth
	•			

b)

O	•	Tth	Hth	Thth
	•			

d)

O	•	Tth	Hth	Thth
	•			

2 **a)** Which decimal is equivalent to $\frac{77}{10}$? Circle your answer.

0·77 77·10 7·7 77·7

b) Which decimal is equivalent to $\frac{370}{100}$? Circle your answer.

0·37 0·037 0·307 3·7

3 Use the fraction wall to help convert these fractions to decimals.

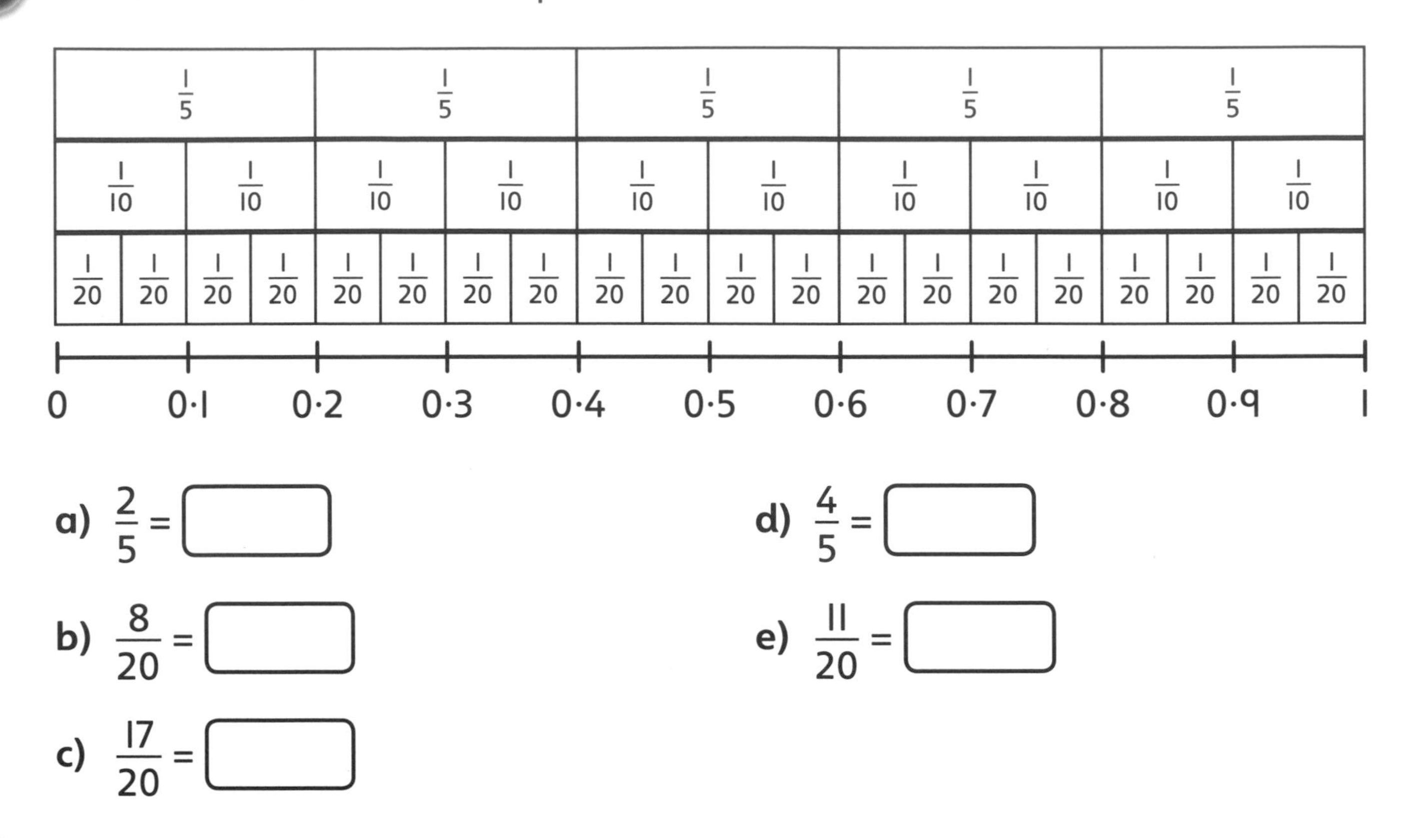

a) $\frac{2}{5} = \square$

b) $\frac{8}{20} = \square$

c) $\frac{17}{20} = \square$

d) $\frac{4}{5} = \square$

e) $\frac{11}{20} = \square$

4 Use equivalent fractions to convert these fractions to decimals.

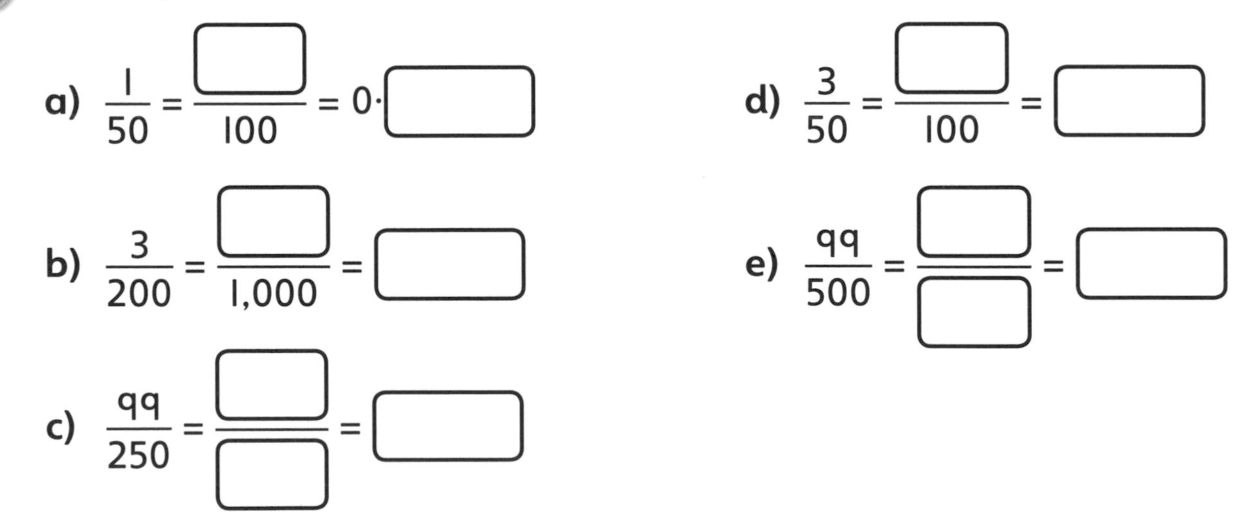

a) $\frac{1}{50} = \frac{\square}{100} = 0\cdot\square$

b) $\frac{3}{200} = \frac{\square}{1,000} = \square$

c) $\frac{99}{250} = \frac{\square}{\square} = \square$

d) $\frac{3}{50} = \frac{\square}{100} = \square$

e) $\frac{99}{500} = \frac{\square}{\square} = \square$

5 Write the decimals that the arrows are pointing to.

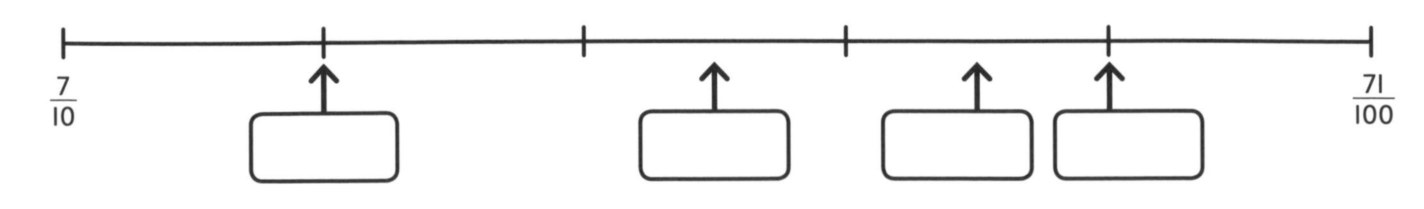

6 Use these digit cards to make fractions, where one card is the denominator and one card is the numerator. Convert each fraction to a decimal and write it in the correct column of the table.

CHALLENGE

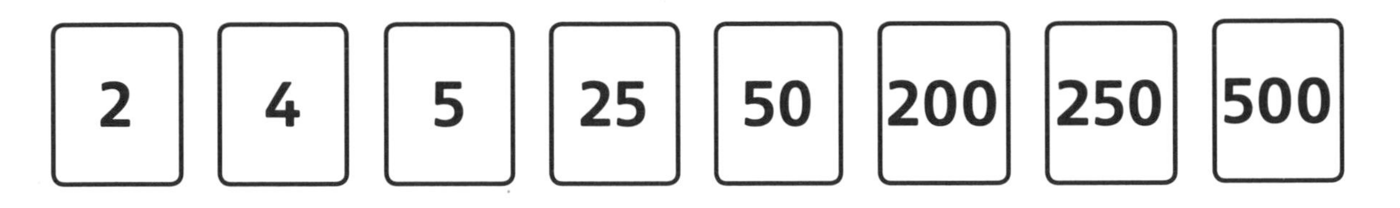

Between 0 and 1	Between 1 and 10	Greater than 10

Reflect

What is the same and what is different about converting from decimals to fractions and converting from fractions to decimals?

→ Textbook 6B p24

Fractions as decimals 2

1 Write each fraction as a decimal.

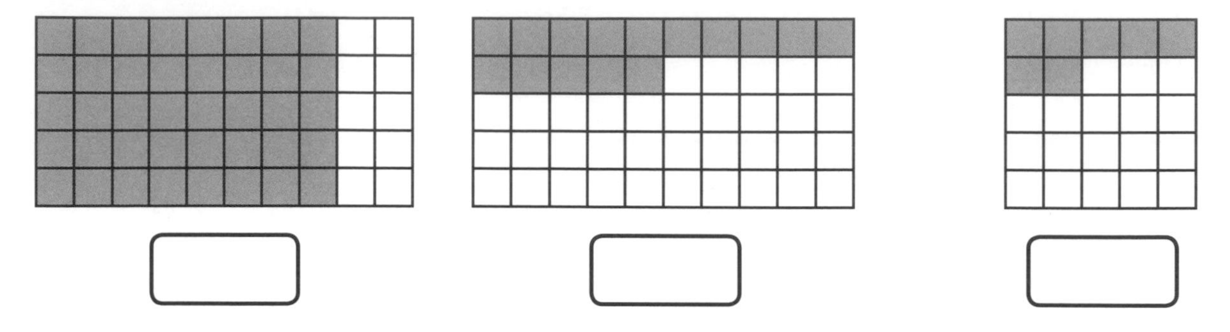

2 Write an equivalent fraction and a decimal for each of the fractions marked on the number lines.

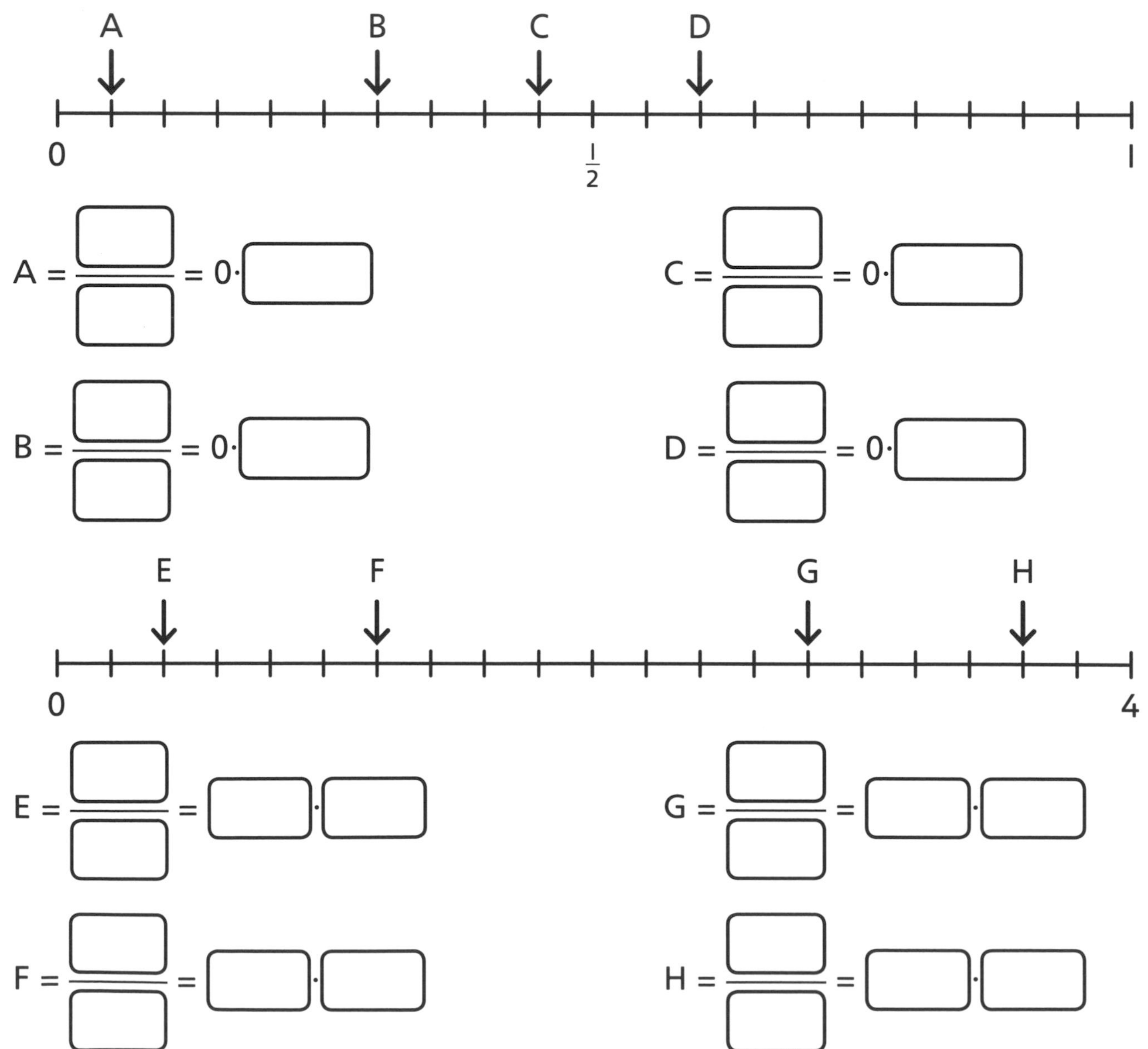

3 Use equivalent fractions to convert these fractions into divisions and decimals.

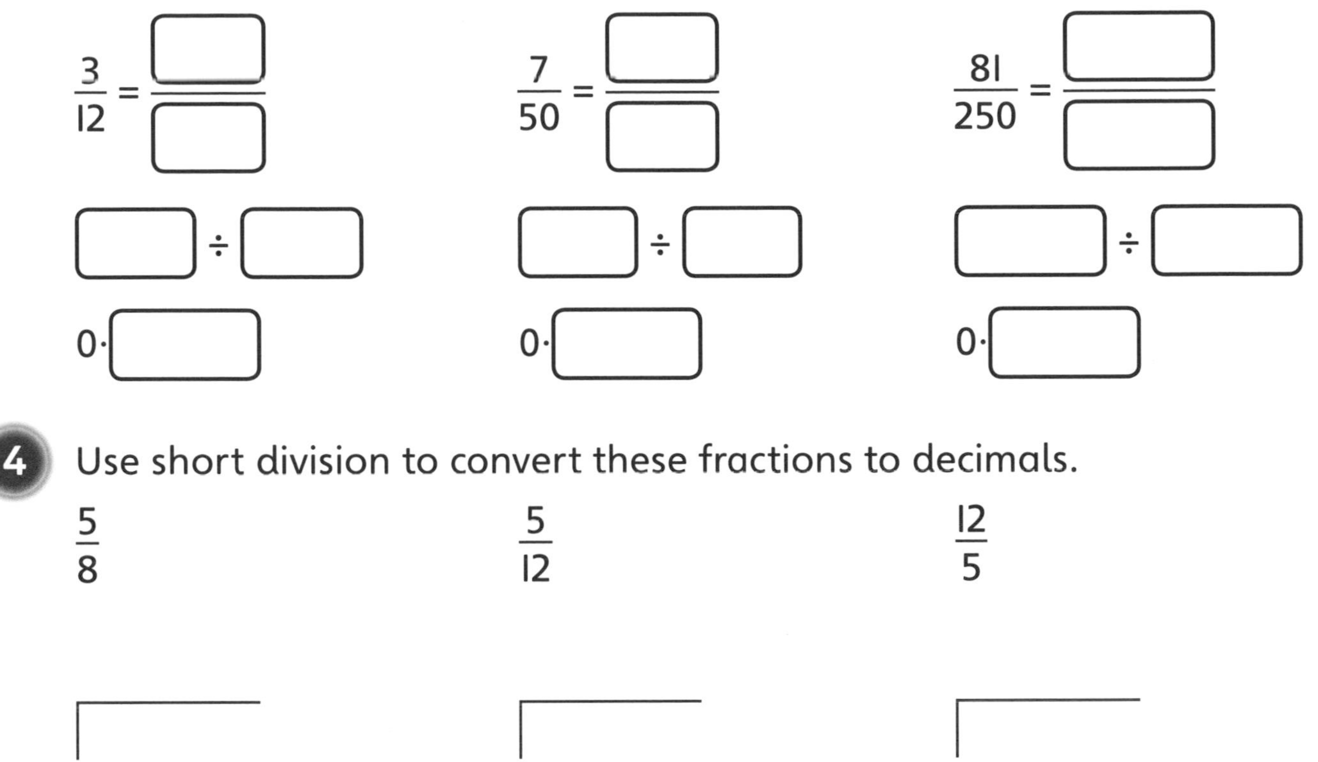

$\frac{3}{12} = \frac{\square}{\square}$ $\qquad$ $\frac{7}{50} = \frac{\square}{\square}$ $\qquad$ $\frac{81}{250} = \frac{\square}{\square}$

$\square \div \square$ $\qquad$ $\square \div \square$ $\qquad$ $\square \div \square$

0·$\square$ $\qquad$ 0·$\square$ $\qquad$ 0·$\square$

4 Use short division to convert these fractions to decimals.

$\frac{5}{8}$ $\qquad$ $\frac{5}{12}$ $\qquad$ $\frac{12}{5}$

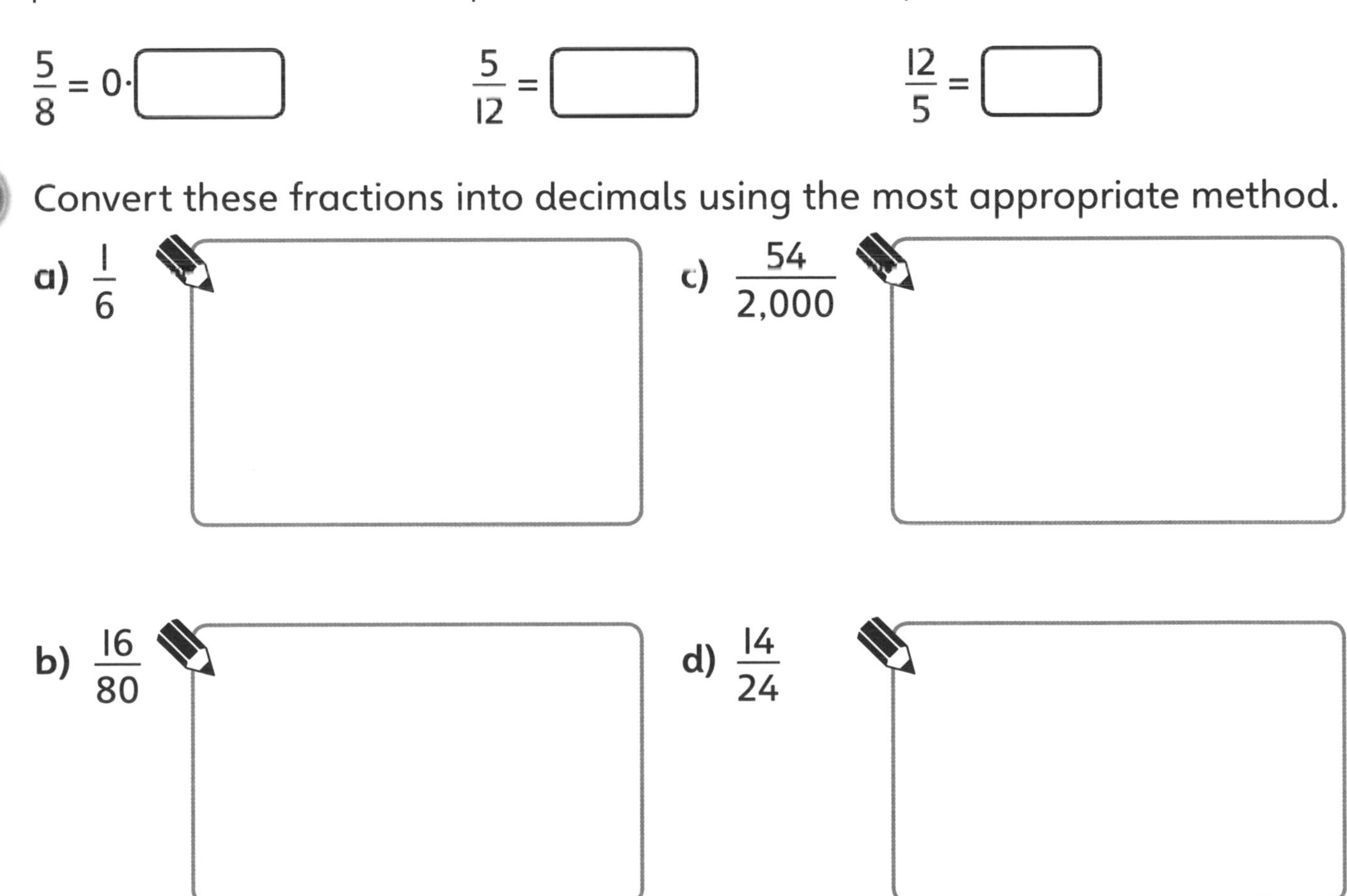

$\frac{5}{8} = 0 \cdot \square$ $\qquad$ $\frac{5}{12} = \square$ $\qquad$ $\frac{12}{5} = \square$

5 Convert these fractions into decimals using the most appropriate method.

a) $\frac{1}{6}$

b) $\frac{16}{80}$

c) $\frac{54}{2,000}$

d) $\frac{14}{24}$

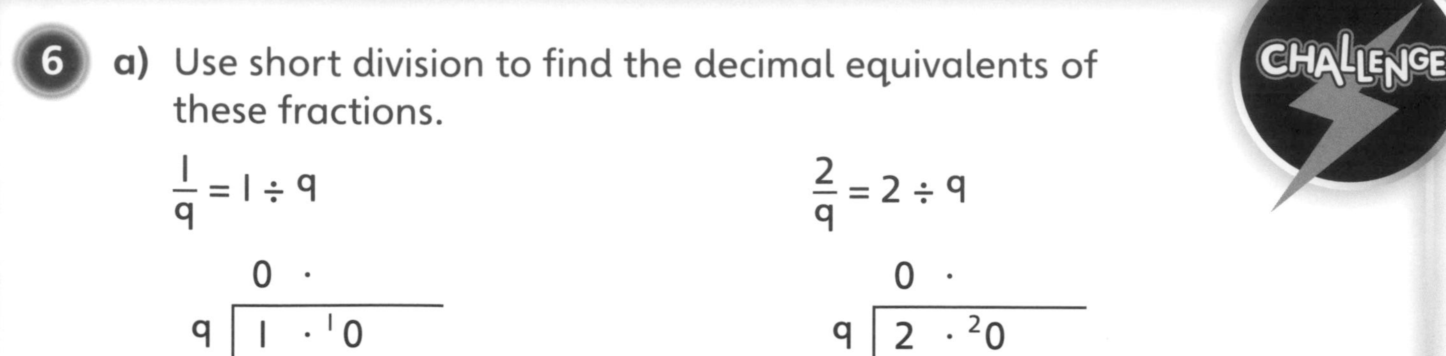

6 **a)** Use short division to find the decimal equivalents of these fractions.

$\frac{1}{9} = 1 \div 9$

$9\overline{)1 \cdot {}^{1}0}$ quotient: 0 ·

$\frac{2}{9} = 2 \div 9$

$9\overline{)2 \cdot {}^{2}0}$ quotient: 0 ·

$\frac{3}{9} = \square \div \square$

$\frac{4}{9} = \square \div \square$

b) Without working them out, predict the missing decimal equivalents to three dp.

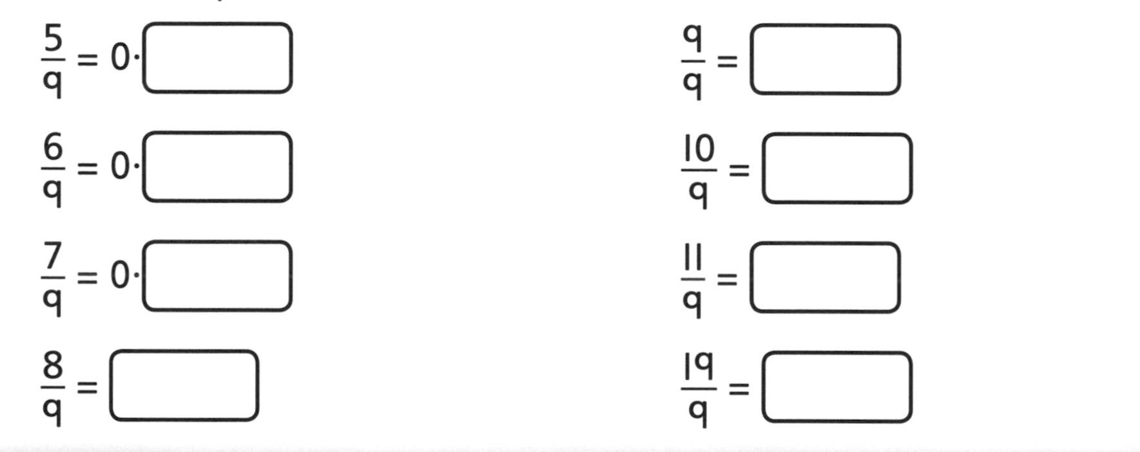

$\frac{5}{9} = 0 \cdot \square$

$\frac{6}{9} = 0 \cdot \square$

$\frac{7}{9} = 0 \cdot \square$

$\frac{8}{9} = \square$

$\frac{9}{9} = \square$

$\frac{10}{9} = \square$

$\frac{11}{9} = \square$

$\frac{19}{9} = \square$

Reflect

Explain how to use decimals to compare $\frac{5}{8}$ and $\frac{55}{100}$.

→ Textbook 6B p28

Multiplying decimals 1

Complete these multiplication calculations.

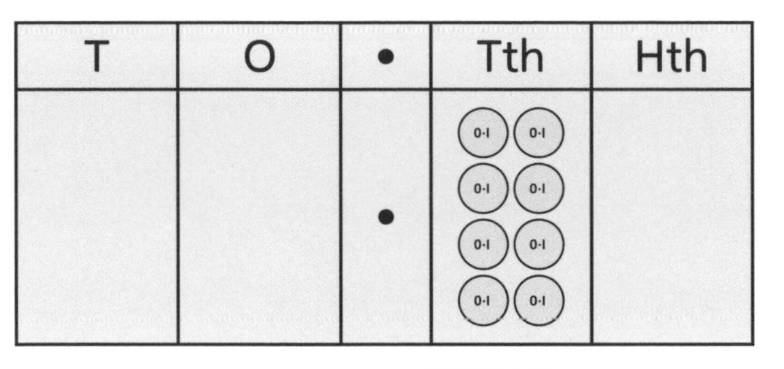

4 × 0·2 = ☐

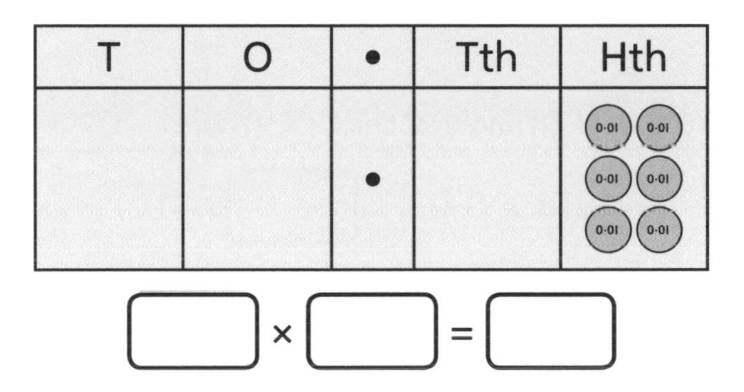

☐ × ☐ = ☐

Complete the number line to represent each calculation, then solve each calculation.

a) 3 × 0·3 = ☐

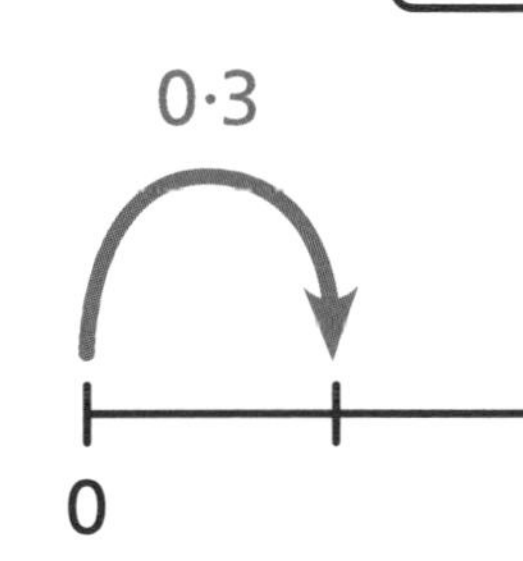

b) 3 × 0·03 = ☐

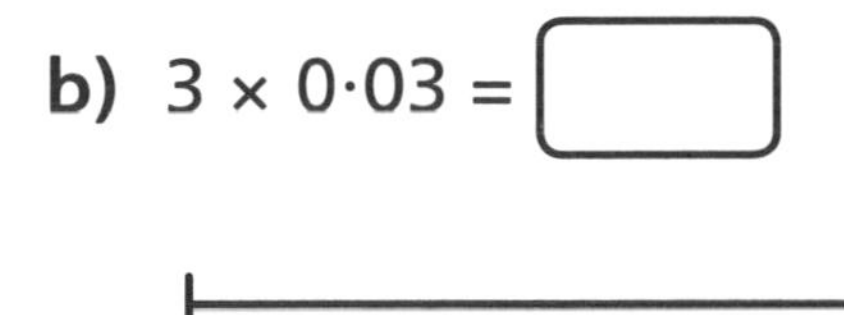

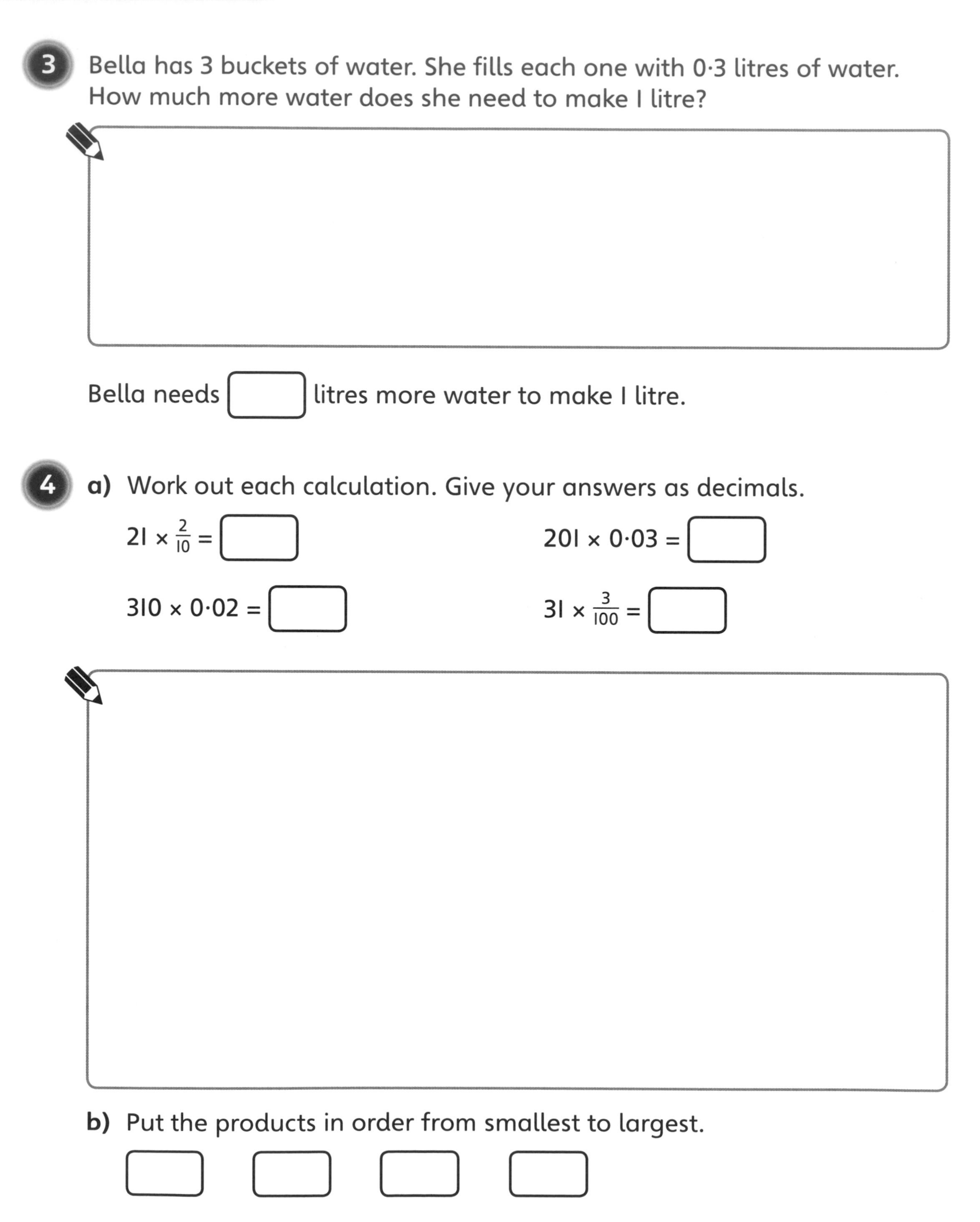

3 Bella has 3 buckets of water. She fills each one with 0·3 litres of water. How much more water does she need to make 1 litre?

Bella needs [ ] litres more water to make 1 litre.

4 **a)** Work out each calculation. Give your answers as decimals.

$21 \times \frac{2}{10} =$ [ ]

$201 \times 0{\cdot}03 =$ [ ]

$310 \times 0{\cdot}02 =$ [ ]

$31 \times \frac{3}{100} =$ [ ]

b) Put the products in order from smallest to largest.

[ ] [ ] [ ] [ ]

5 a) Complete the multiplications on this diagram.

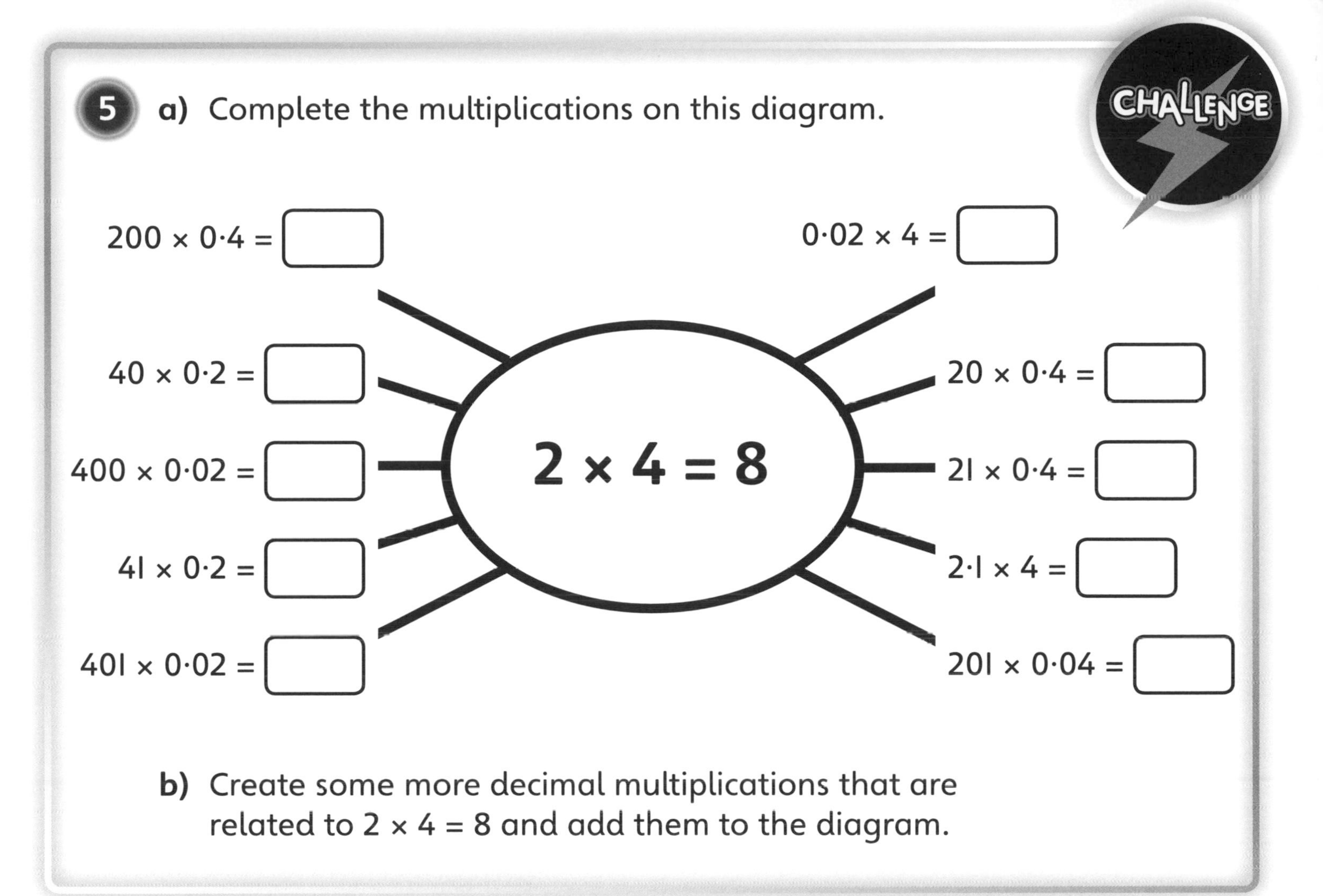

b) Create some more decimal multiplications that are related to 2 × 4 = 8 and add them to the diagram.

Reflect

What advice would you give to your partner about multiplying numbers with decimals?

→ Textbook 6B p32

Multiplying decimals 2

1 Write two multiplications to match each representation.

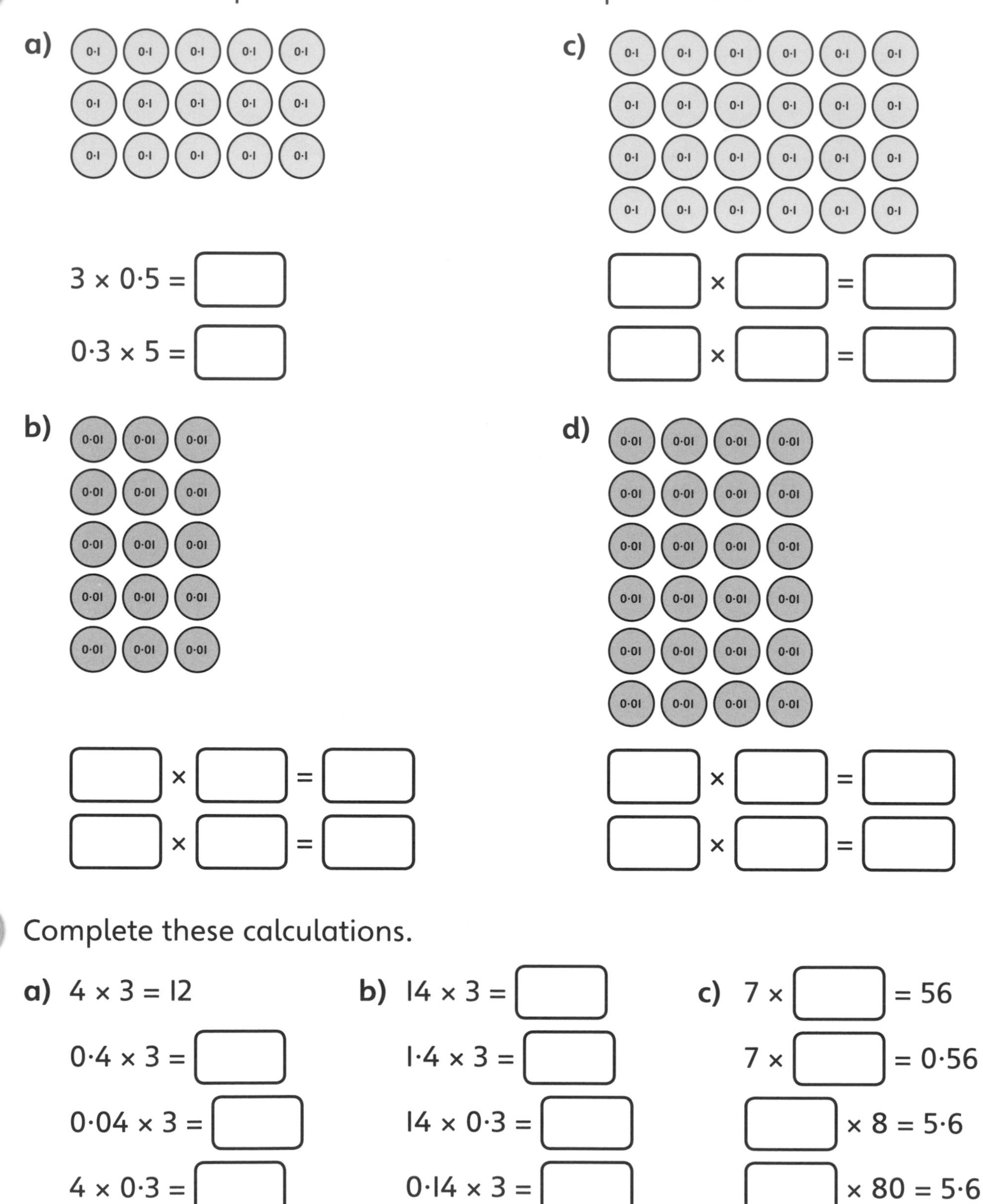

2 Complete these calculations.

a) 4 × 3 = 12

0·4 × 3 = ☐

0·04 × 3 = ☐

4 × 0·3 = ☐

4 × 0·03 = ☐

b) 14 × 3 = ☐

1·4 × 3 = ☐

14 × 0·3 = ☐

0·14 × 3 = ☐

0·03 × 14 = ☐

c) 7 × ☐ = 56

7 × ☐ = 0·56

☐ × 8 = 5·6

☐ × 80 = 5·6

700 × ☐ = 560

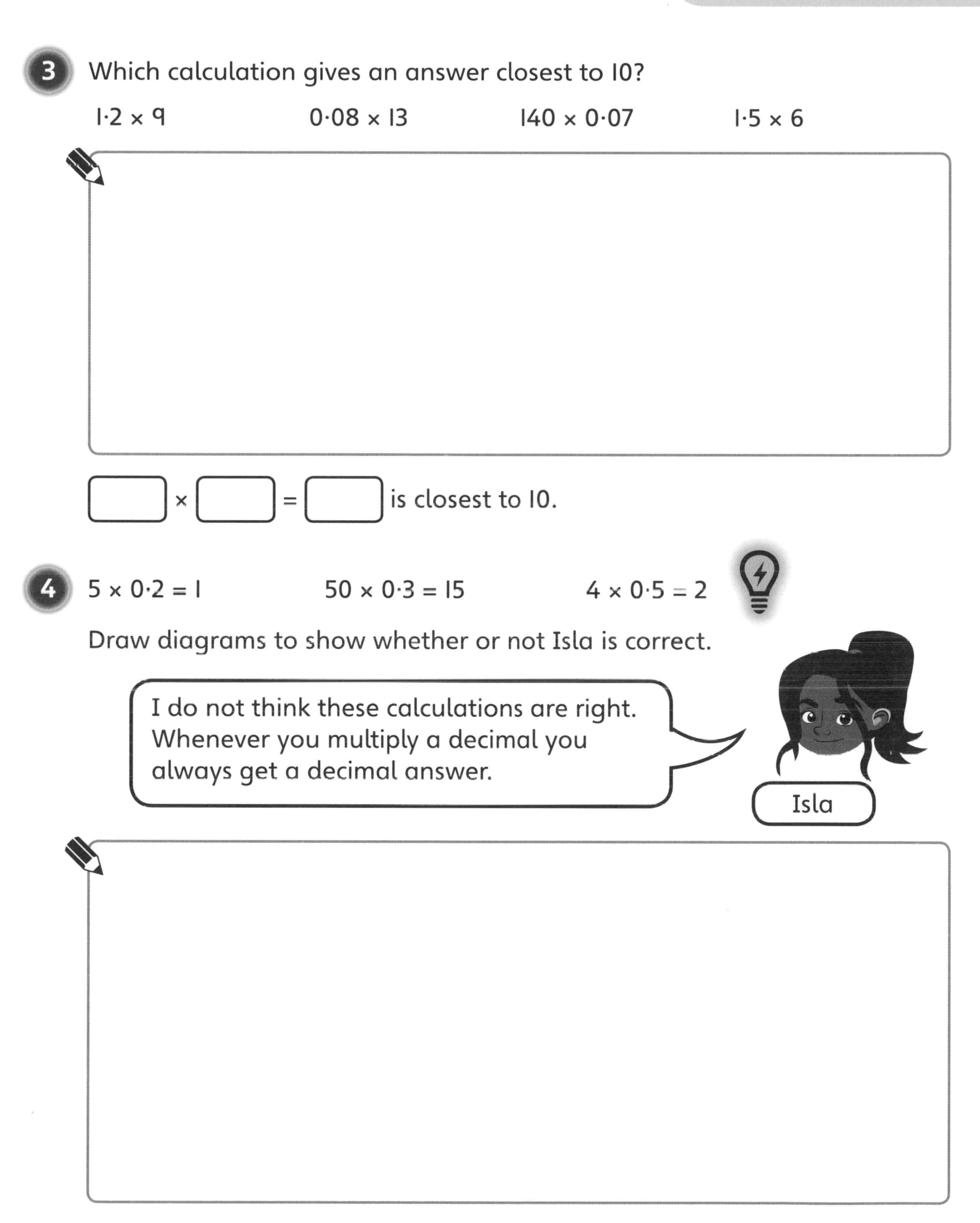

3 Which calculation gives an answer closest to 10?

1·2 × 9 0·08 × 13 140 × 0·07 1·5 × 6

☐ × ☐ = ☐ is closest to 10.

4 5 × 0·2 = 1 50 × 0·3 = 15 4 × 0·5 = 2

Draw diagrams to show whether or not Isla is correct.

5 **a)** Use each card once to create four different calculations. Find the answer to each calculation.

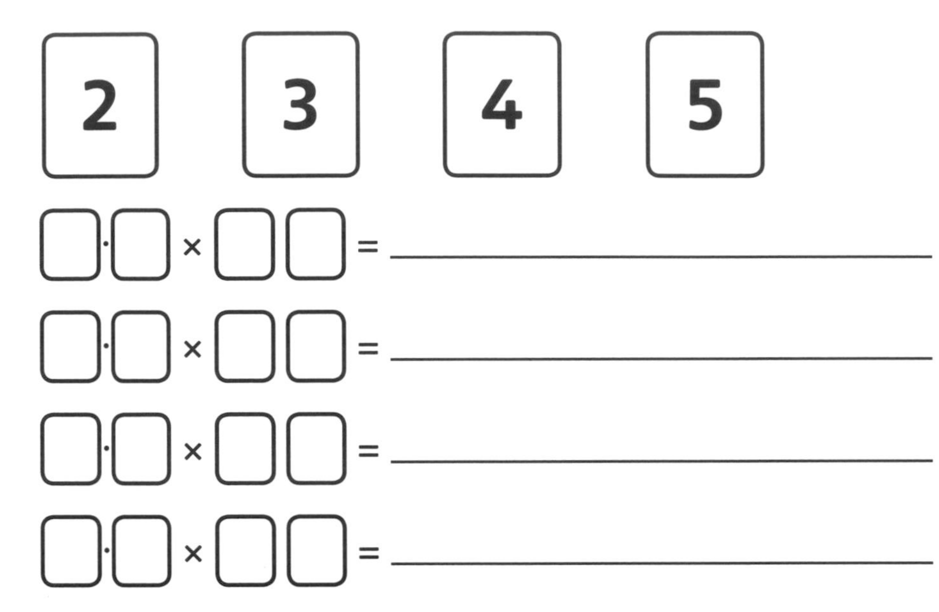

b) What is the difference between the largest and the smallest product you can make using these cards?

Reflect

Write three different multiplications with a product of 0·36.

→ Textbook 6B p36

Dividing decimals 1

1 Complete the divisions.

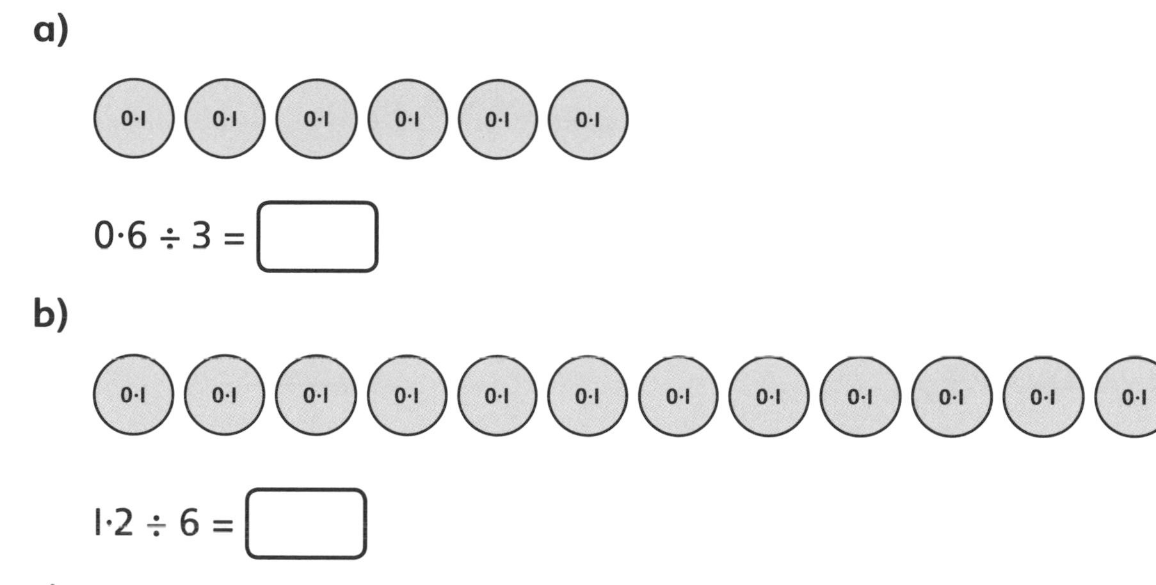

a)

0·6 ÷ 3 = ☐

b)

1·2 ÷ 6 = ☐

c)

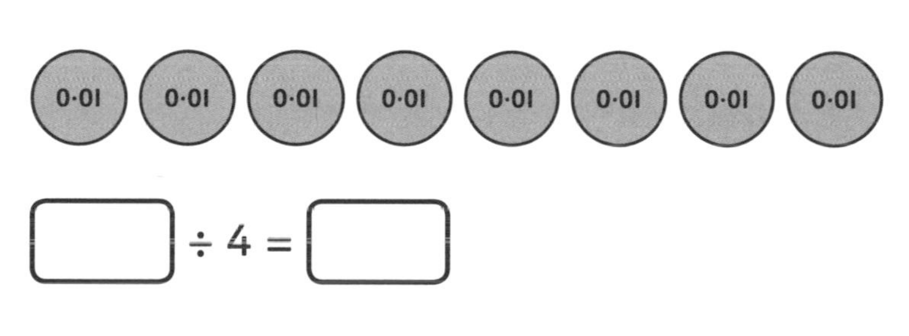

☐ ÷ 4 = ☐

2 a) Complete these division calculations.

36 ÷ 4 = ☐	48 ÷ 4 = ☐	16 ÷ 4 = ☐	28 ÷ 4 = ☐
3·6 ÷ 4 = ☐	4·8 ÷ 4 = ☐	1·6 ÷ 4 = ☐	2·8 ÷ 4 = ☐
0·36 ÷ 4 = ☐	0·48 ÷ 4 = ☐	0·16 ÷ 4 = ☐	0·28 ÷ 4 = ☐

b) Complete these division calculations.

3·6 ÷ 6 = ☐ 4·8 ÷ 6 = ☐

0·72 ÷ 6 = ☐ 0·18 ÷ 6 = ☐

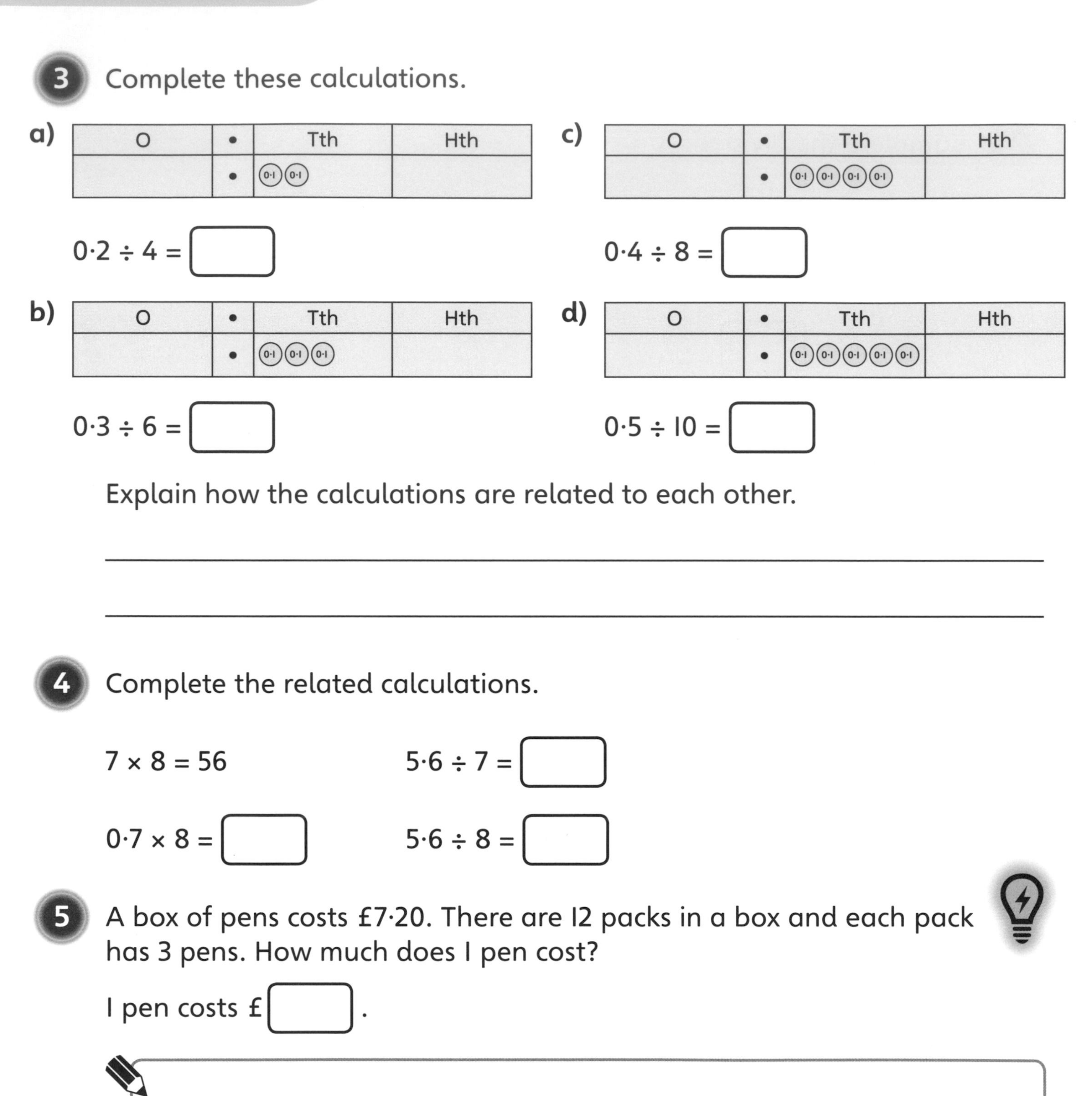

3 Complete these calculations.

a)

O	•	Tth	Hth
	•	0·1 0·1	

$0·2 \div 4 =$ ☐

b)

O	•	Tth	Hth
	•	0·1 0·1 0·1	

$0·3 \div 6 =$ ☐

c)

O	•	Tth	Hth
	•	0·1 0·1 0·1 0·1	

$0·4 \div 8 =$ ☐

d)

O	•	Tth	Hth
	•	0·1 0·1 0·1 0·1 0·1	

$0·5 \div 10 =$ ☐

Explain how the calculations are related to each other.

____

____

4 Complete the related calculations.

$7 \times 8 = 56$

$5·6 \div 7 =$ ☐

$0·7 \times 8 =$ ☐

$5·6 \div 8 =$ ☐

5 A box of pens costs £7·20. There are 12 packs in a box and each pack has 3 pens. How much does 1 pen cost?

1 pen costs £ ☐ .

6 Amelia, Bella and Lee are growing sunflowers.

CHALLENGE

Bella's sunflower is three times as tall as Amelia's. Lee's sunflower is 0·5 m taller than Bella's. The sunflowers are 5·4 m tall in total.

How tall is each sunflower?

I will use bar models to help me set out the information that I know.

Reflect

Write a word problem for the division $3{\cdot}2 \div 8 = \square$.

→ Textbook 6B p40

Dividing decimals 2

1 Complete these divisions.

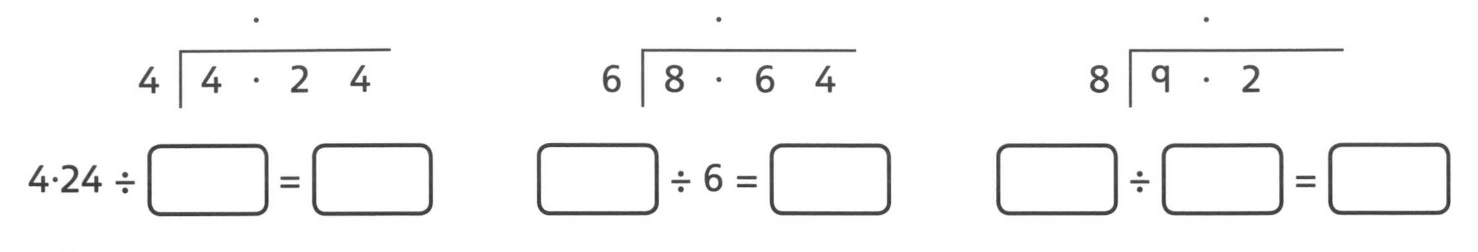

4·24 ÷ ☐ = ☐ ☐ ÷ 6 = ☐ ☐ ÷ ☐ = ☐

2 **a)** Predict if the answer to each of these divisions will have no decimal places, one decimal place or two decimal places. Write the letters in the table.

A	B	C	D	E	F
25 ÷ 4	2·6 ÷ 2	100·5 ÷ 5	8·72 ÷ 4	1,080 ÷ 4	1·38 ÷ 3

No decimal places	One decimal place	Two decimal places

b) Complete each division to check your predictions.

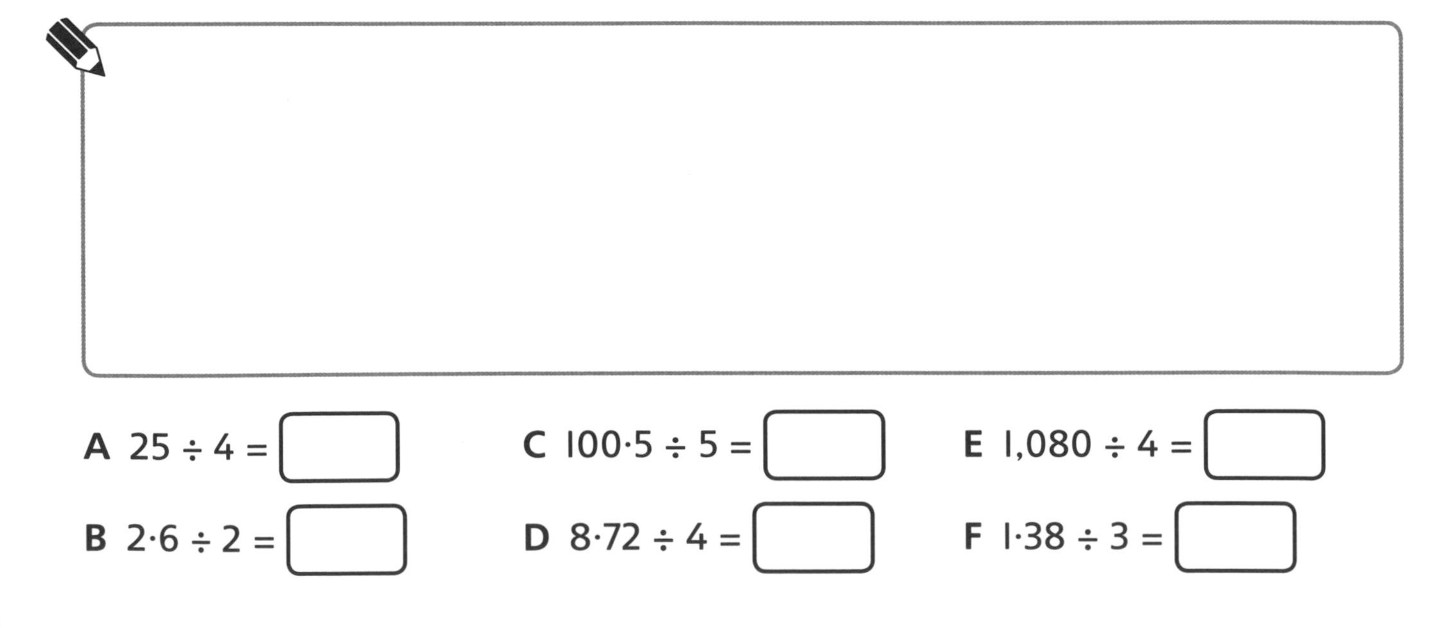

A 25 ÷ 4 = ☐ **C** 100·5 ÷ 5 = ☐ **E** 1,080 ÷ 4 = ☐

B 2·6 ÷ 2 = ☐ **D** 8·72 ÷ 4 = ☐ **F** 1·38 ÷ 3 = ☐

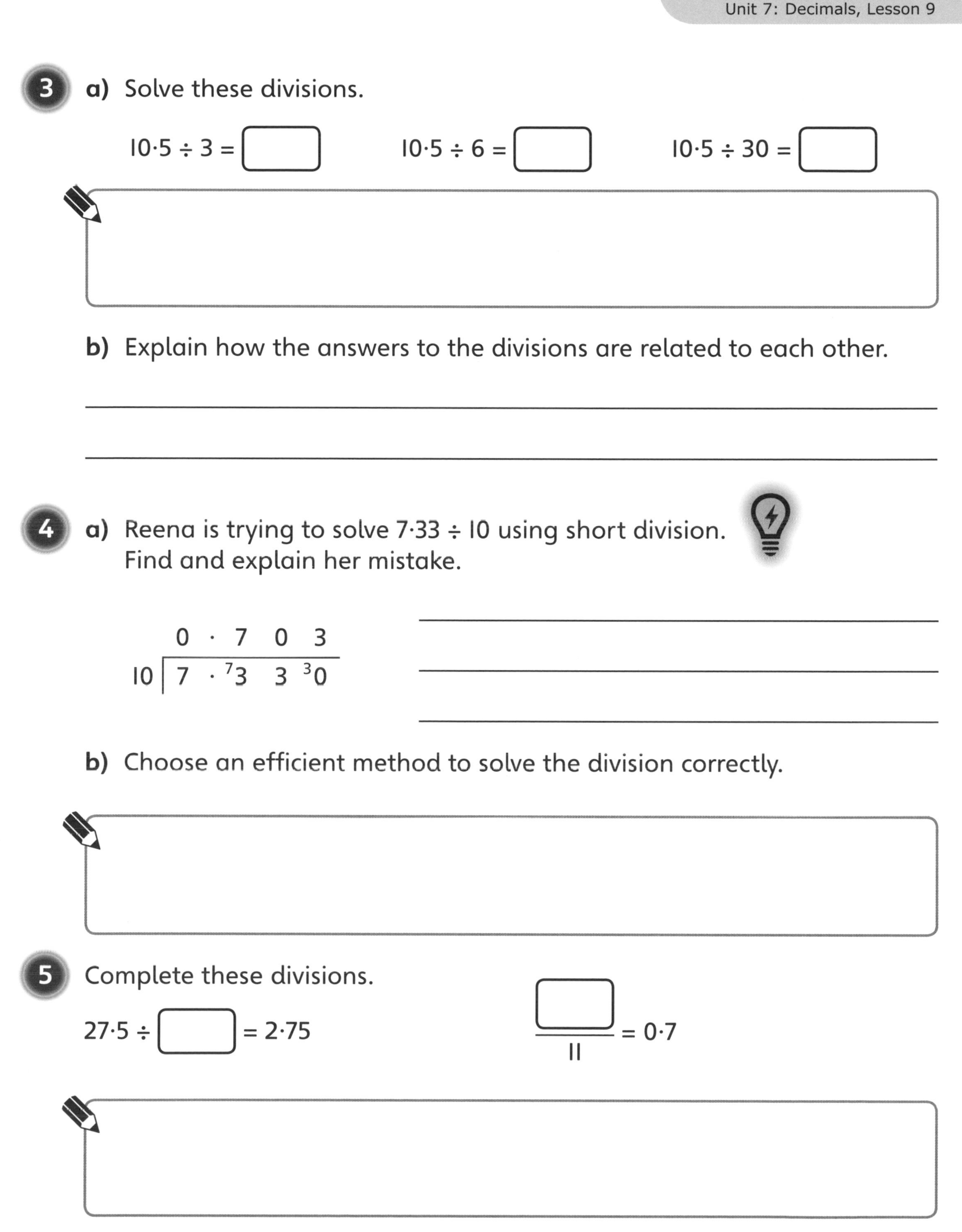

3 **a)** Solve these divisions.

$10{\cdot}5 \div 3 = \square$ $10{\cdot}5 \div 6 = \square$ $10{\cdot}5 \div 30 = \square$

b) Explain how the answers to the divisions are related to each other.

4 **a)** Reena is trying to solve 7·33 ÷ 10 using short division. Find and explain her mistake.

```
      0 · 7  0  3
10 | 7 · ⁷3  3 ³0
```

b) Choose an efficient method to solve the division correctly.

5 Complete these divisions.

$27{\cdot}5 \div \square = 2{\cdot}75$ $\frac{\square}{11} = 0{\cdot}7$

CHALLENGE

6 8 small blocks have the same mass as 6 large blocks. The mass of 1 large block is 14·2 kg. Calculate the mass of 1 small block.

The mass of 1 small block is [ ] kg.

Reflect

Show how to work out 123 ÷ 4 = 30 r 3, giving the answer as a decimal number.

→ Textbook 6B p44

End of unit check

My journal

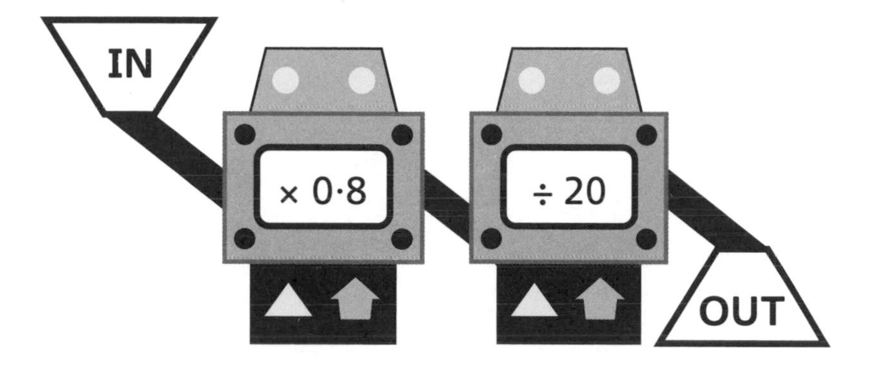

Try each of these inputs in the function machine.

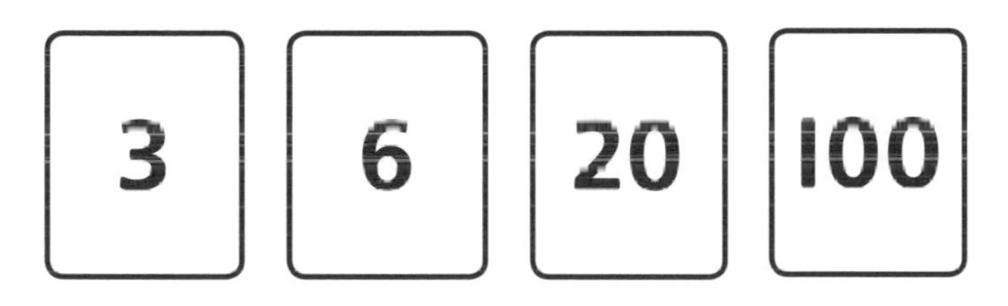

What are the outputs?

Show your working and explain any patterns you notice.

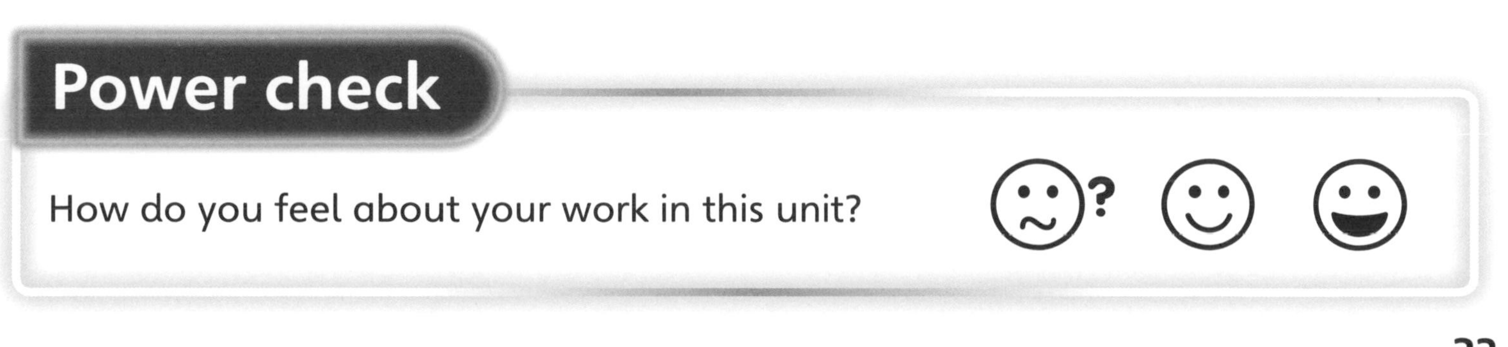

Power check

How do you feel about your work in this unit?

Power play

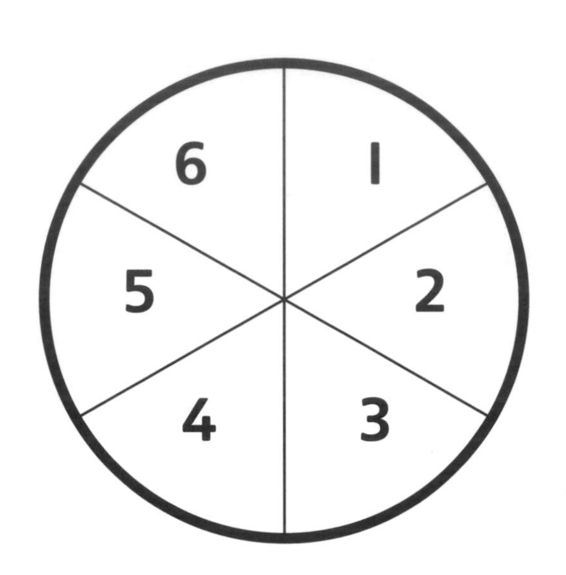

With a partner, take it in turns to use the spinner or roll a dice to get three digits.

Choose how to use the digits to complete this multiplication, and then calculate the answer.

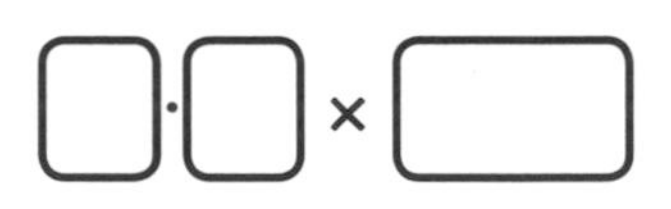

Mark your number on this number line with your initials.

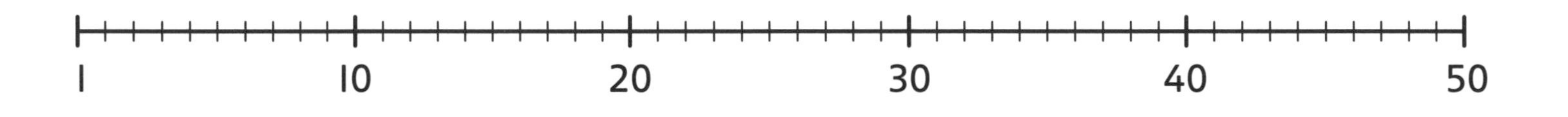

The winner is the first person to get three numbers in a row on the number line, without their partner getting any of the numbers in between.

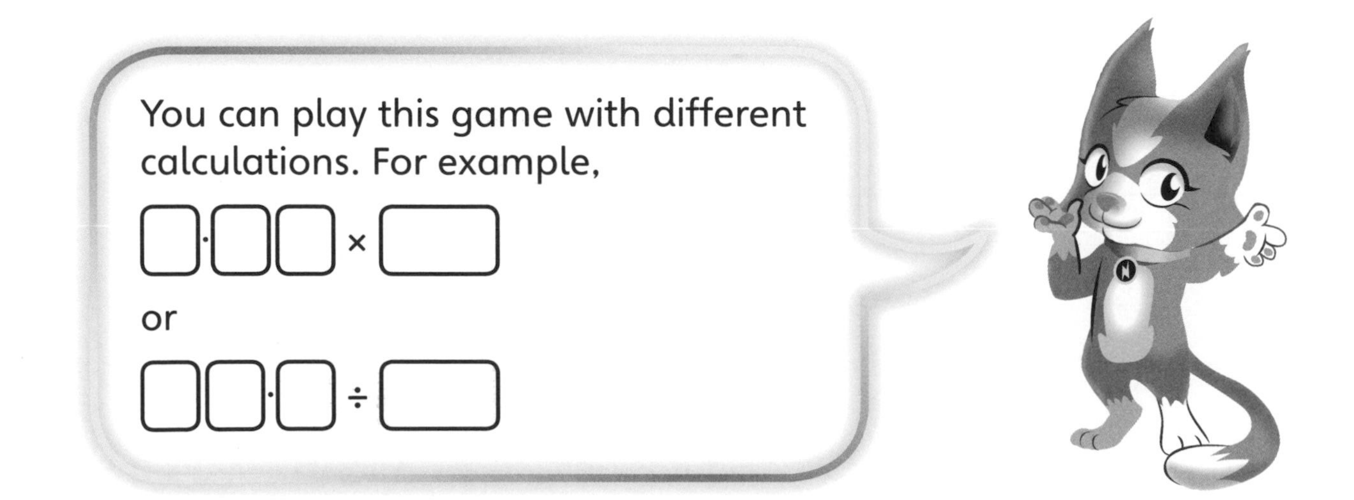

→ Textbook 6B p48

Percentage of 1

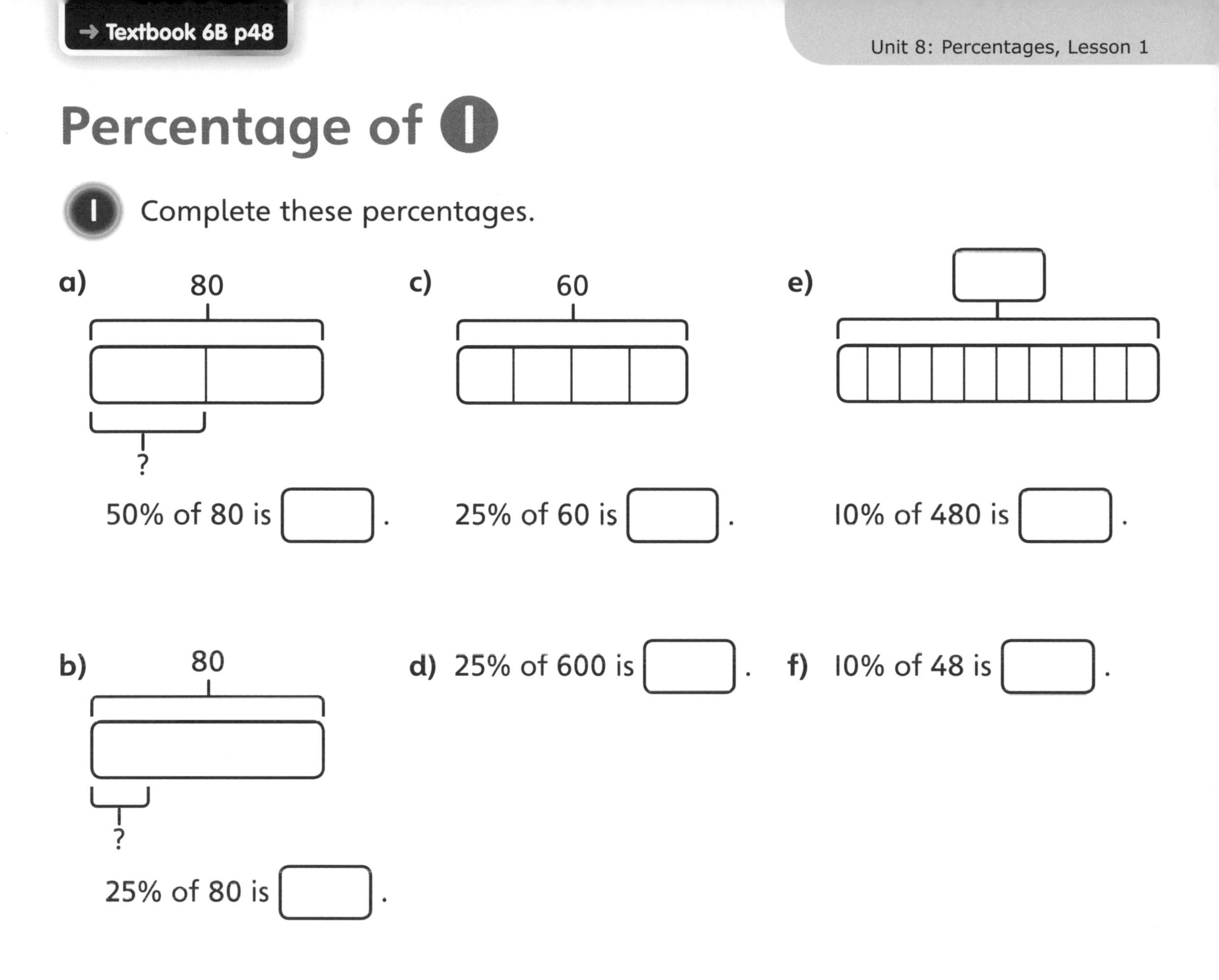

1 Complete these percentages.

a) 50% of 80 is ☐.

b) 25% of 80 is ☐.

c) 25% of 60 is ☐.

d) 25% of 600 is ☐.

e) 10% of 480 is ☐.

f) 10% of 48 is ☐.

2 Colour the grids 50% yellow, 25% red and 10% blue.

a)

b)

3 Calculate the amount of money taken off each item.

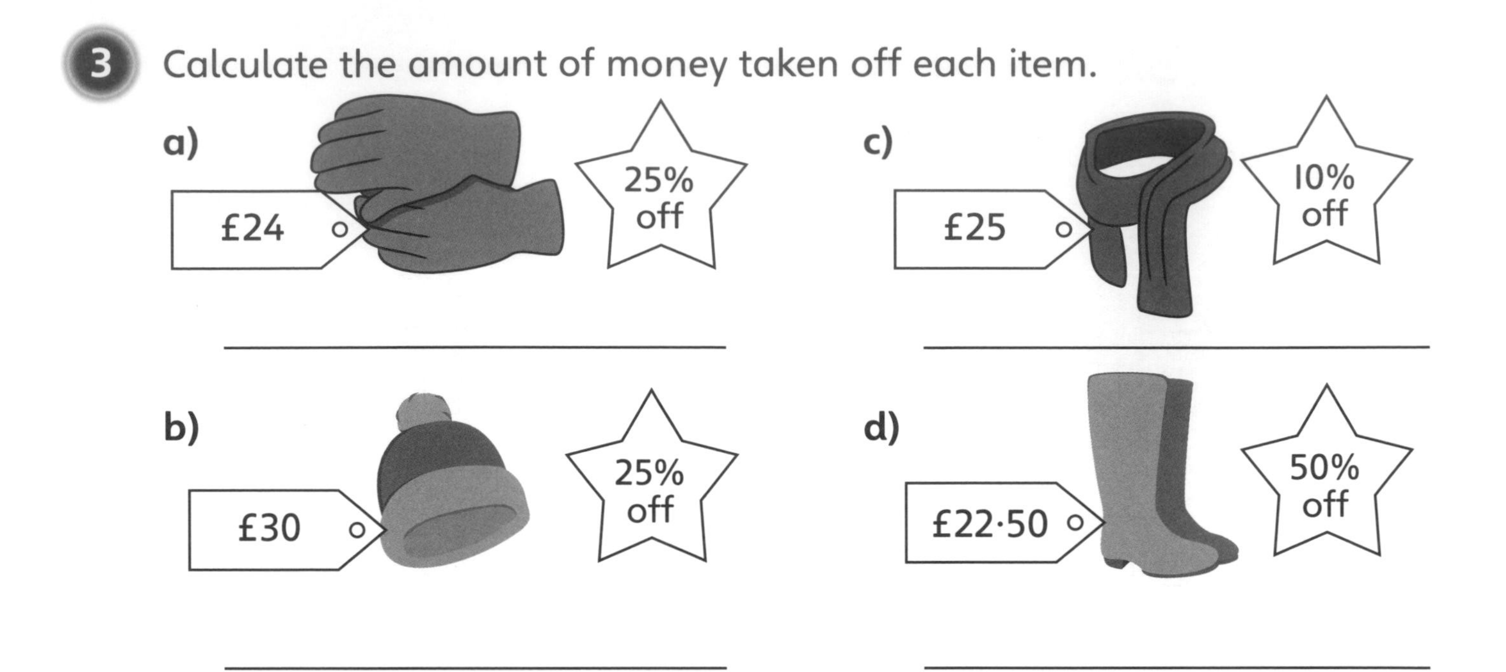

4 **a)** Emma bought 2 kg of fruit. 25% of the weight was pineapple. 10% of the weight was bananas. The rest was apples. How many more grams of apples than bananas did Emma buy?

Emma bought [ ] more grams of apples than bananas.

b) Aki bought $1\frac{1}{2}$ kg of vegetables. 25% was potatoes.

Bella bought $3\frac{1}{2}$ kg of vegetables. 10% was potatoes. Who bought more potatoes?

__________ bought more potatoes.

5 Find the percentages.

50% of 50 = ☐ 25% of 50 = ☐ 10% of 30 = ☐

50% of 5 = ☐ 25% of 500 = ☐ 10% of ☐ = 30

50% of 0·5 = ☐ 25% of 1,000 = ☐ 10% of 3 = ☐

CHALLENGE

6 Richard has £40. He spends 50% on Saturday. On Sunday he spends 10% of what is left. On Monday he gives 25% of the remaining amount to charity. He then spends £5·75 at the cinema. How much money does Richard have left?

Richard has £ ☐ left.

Reflect

Create a diagram to show how to find 10% of any number. Explain what you did.

To find 10% of a number ______________________

____

______________________.

→ Textbook 6B p52

Percentage of 2

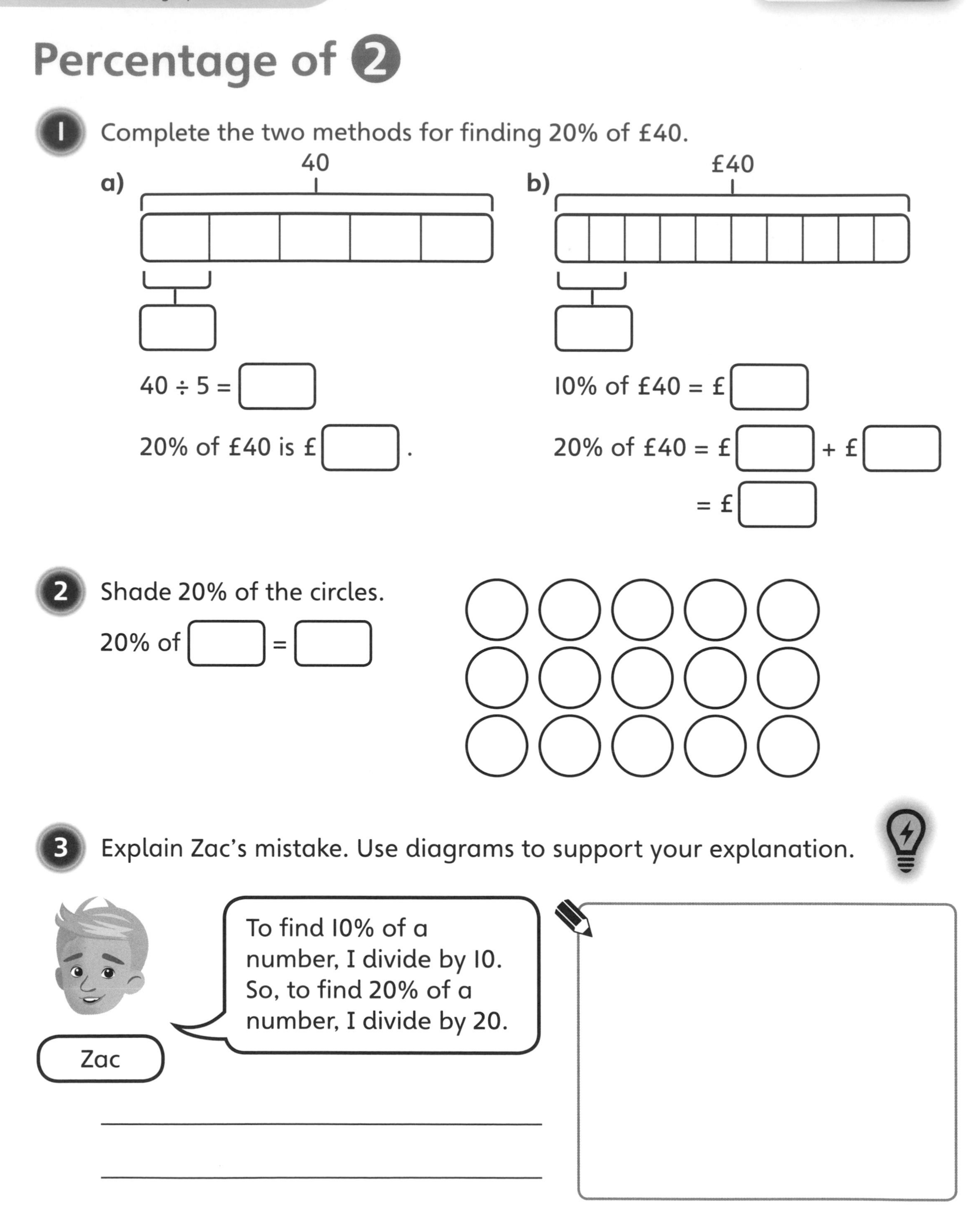

1 Complete the two methods for finding 20% of £40.

a) 40

40 ÷ 5 = ☐

20% of £40 is £☐.

b) £40

10% of £40 = £☐

20% of £40 = £☐ + £☐

= £☐

2 Shade 20% of the circles.

20% of ☐ = ☐

3 Explain Zac's mistake. Use diagrams to support your explanation.

4 Complete the table.

Starting number	10% of the number	20% of the number
400		
410		
41		
401		
	1·4	
		4·1

5 **a)** Ambika takes part in a 24 km cycle ride. She has completed 20% of the journey. How many metres has she cycled?

24 km

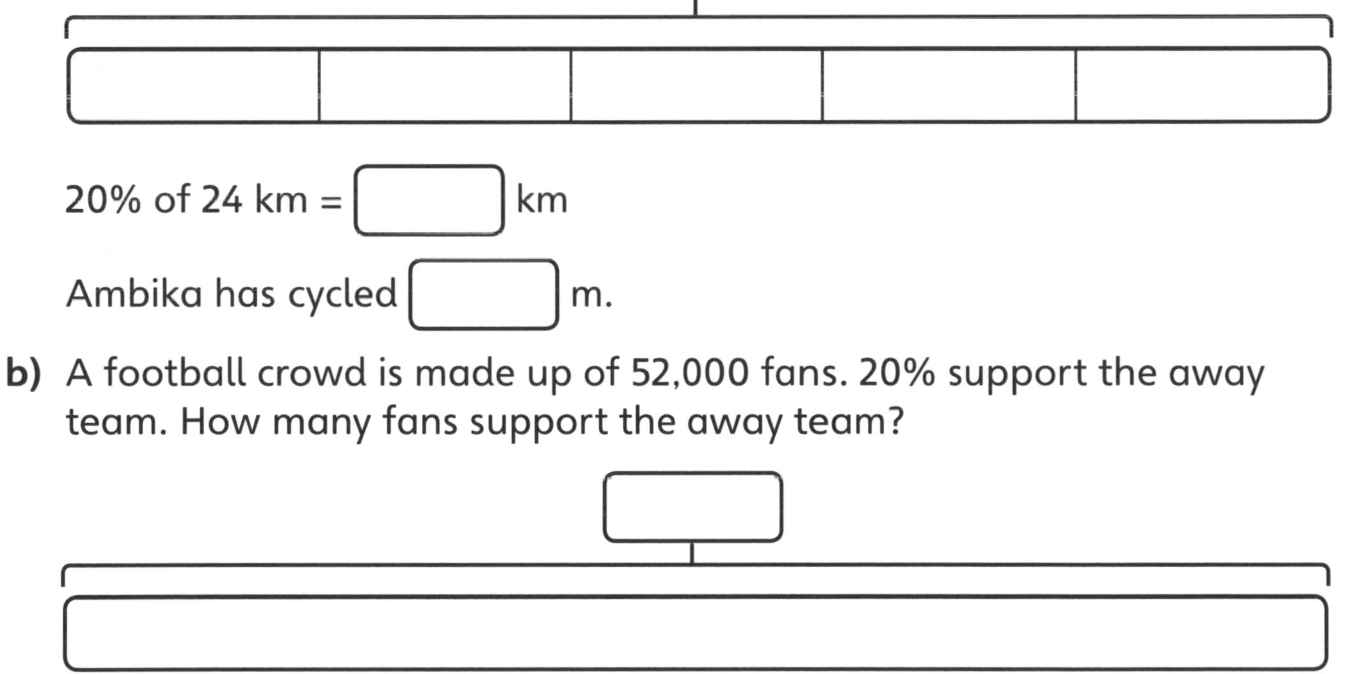

20% of 24 km = ☐ km

Ambika has cycled ☐ m.

b) A football crowd is made up of 52,000 fans. 20% support the away team. How many fans support the away team?

20% of ☐ is ☐ .

☐ fans support the away team.

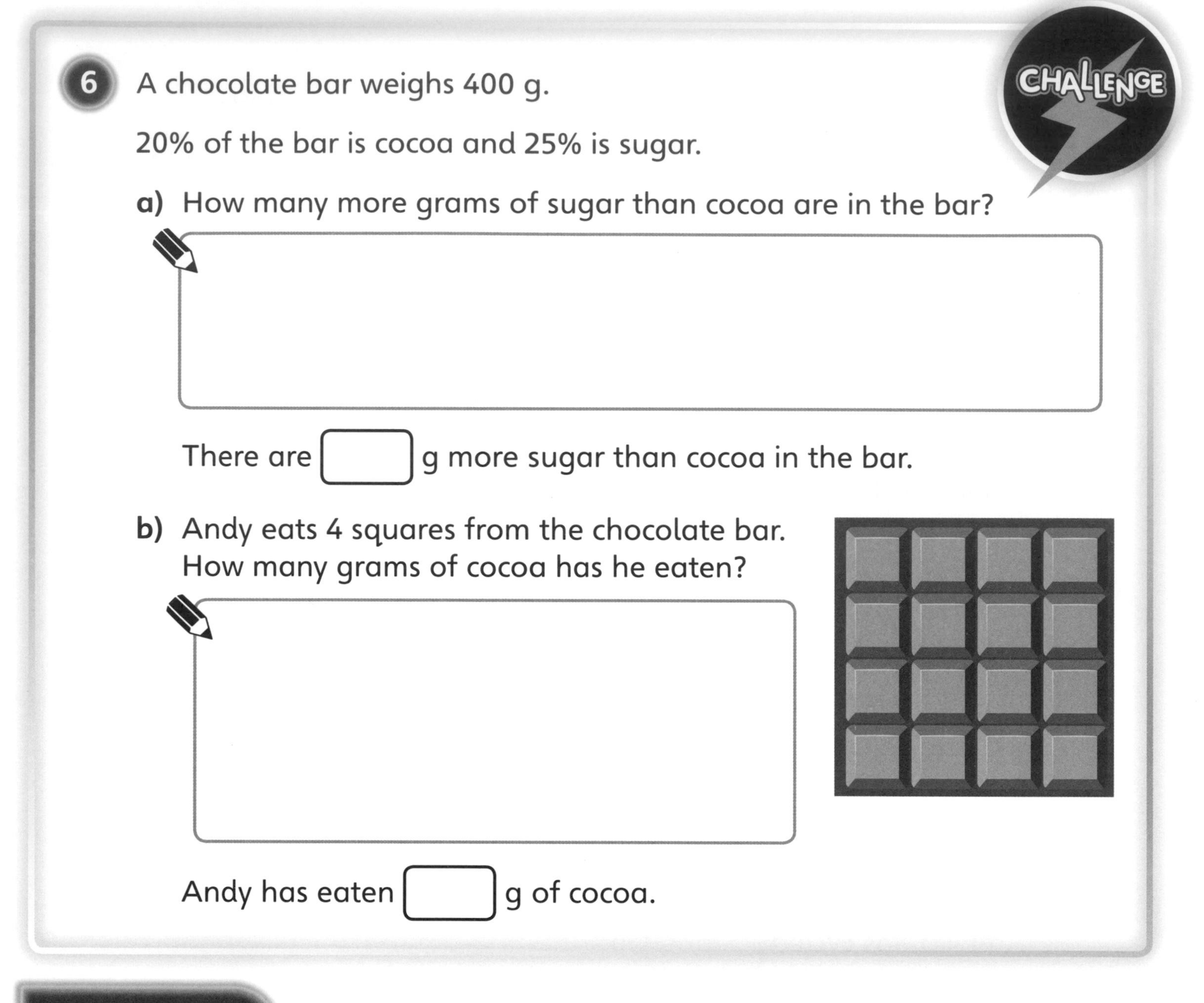

6 A chocolate bar weighs 400 g.

20% of the bar is cocoa and 25% is sugar.

a) How many more grams of sugar than cocoa are in the bar?

There are [ ] g more sugar than cocoa in the bar.

b) Andy eats 4 squares from the chocolate bar. How many grams of cocoa has he eaten?

Andy has eaten [ ] g of cocoa.

Reflect

Lexi says that if she knows 10% of an amount, she can work out any other amount. Is she correct? Explain your answer.

→ Textbook 6B p56

Percentage of 3

Find 1% of each number.

a)

	Th	H	T	O
Whole amount		7	0	0
1% of whole amount				

b)

	Th	H	T	O
Whole amount		6	0	0
1% of whole amount				

c)

	Th	H	T	O
Whole amount	1	7	0	0
1% of whole amount				

d)

	Th	H	T	O	•	Tth	Hth
Whole amount			6	1	•		
1% of whole amount					•		

Match the calculations and complete the missing answers.

1% of 300 = ☐

10% of 3,000 = ☐

1% of 30 = ☐

10% of 300 = ☐

$\frac{1}{10}$ of 3,000 = 300

	H	T	O
Whole amount	3	0	0
$\frac{1}{10}$ of whole amount		3	0

30 ÷ 100 = 0·3

300 ÷ 100 = 3

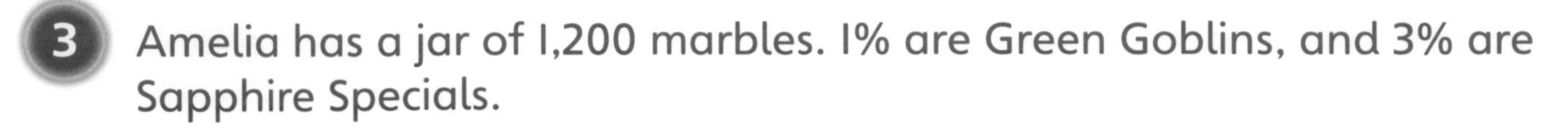

3 Amelia has a jar of 1,200 marbles. 1% are Green Goblins, and 3% are Sapphire Specials.

How many of each type are there?

a) 1% of 1,200 = ☐

There are ☐ Green Goblins.

b) ☐ × 3 = ☐

3% of 1,200 = ☐

There are ☐ Sapphire Specials.

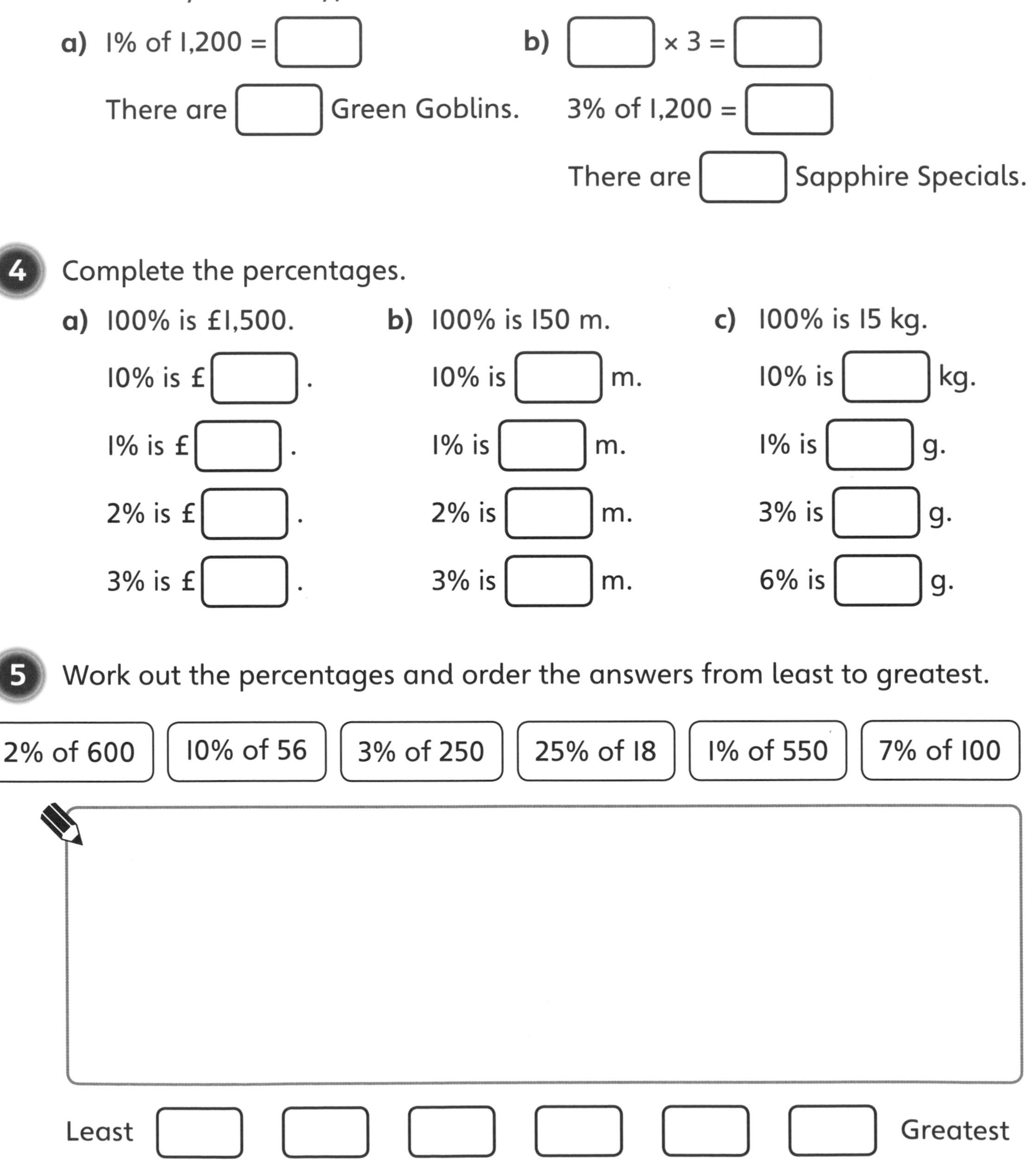

4 Complete the percentages.

a) 100% is £1,500.

10% is £ ☐ .

1% is £ ☐ .

2% is £ ☐ .

3% is £ ☐ .

b) 100% is 150 m.

10% is ☐ m.

1% is ☐ m.

2% is ☐ m.

3% is ☐ m.

c) 100% is 15 kg.

10% is ☐ kg.

1% is ☐ g.

3% is ☐ g.

6% is ☐ g.

5 Work out the percentages and order the answers from least to greatest.

2% of 600	10% of 56	3% of 250	25% of 18	1% of 550	7% of 100

Least ☐ ☐ ☐ ☐ ☐ ☐ Greatest

CHALLENGE

6 **a)** Do you agree with Reena? Explain your answer.

Reena

I think 3% of 200 must be equal to 2% of 300.

b) Explore other examples like this. Explain what you notice and write a statement of your own.

Reflect

Draw a diagram and explain how to find 3% of any number.

→ Textbook 6B p60

Percentage of 4

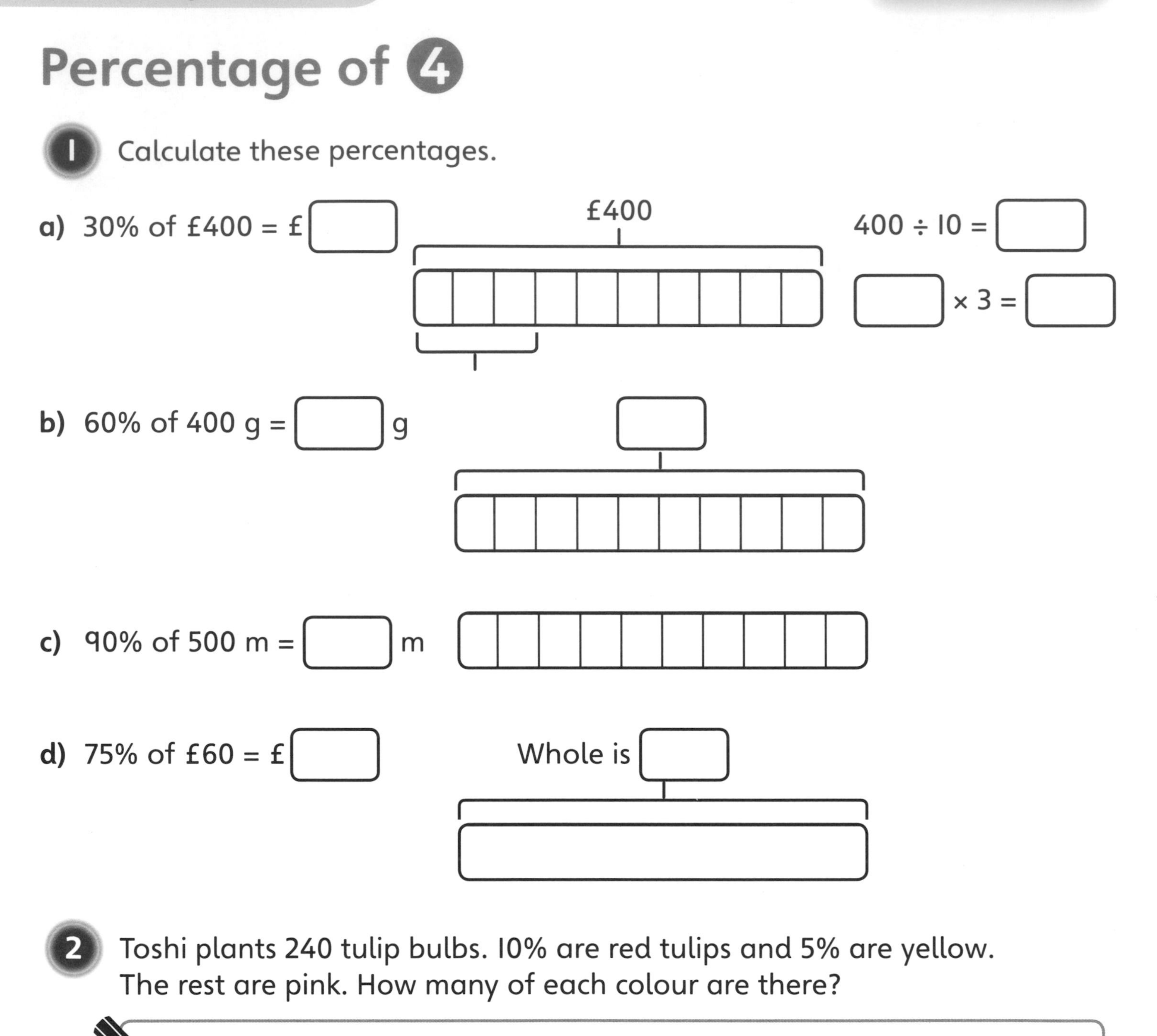

1 Calculate these percentages.

a) 30% of £400 = £ ☐

£400

400 ÷ 10 = ☐

☐ × 3 = ☐

b) 60% of 400 g = ☐ g

c) 90% of 500 m = ☐ m

d) 75% of £60 = £ ☐

Whole is ☐

2 Toshi plants 240 tulip bulbs. 10% are red tulips and 5% are yellow. The rest are pink. How many of each colour are there?

There are ☐ red tulips.

There are ☐ yellow tulips.

There are ☐ pink tulips.

3 **a)** Complete these percentages.

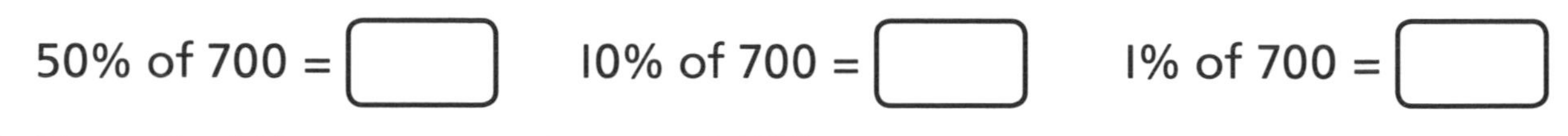

b) Now find these percentages of 700.

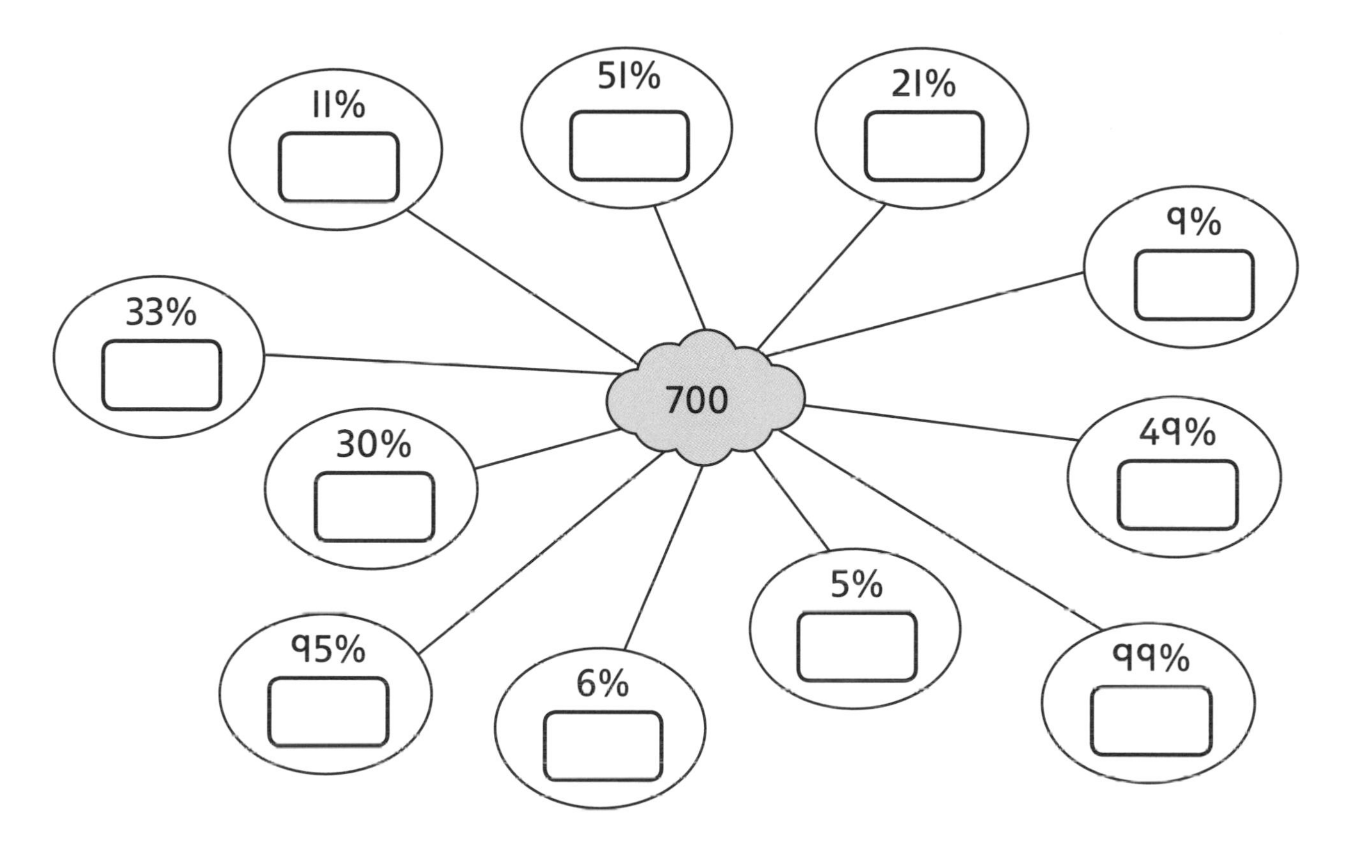

4 32,500 people signed up to run a marathon.

11% dropped out before race day. 29% did not complete the course.

How many people finished the marathon?

[ ] people finished the marathon.

CHALLENGE

5 On Monday, the groundskeeper mowed 30% of the football pitch.

On Tuesday, she mowed half of the remaining area.

On Wednesday, she mowed 1,250 square metres.

What area of the pitch was left to mow on Thursday?

70 m

100 m

[ ] square metres of the pitch still needed mowing on Thursday.

Reflect

Show two different ways to find 85% of 300.

→ Textbook 6B p64

Finding missing values

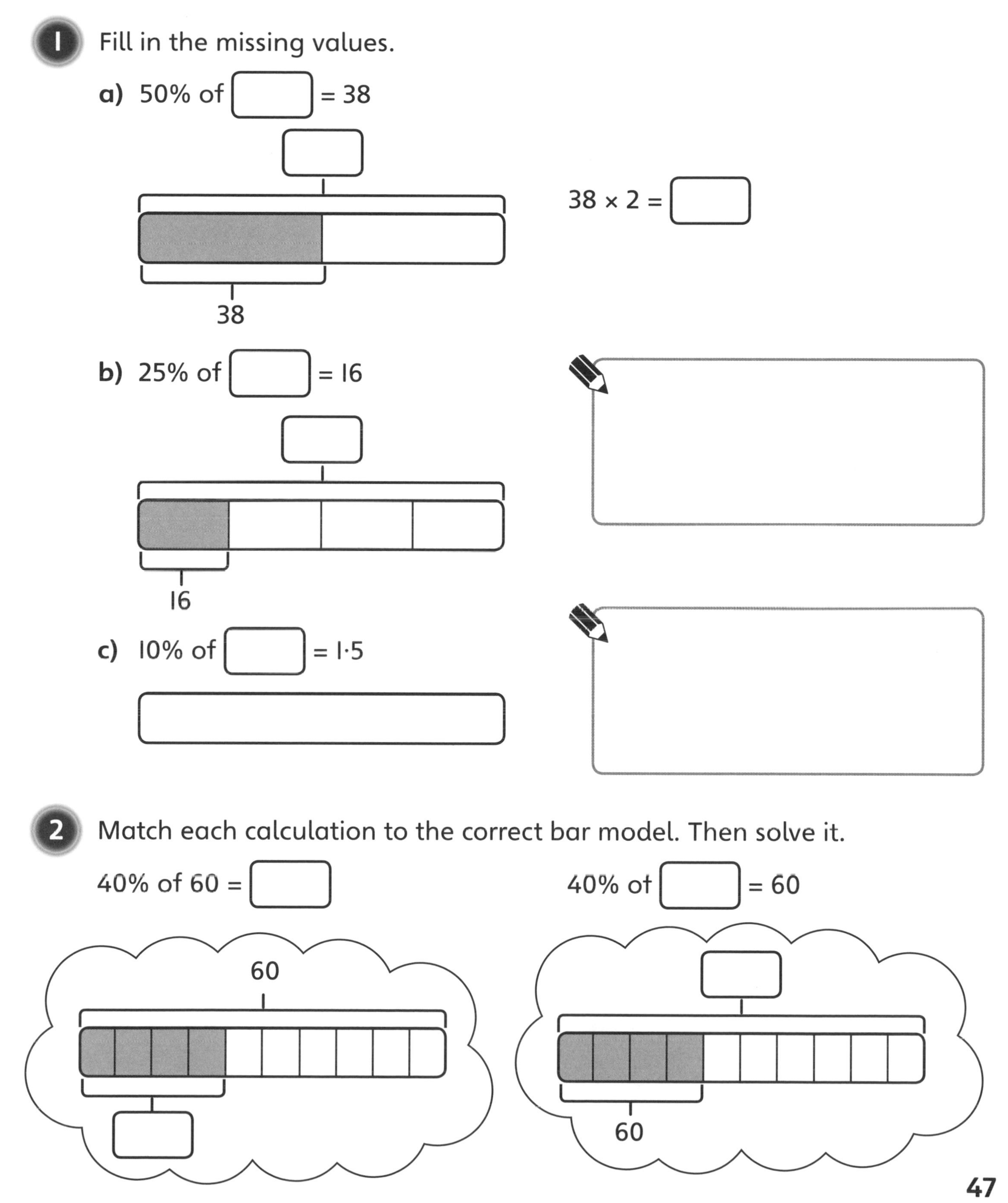

1 Fill in the missing values.

a) 50% of [ ] = 38

38 × 2 = [ ]

b) 25% of [ ] = 16

c) 10% of [ ] = 1·5

2 Match each calculation to the correct bar model. Then solve it.

40% of 60 = [ ]

40% of [ ] = 60

3 **a)** In a bag of orange and lemon sweets, 30% are orange and 63 sweets are lemon. How many orange sweets are there?

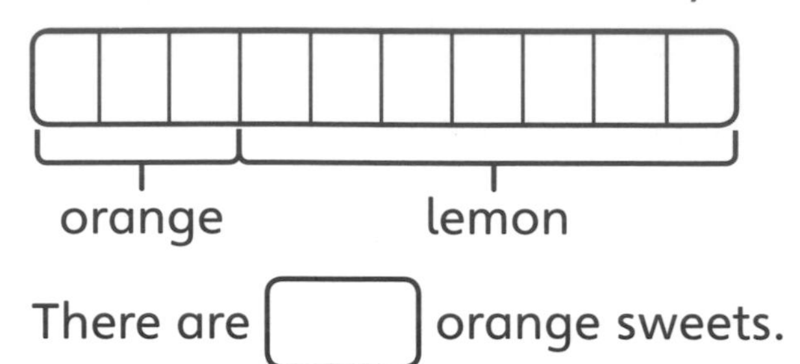

There are ☐ orange sweets.

b) Amelia has a piece of string. She cuts off 25%. The piece that is left is 240 cm long. How long was the string before she cut it?

The string was ☐ cm long before Amelia cut it.

4 **a)** Find a solution to Aki's percentage puzzle.

I am thinking of a number. I subtract 20. I then find 10% of what is left. I finish on 40. What number did I start with?

Aki

b) Find a solution to Alex's percentage puzzle.

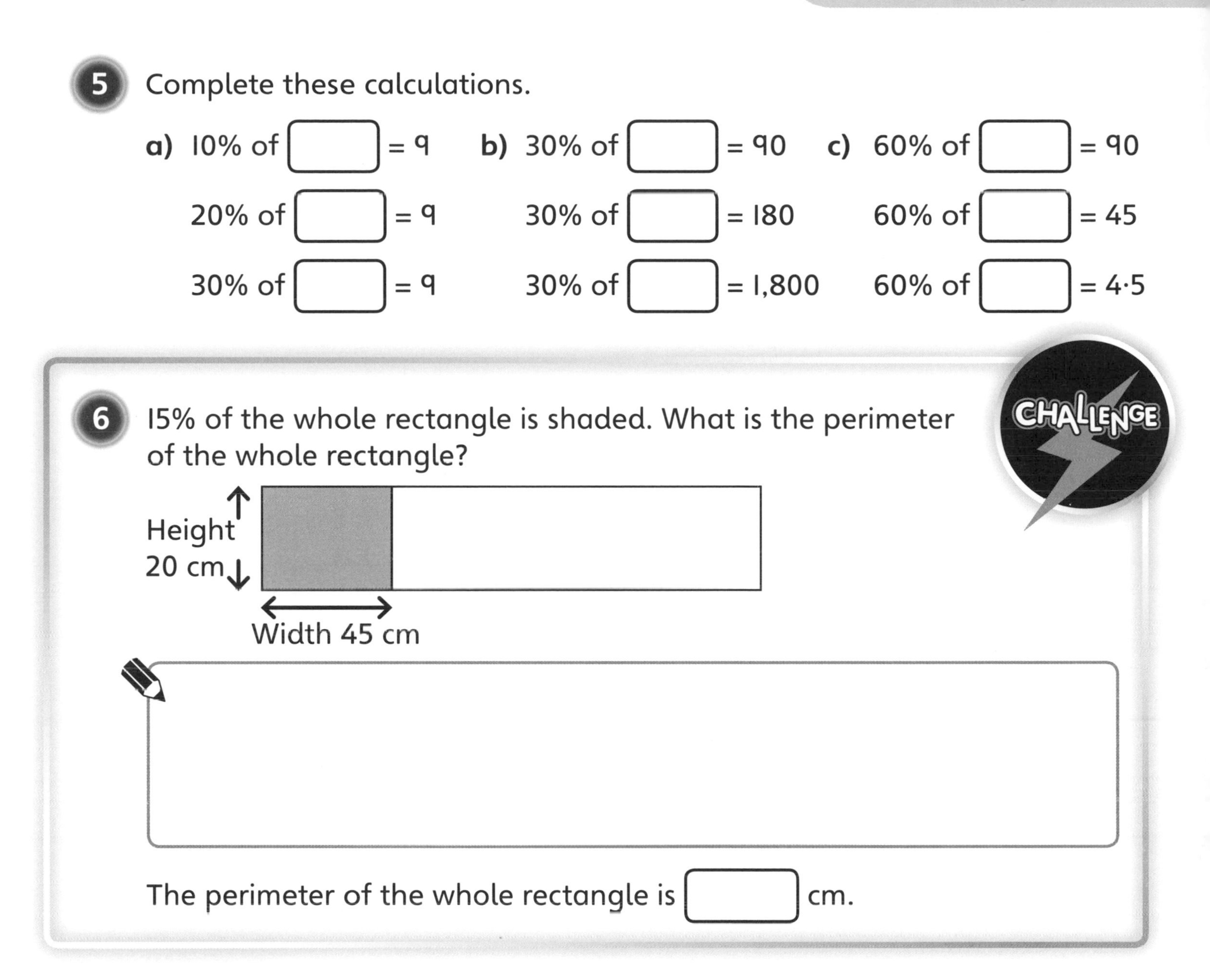

5 Complete these calculations.

a) 10% of ☐ = 9
20% of ☐ = 9
30% of ☐ = 9

b) 30% of ☐ = 90
30% of ☐ = 180
30% of ☐ = 1,800

c) 60% of ☐ = 90
60% of ☐ = 45
60% of ☐ = 4·5

CHALLENGE

6 15% of the whole rectangle is shaded. What is the perimeter of the whole rectangle?

The perimeter of the whole rectangle is ☐ cm.

Reflect

Draw diagrams to show the differences between '20% of 45 = ?' and '20% of ? = 45'.

→ Textbook 6B p68

Converting fractions to percentages

What percentage is shaded?

a)

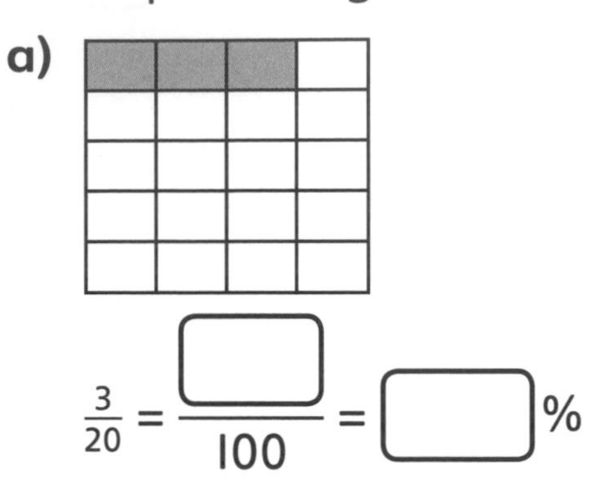

$\frac{3}{20} = \frac{\square}{100} = \square\%$

c)

$\frac{\square}{\square} = \frac{\square}{100} = \square\%$

b)

d)

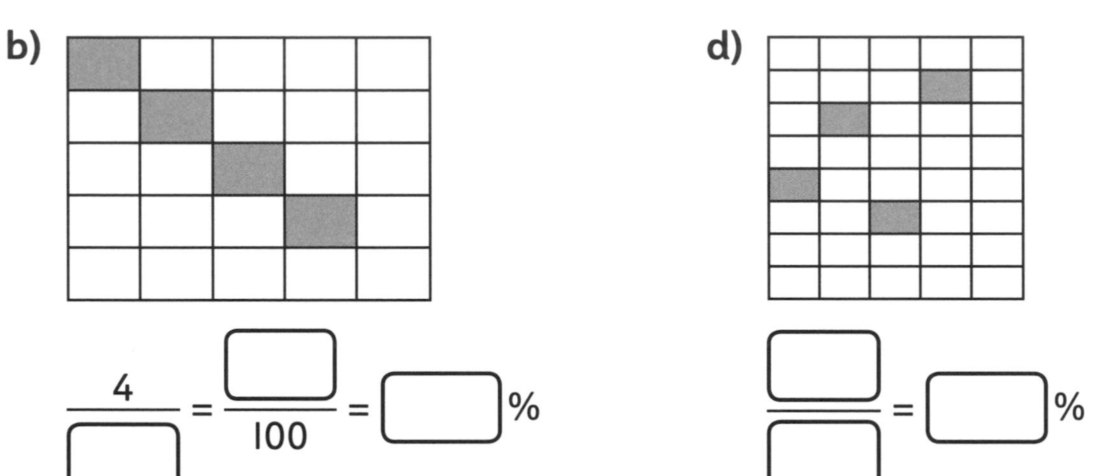

$\frac{4}{\square} = \frac{\square}{100} = \square\%$

$\frac{\square}{\square} = \square\%$

2 Complete each equivalent fraction and then draw a line to its matching percentage.

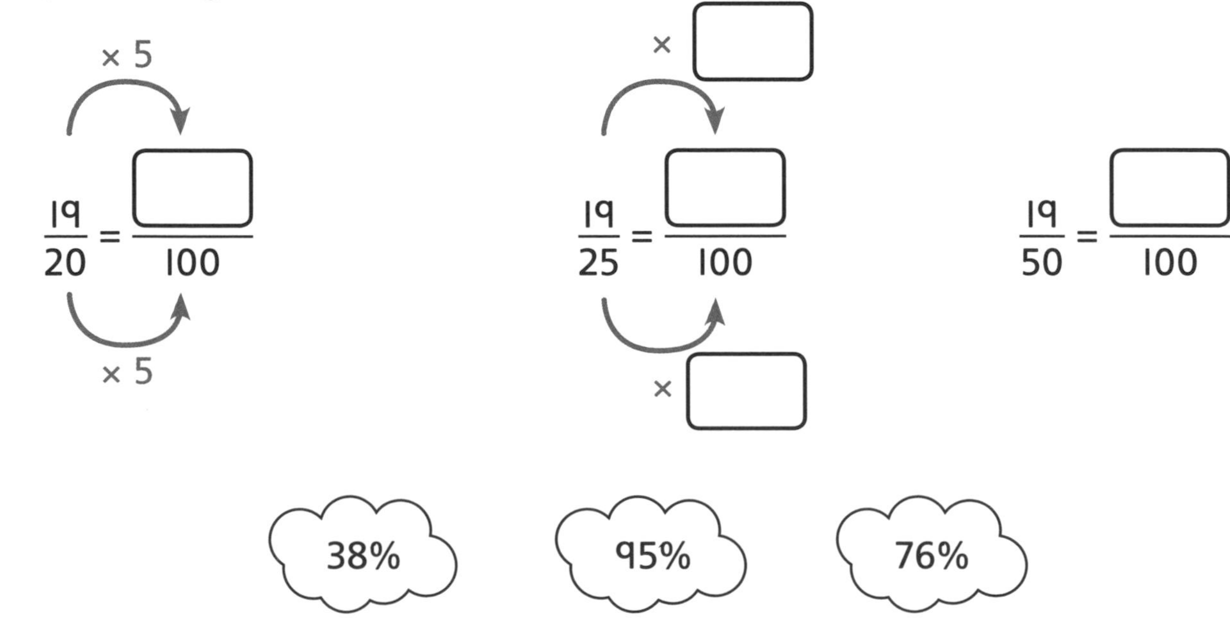

$\frac{19}{20} = \frac{\square}{100}$ (× 5, × 5)

$\frac{19}{25} = \frac{\square}{100}$ (× $\square$, × $\square$)

$\frac{19}{50} = \frac{\square}{100}$

3 Luis and Kate practised penalty kicks. Luis scored 14 out of 20. Kate scored 28 out of 40. What percentage of their penalties did they each score?

4 Reena keeps a record of her hens' eggs. Complete the table.

Week	Number of eggs laid	Number of eggs that hatched	Percentage of eggs hatched
Week 1	10	6	$\frac{6}{10}$ = 60%
Week 2	20	6	$\frac{6}{20}$ = ☐ %
Week 3	8	6	$\frac{6}{☐}$ = ☐ %
Week 4	12	6	

What percentage of each picture is shaded?

a)

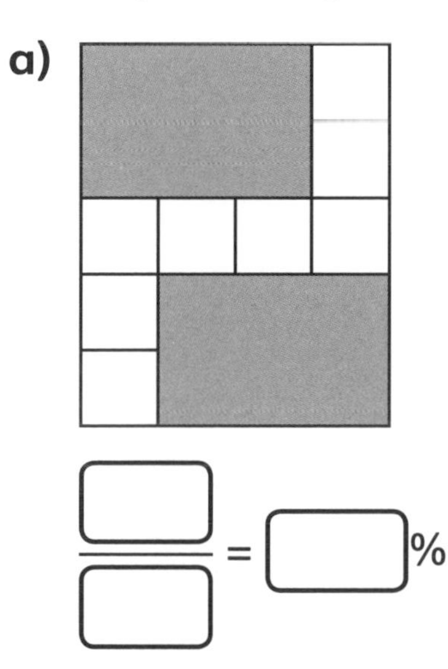

b)

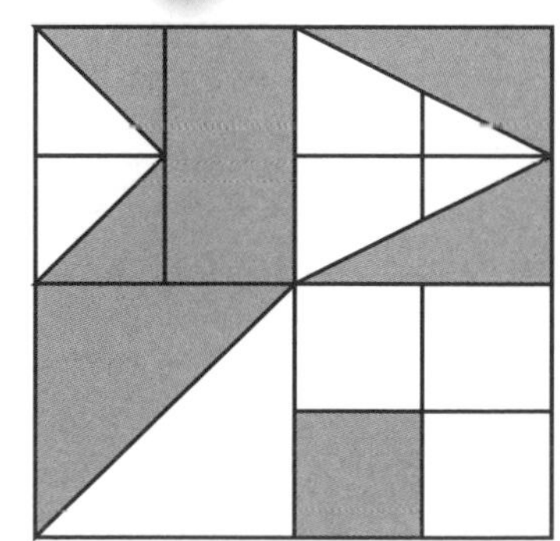

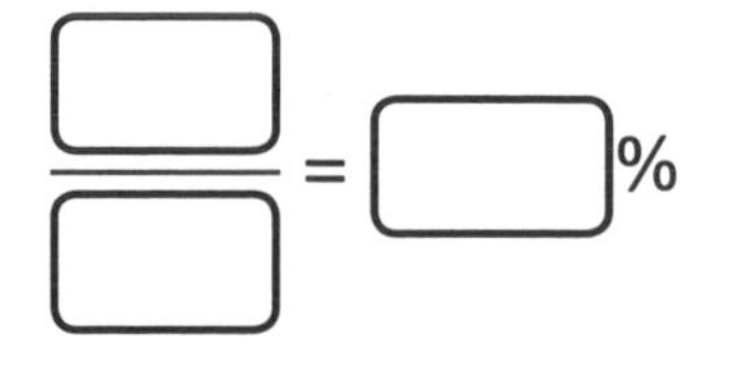

CHALLENGE

6 Mo recorded the number of different-coloured cars in a car park. The bar chart shows his results. What percentage of each car colour did Mo see?

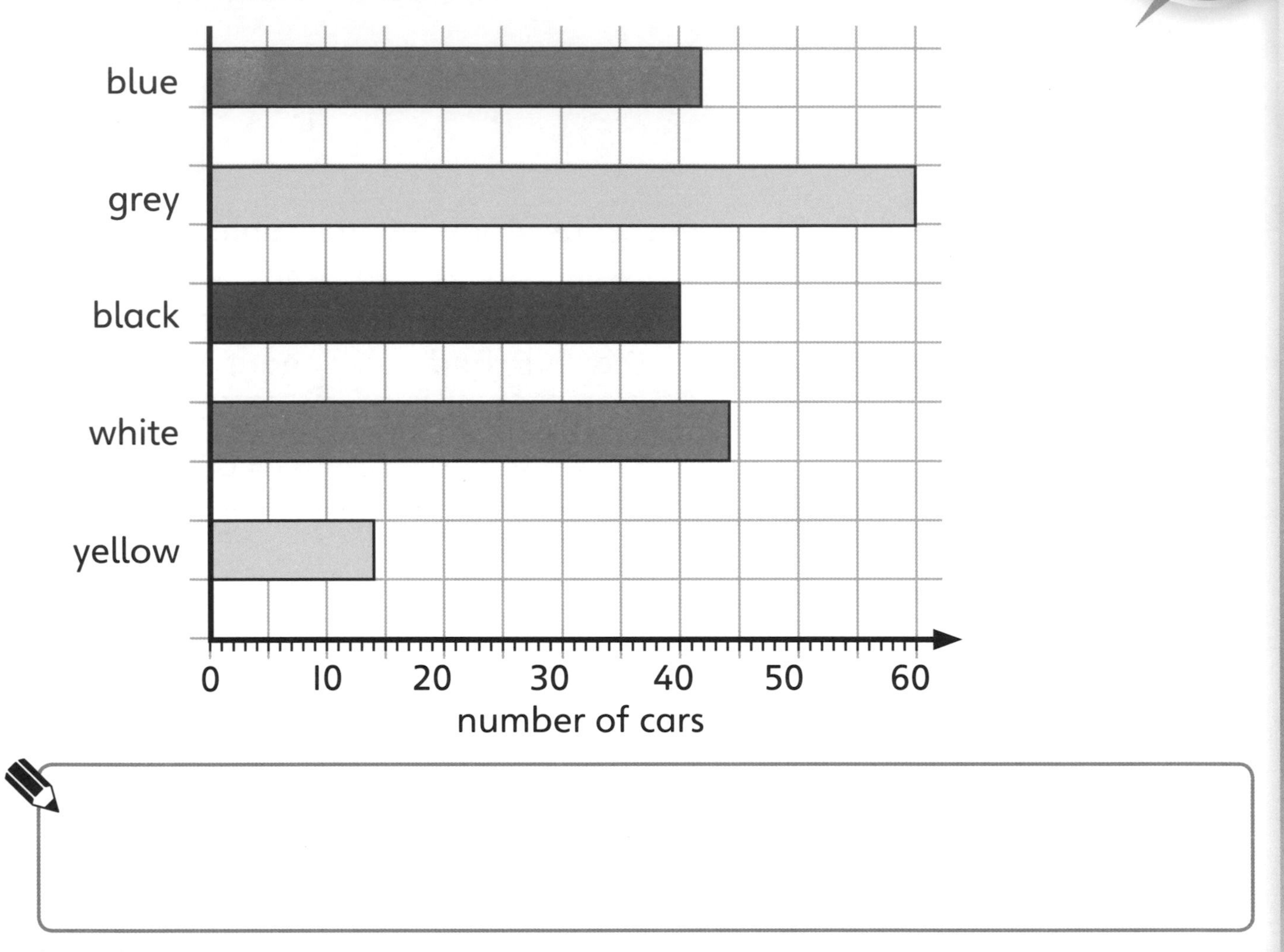

Reflect

Explain how to convert $\frac{3}{25}$ into a percentage.

→ Textbook 6B p72

Equivalent fractions, decimals and percentages 1

1 Complete the equivalent decimals, fractions and percentages for this number line.

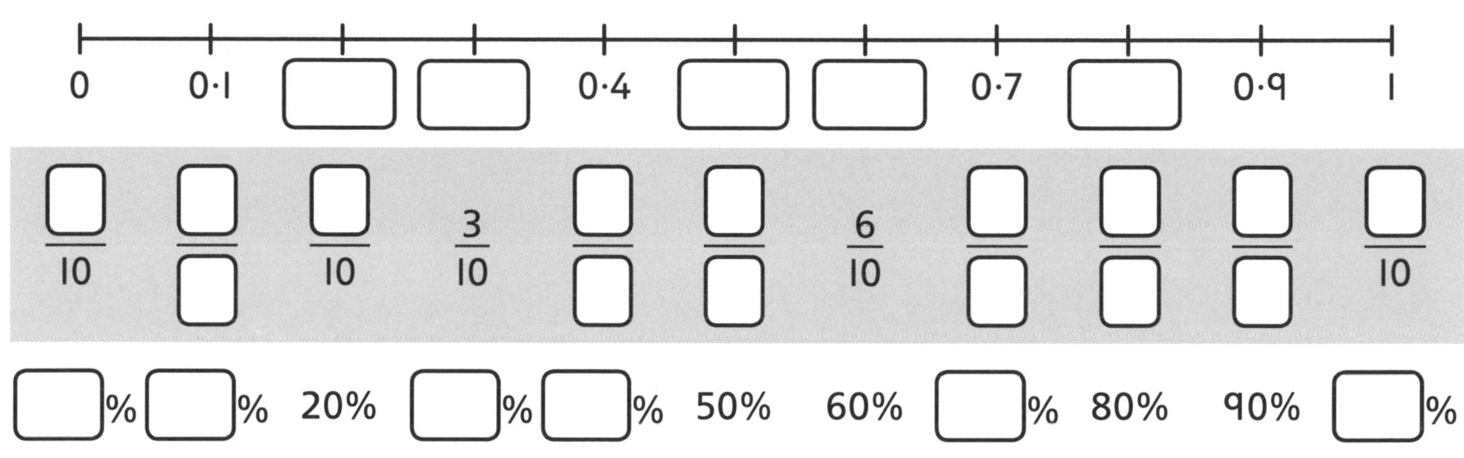

2 Write the fraction, decimal and percentage represented in each diagram.

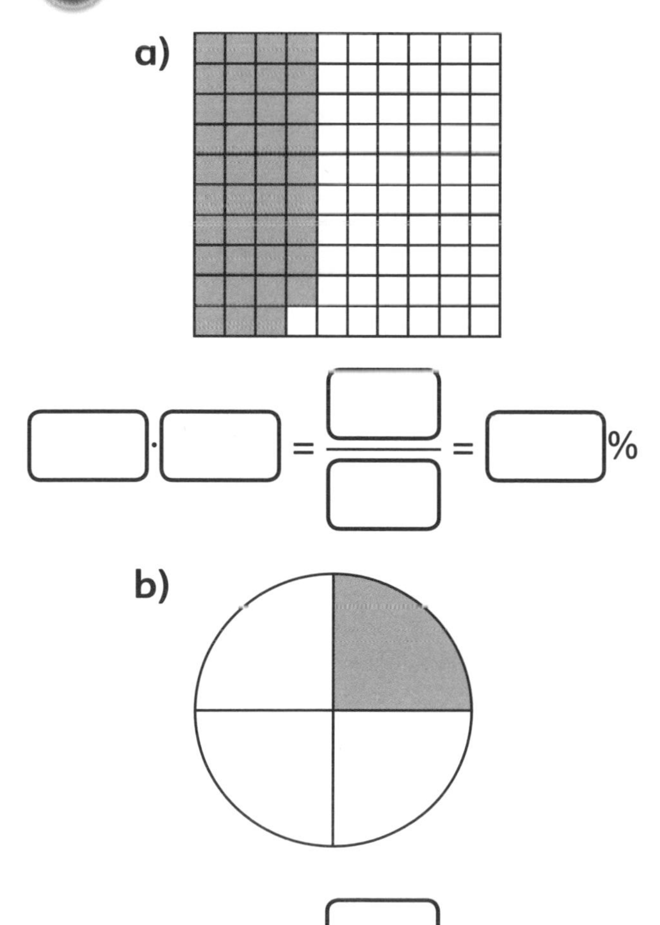

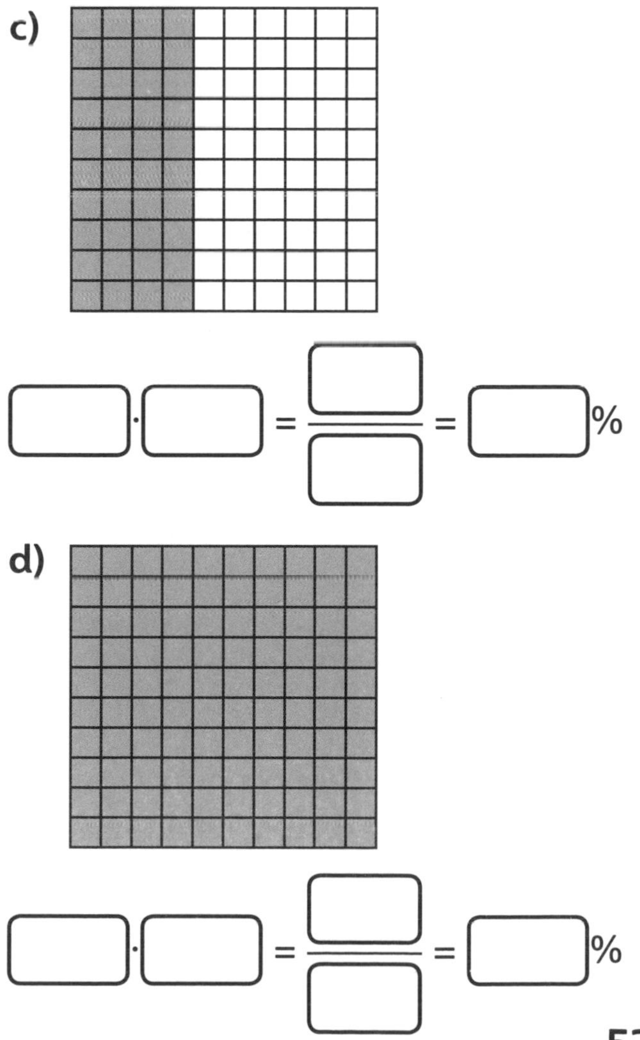

3 Match the equivalent amounts.

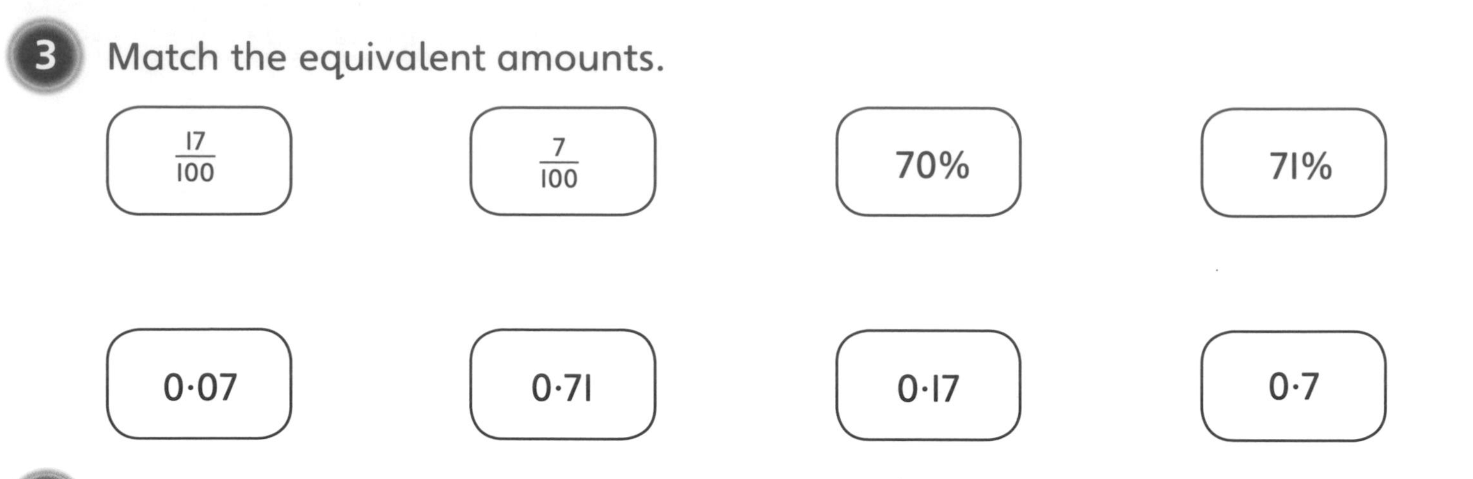

4 Complete the table.

Percentage	**Decimal**	**Fraction**
66%		
	0·6	
		$\frac{9}{100}$
0%		
	0·9	

5 Jamie says that to convert a decimal to a percentage, all you have to do is remove the '0·' and add '%' to the end. For example, 0·43 = 43%.

Explain Jamie's mistakes.

____

____

____

____

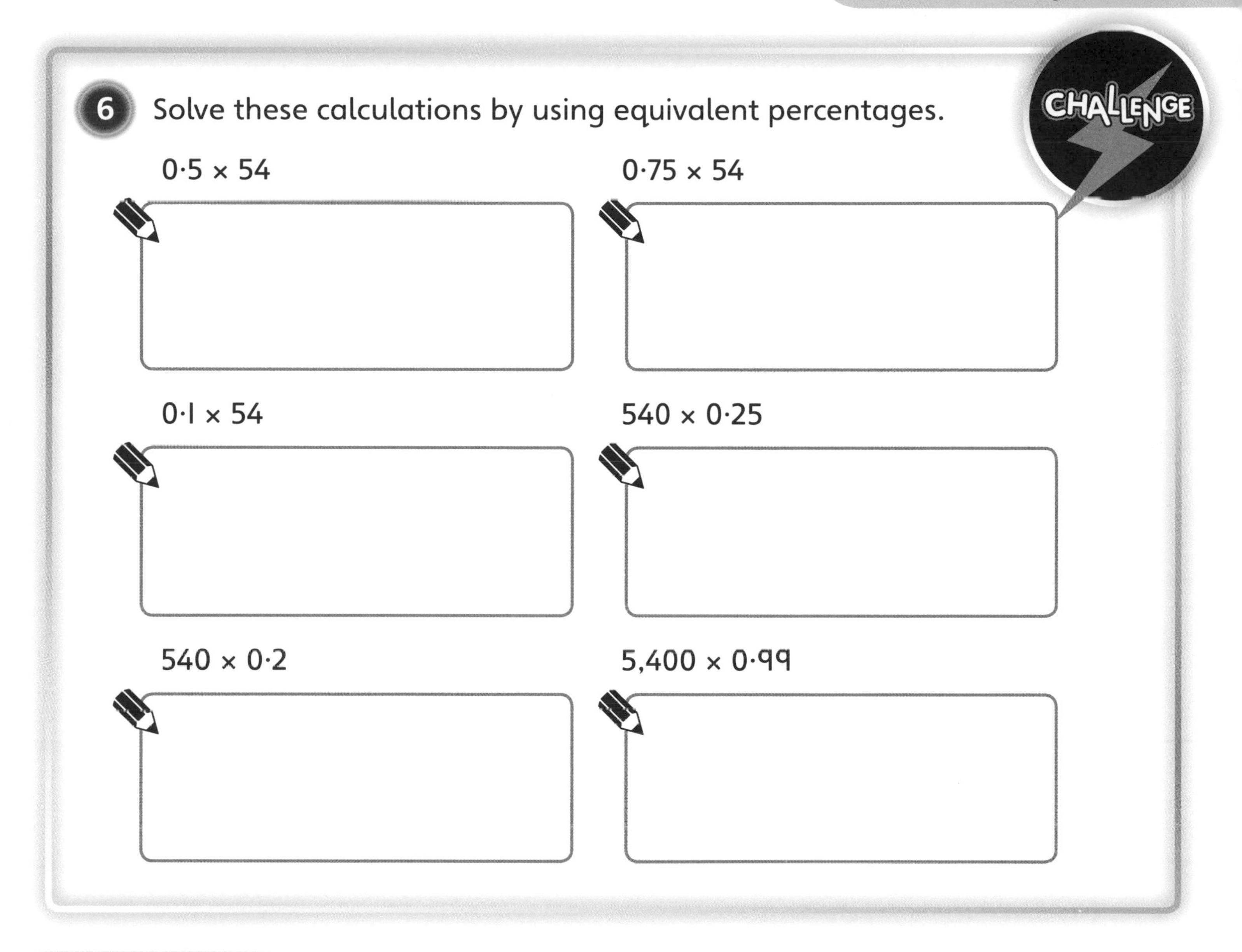

6 Solve these calculations by using equivalent percentages.

0·5 × 54

0·75 × 54

0·1 × 54

540 × 0·25

540 × 0·2

5,400 × 0·99

Reflect

Estimate the fraction, decimal and percentage shown by this bar.

→ Textbook 6B p76

Equivalent fractions, decimals and percentages 2

1 Fill in the blanks with a < or > sign.

a) $\frac{4}{5}$ ◯ 85%

b) 0·404 ◯ $\frac{100}{250}$

c) 99% ◯ $\frac{199}{200}$

2 Which two amounts are equal?

$\frac{7}{8}$ 90% $\frac{88}{1,000}$ 88% $\frac{9}{100}$ 0·009 0·088 0·7 0·78

$\square = \square$

3 Order these amounts from smallest to greatest.

57% $\frac{3}{10}$ $\frac{17}{25}$ 61% 0·55 0·62 $\frac{41}{50}$

$\square < \square < \square < \square < \square < \square < \square$

4 Is $1{\cdot}8$ more than $1\frac{17}{20}$? Explain your answer.

5 Find the mid-point between the two amounts on each number line.

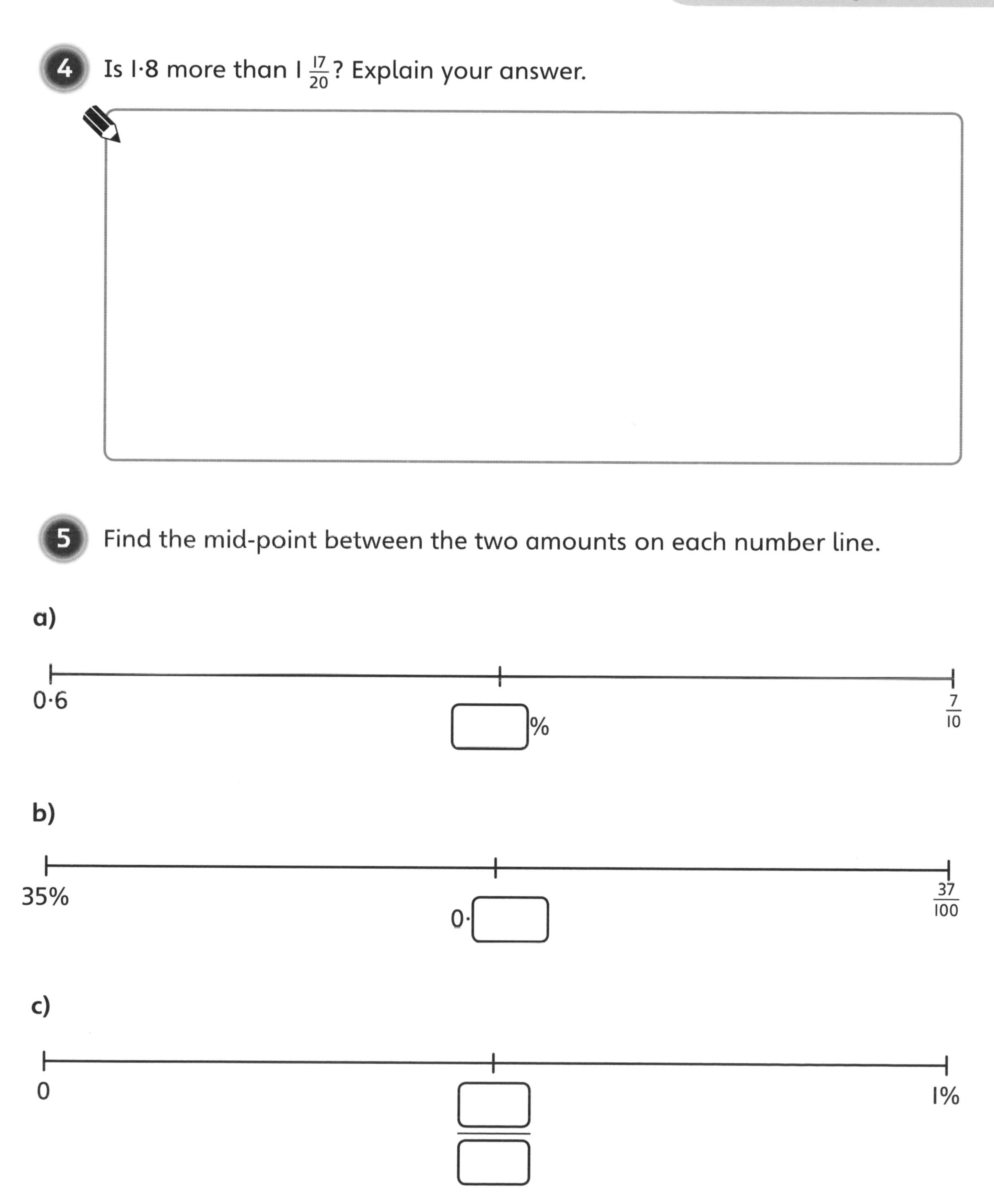

CHALLENGE

6 **a)** Ebo has eaten 87% of an apple. Lexi has eaten $\frac{4}{9}$ of 2 apples. Who has eaten the most apple?

Draw a diagram to show your reasoning.

______________ has eaten the most apple.

b) Write your own similar problem.

____

____

____

Reflect

Explain how to order fractions, decimals and percentages.

- To order fractions, decimals and percentages ______________
- ____
- ____
- ____.
-

→ Textbook 6B p80

Mixed problem solving

Patterns are made from these two tiles.

What fraction of each design is shaded?

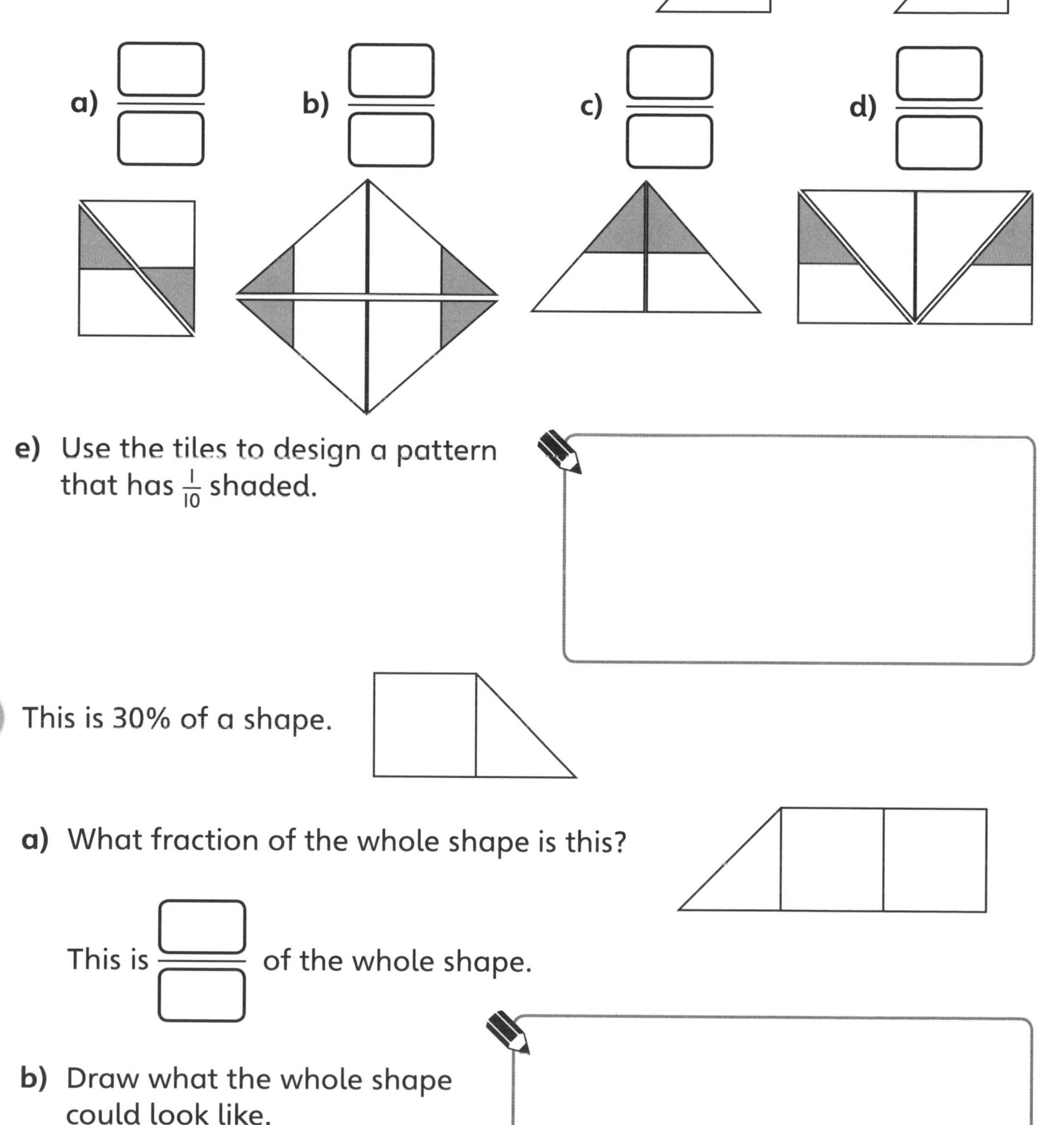

e) Use the tiles to design a pattern that has $\frac{1}{10}$ shaded.

2 This is 30% of a shape.

a) What fraction of the whole shape is this?

This is $\frac{\square}{\square}$ of the whole shape.

b) Draw what the whole shape could look like.

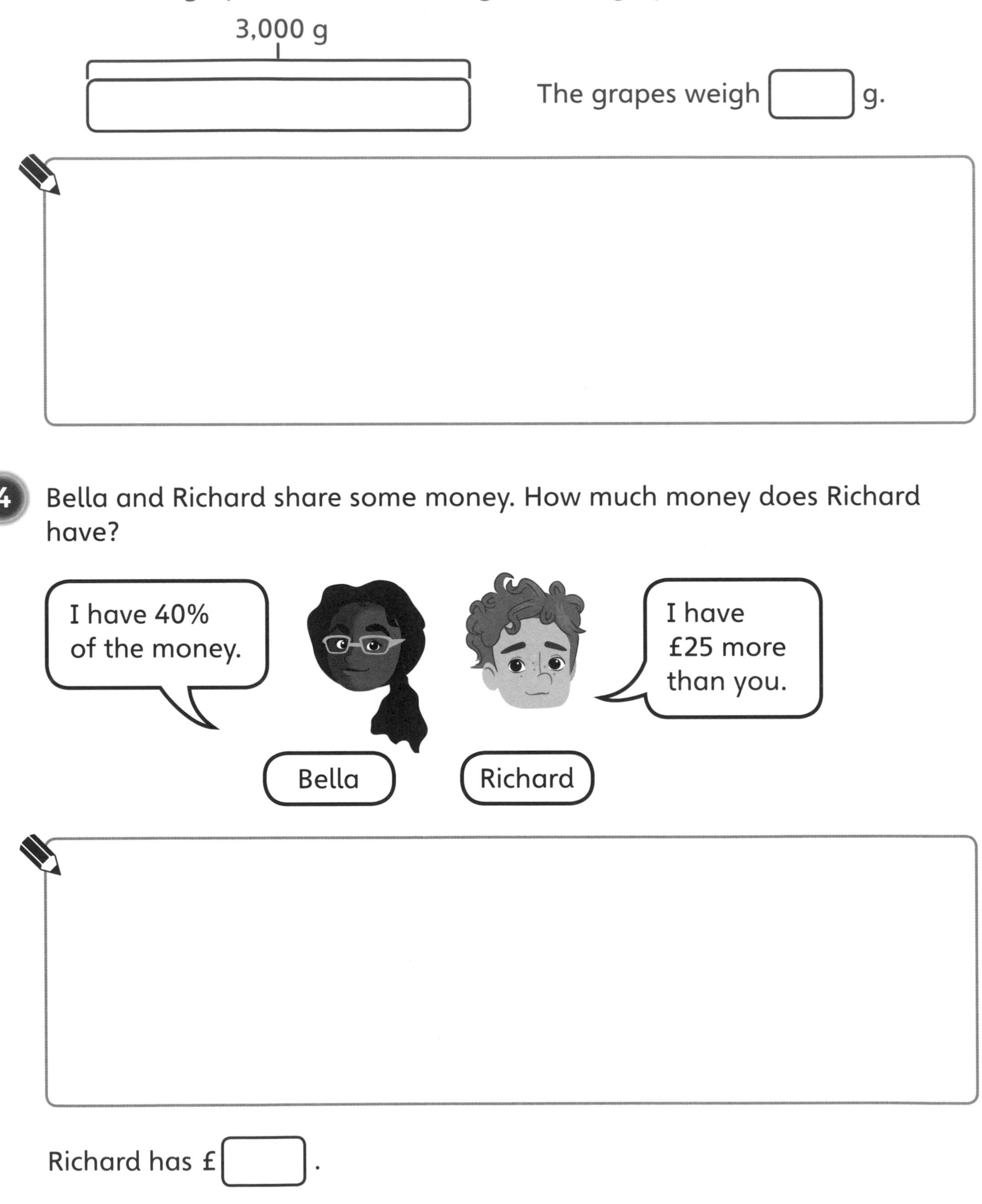

3 Andy buys 3,000 g of fruit. $\frac{3}{10}$ of the weight is apples. 45% is bananas. The rest is grapes. What is the weight of the grapes?

The grapes weigh [ ] g.

4 Bella and Richard share some money. How much money does Richard have?

Richard has £[ ].

5 Max scored 45% on the first half of a test and 50% on the second half. He thinks he scores 95% altogether. Explain Max's mistake.

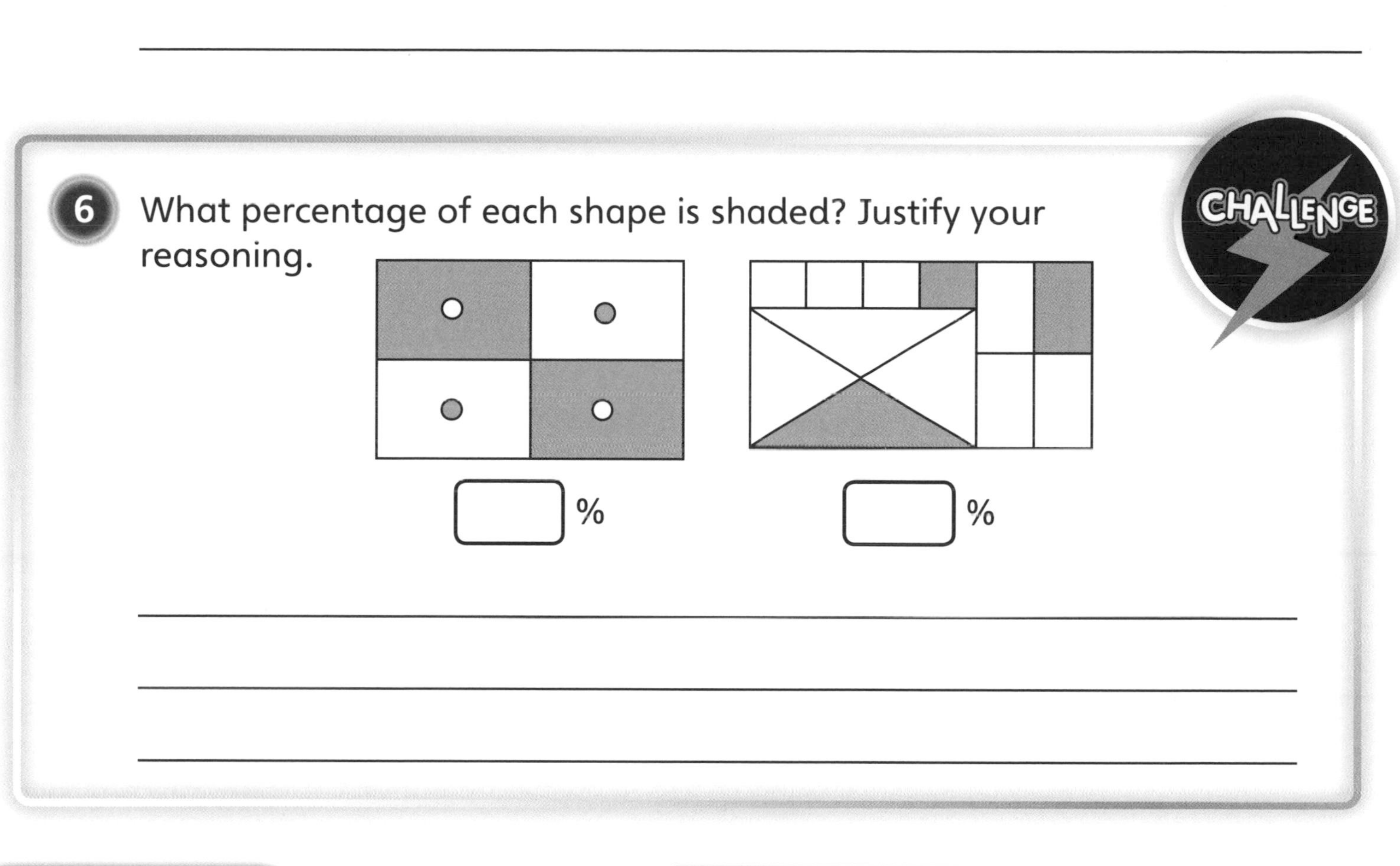

6 What percentage of each shape is shaded? Justify your reasoning.

Reflect

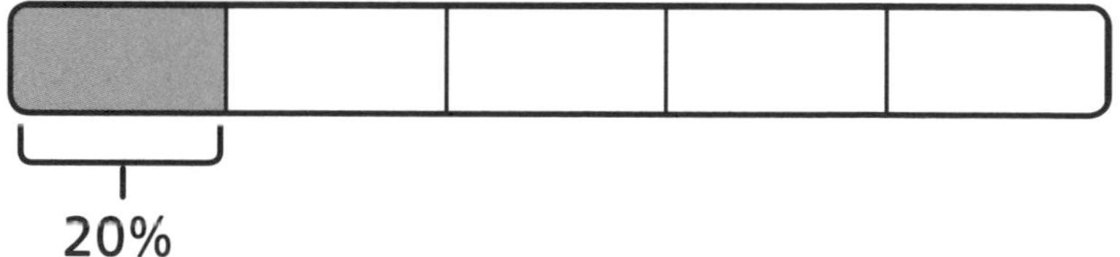

Write a story problem about percentages and fractions that fits this bar model.

→ Textbook 6B p84

End of unit check

My journal

a) Shade 25% of the diagram. Explain your decisions.

b) Shade 35% of this diagram.

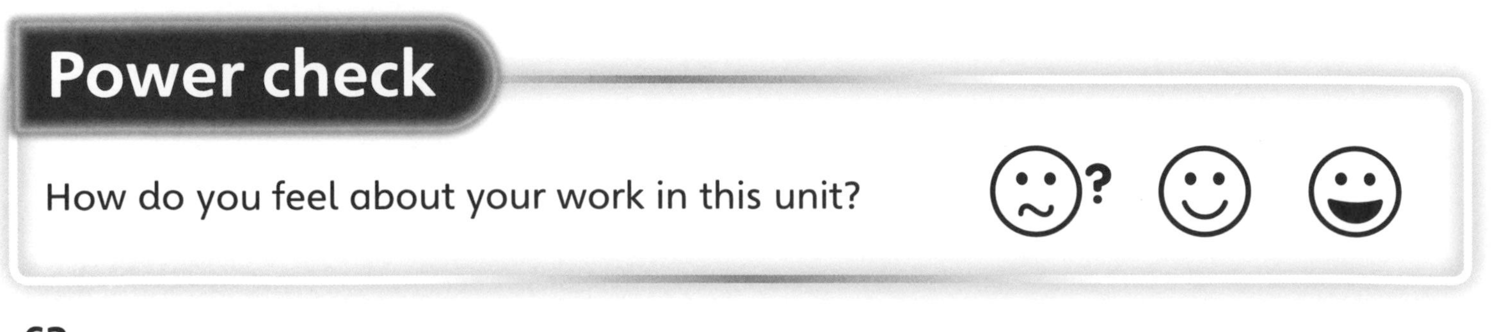

Power check

How do you feel about your work in this unit?

Power play

- Play in pairs with two different-coloured counters.
- Take it in turns to choose a problem to solve (for example, 10% of 900 = ?). If your answer is correct, place one of your counters on the square where the answer would go.
- The first person to get a full row of counters wins!

of	900		260		1
10%		17			
	9				
75%					
		170		25	
99%					

Try creating your own game and then swap with a partner.

→ Textbook 6B p88

Finding a rule 1

1 Reena makes some fairy cakes.
Each cake has 3 stars on top.

a) Complete the table.

Number of cakes	1	2	3	5	10	100	1,500
Number of stars	1 × 3 = 3						

b) Write the rule for n fairy cakes.

For n fairy cakes, you need ☐ × ☐ stars.

2 This is the table for Ebo's cakes.

Number of cakes	5	6	12	20		b
Number of stars	25	30			505	

Complete the table. Draw what one fairy cake could look like.

3 Draw a line to match each repeating pattern with the rule for n repeats.

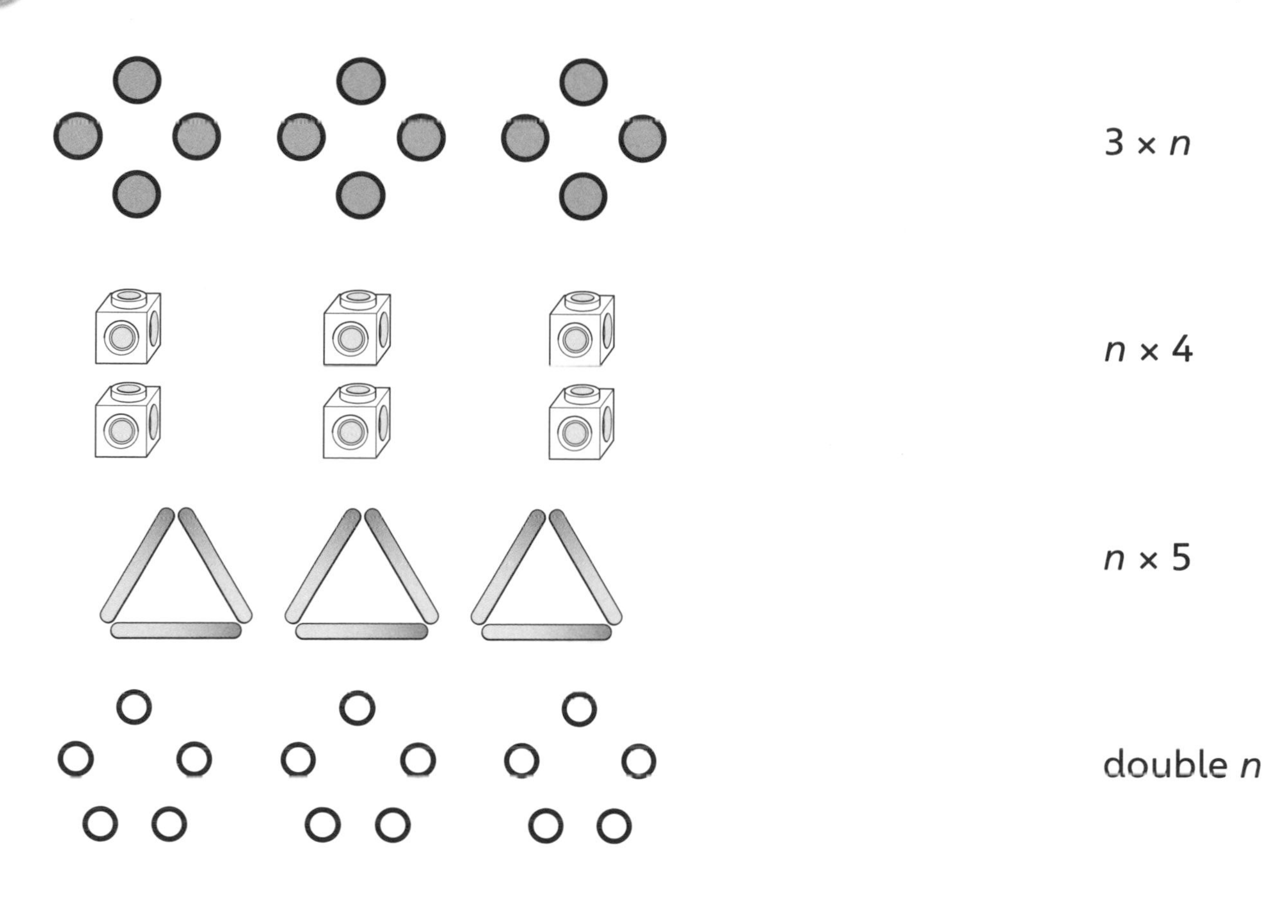

4 Zac started his painting 30 minutes before Kate. Complete the table for how long they have been painting.

Minutes Zac has been painting	45	50	90		x
Minutes Kate has been painting				90	

Complete these rules.

If Zac has been painting for x minutes, Kate has been painting for

____

If Kate has been painting for y minutes, Zac has been painting for

____

5 **a)** Complete the following rules.

The number of legs on b spiders is ________ .

The number of wheels on x tricycles is ________ .

The number of days in m weeks is ________ .

The number of weeks in k years is ________ .

b) What could this rule be for?

The number of ______________________________ is $365 \times d$.

CHALLENGE

6 Complete the tables. What are the rules?

1	3	12	15·5	x
5	7	16		

1	2	4	8	
	5	10	20	y

____

____

Reflect

What is the same and what is different about the rules $a \times 5$ and $5 + a$?

→ Textbook 6B p92

Finding a rule 2

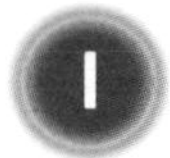

1 **a)** Olivia has £25 in the bank. Each week she saves £3. Complete the table.

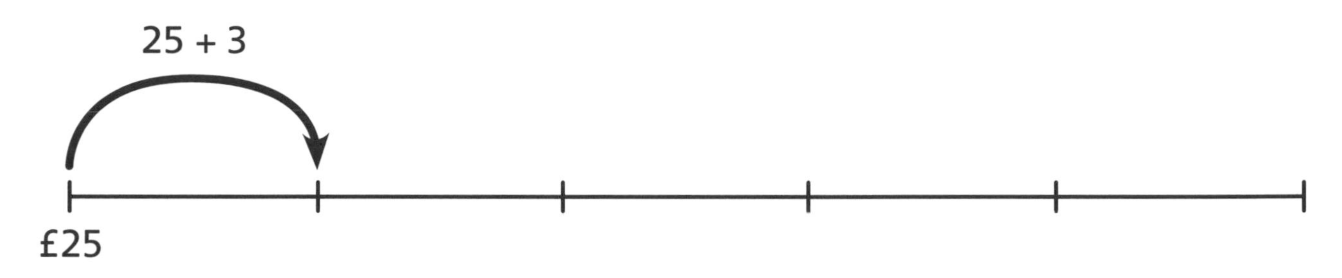

Week	1	2	3	5	10	11
Total savings	28					

b) Complete the rule for how much Olivia has saved after y weeks.

After y weeks, Olivia has saved ☐ + ☐ × ☐ pounds.

2 Max has £50 in the bank. Each week he spends £4 on a comic.

Complete the table and the rule.

£50

Week	1	2	3	5	10	n
Money left						

After n weeks, he has ☐ ◯ ☐ × ☐ pounds left.

Here is a growing pattern of triangles made from sticks.

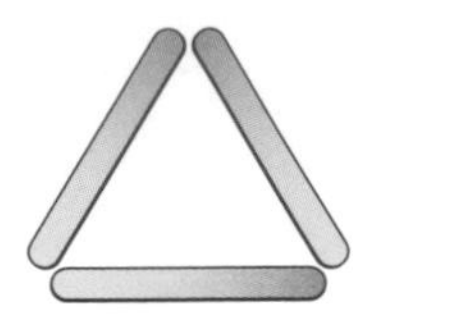 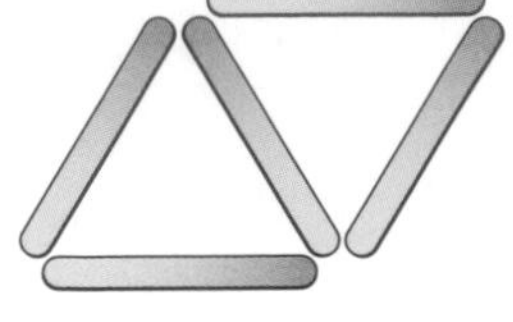 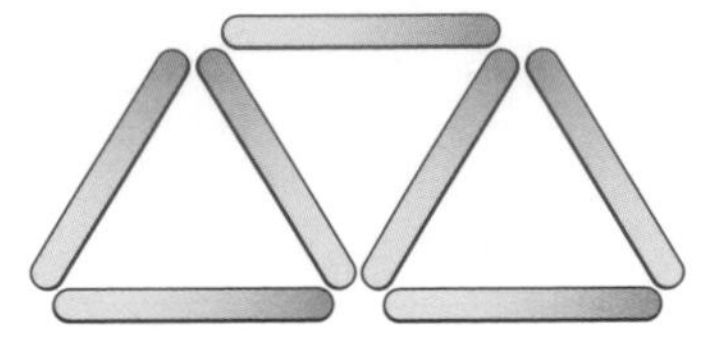

In a growing pattern, there is a rule for how it grows each time.

Complete the table.

Number of triangles	1	2	3	4	5	10	100
Number of sticks used							

Write the rule for the number of sticks needed to make *n* triangles.

To make 1 triangle, ☐ sticks are used.

To make 2 triangles, ☐ sticks are used.

To make 3 triangles, ☐ sticks are used.

To make *n* triangles, ____________________ sticks are used.

4 Ebo makes this pattern of houses. What is the rule for the number of sticks needed for a pattern with *g* houses?

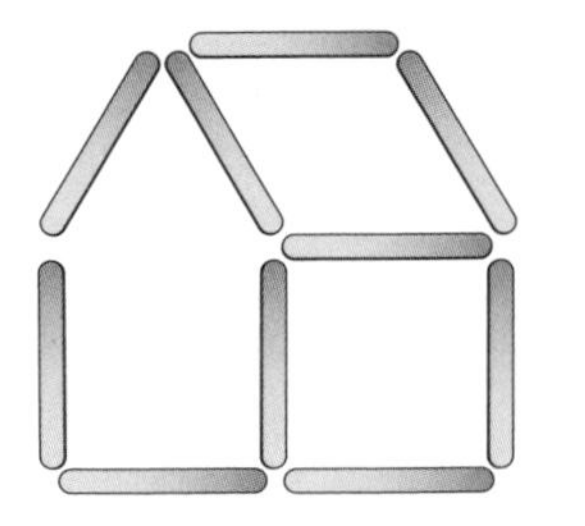 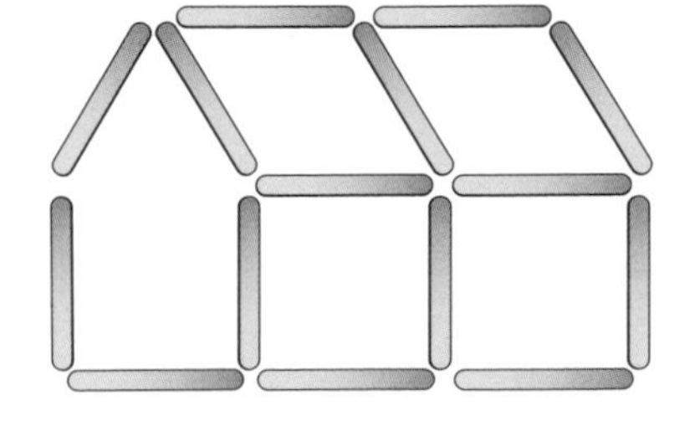 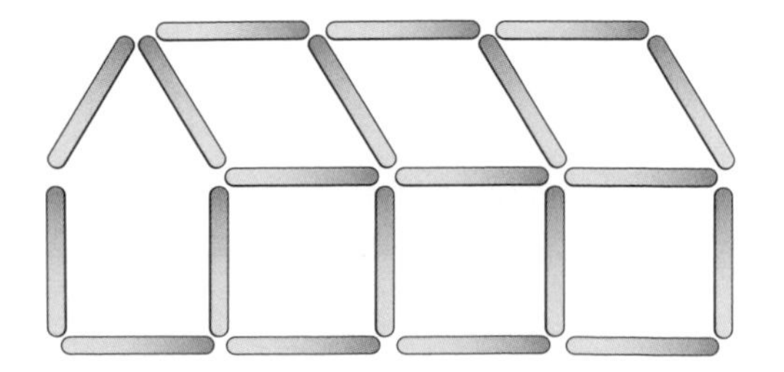

For *g* houses, you need ____ sticks.

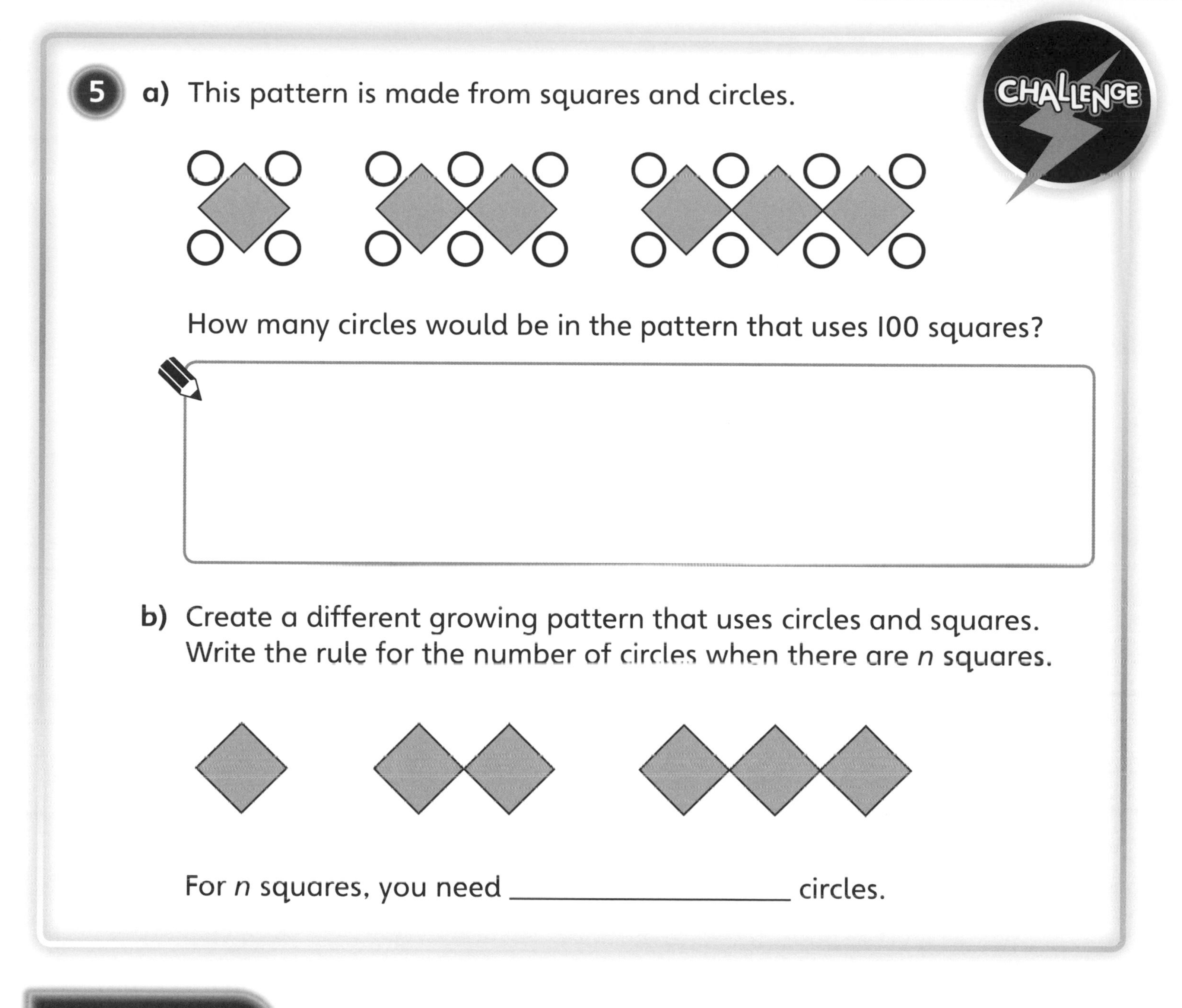

5 **a)** This pattern is made from squares and circles.

How many circles would be in the pattern that uses 100 squares?

b) Create a different growing pattern that uses circles and squares. Write the rule for the number of circles when there are n squares.

For n squares, you need ______________ circles.

Reflect

Create a situation for this rule: $100 - 3y$.

→ Textbook 6B p96

Using a rule 1

Richard has x pet guinea pigs. Luis has 2 more than Richard. Ambika has 3 times as many as Luis.

a) Complete the rule for how many pets Luis has.

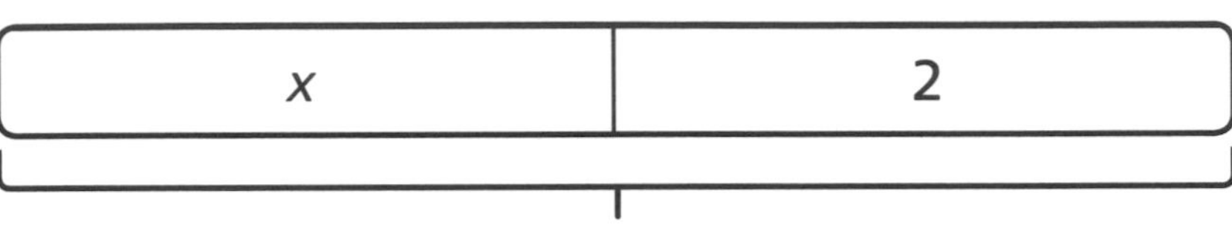

If Richard has x guinea pigs, Luis has ☐ ◯ ☐ guinea pigs.

b) Draw a bar model to represent how many guinea pigs Ambika has.

c) Calculate the number of guinea pigs for Ambika, if Richard has 3 guinea pigs.

Ambika has ☐ guinea pigs.

d) Complete the table.

	Number of guinea pigs				
Richard	1	2	5	10	20
Luis	3				
Ambika	9				

2 Complete the table of inputs and outputs from each function machine.

a)

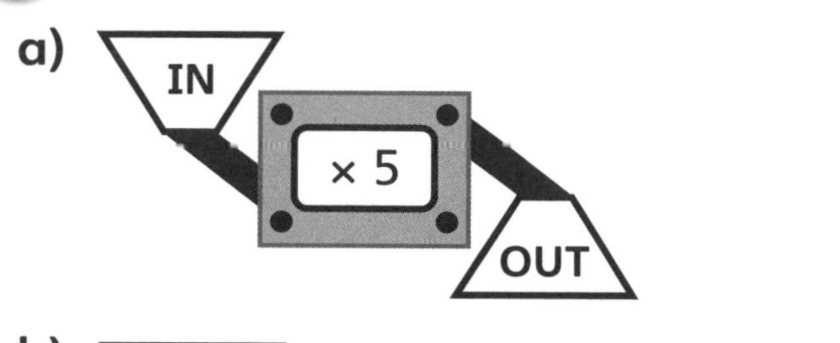

Input	1	2	3	5	10
Output					

If the input is *a*, the output is ________

b)

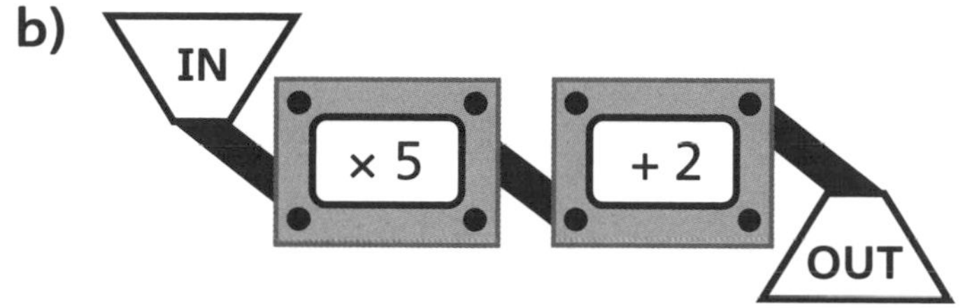

Input	1	2	3	5	10
Output					

If the input is *b*, the output is ________

c)

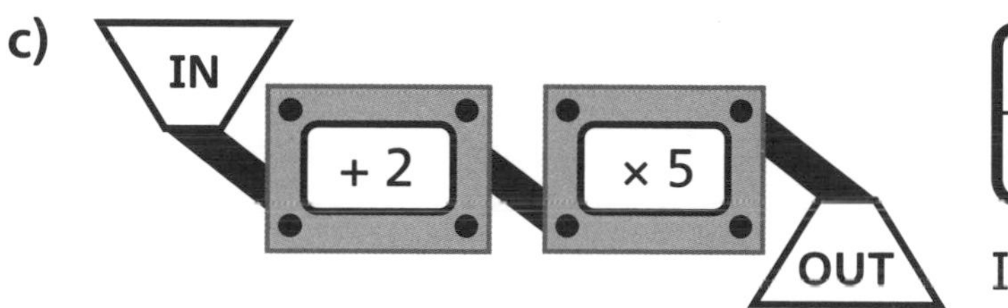

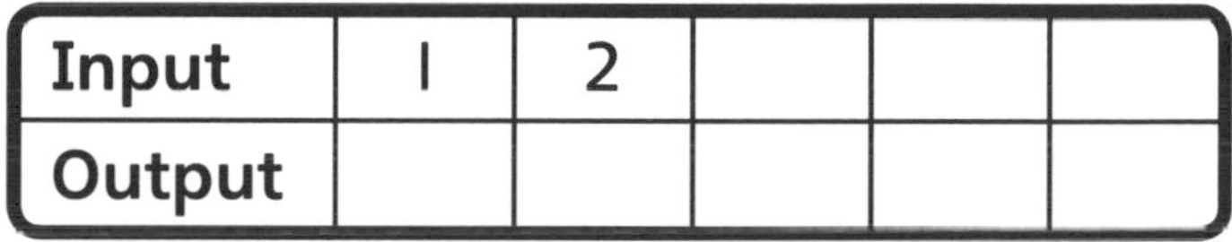

Input	1	2			
Output					

If the input is *b*, the output is ________

d)

IN × 2 × 5 OUT

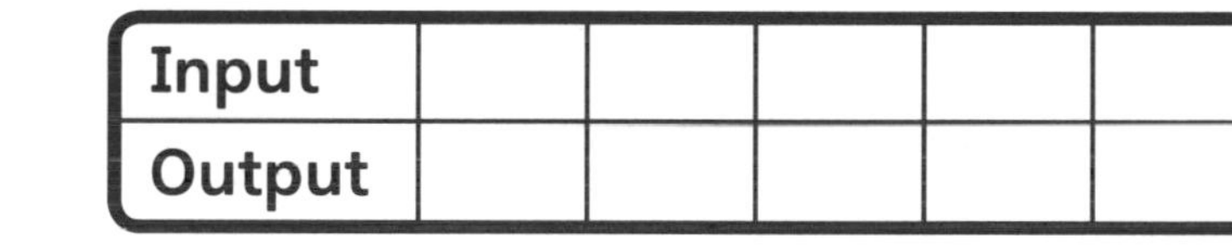

Input					
Output					

If the input is *b*, the output is ________

3 Max says: 'This is just the same as having a machine with one function of – 10.'

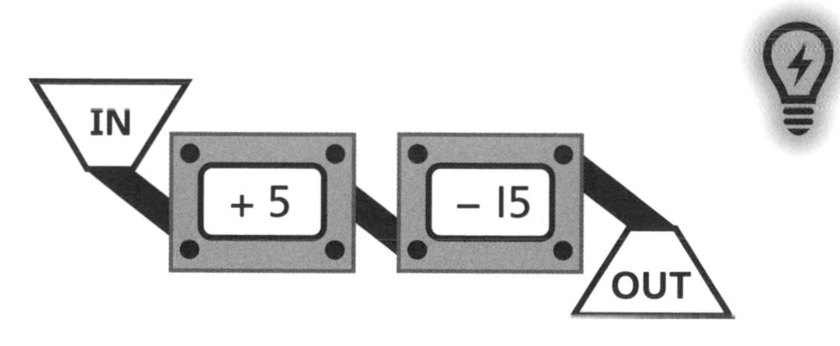

Do you agree? Compare the outputs in the table.

Input	1	2	5	100	1,000	*a*
Output for – 10						
Output for + 5 – 15						

____

4 Kate is investigating two function machines. She inputs 10 and the output is 100. What could the functions be?

CHALLENGE

Explore different possibilities. Create a table of outputs.

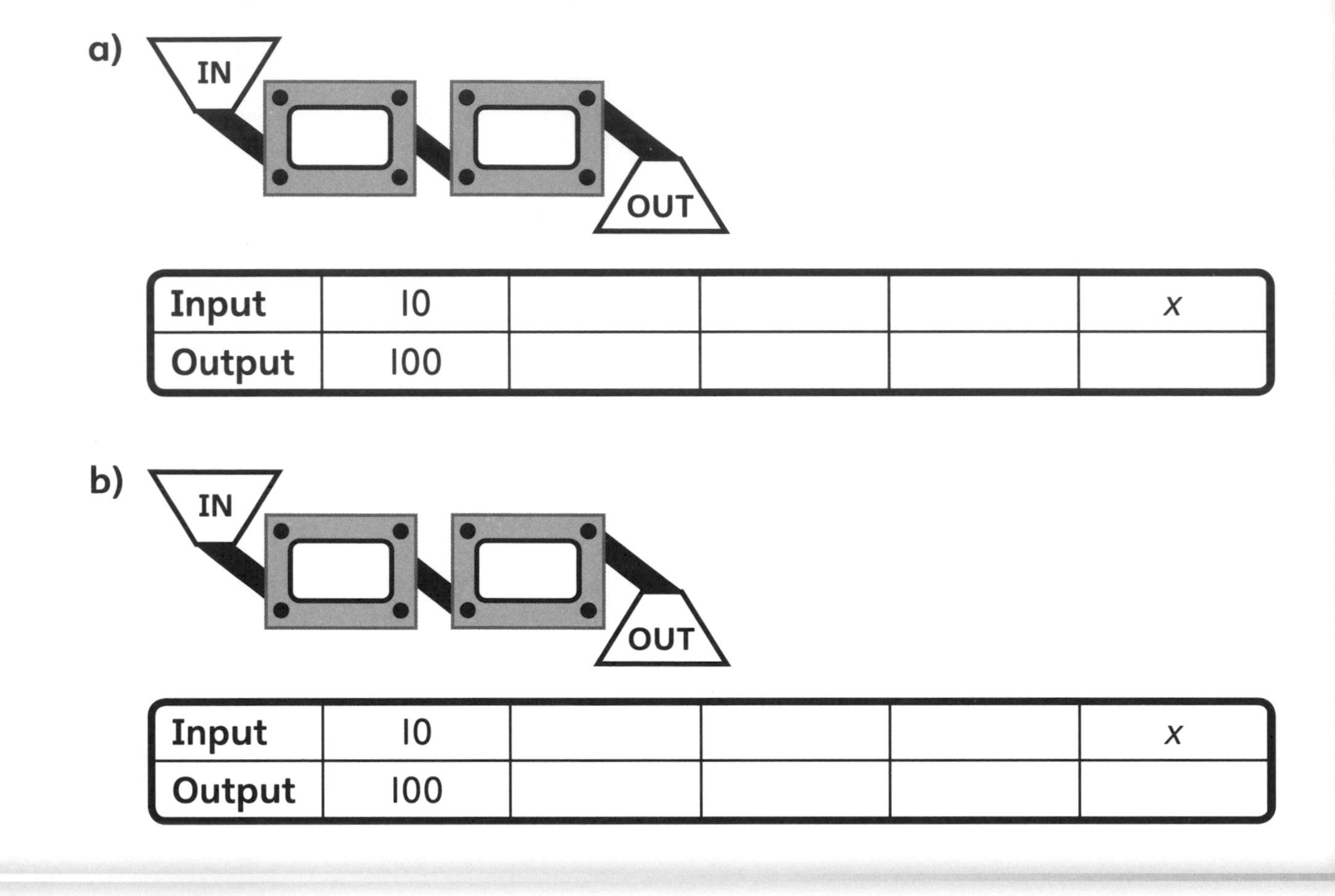

a)

Input	10				x
Output	100				

b)

Input	10				x
Output	100				

Reflect

Emma has the rule $3x + 2$. She wants to find the value when x is 100. Emma says: 'I will just find the output for 10, then multiply by 10.' Does this method work? Explore and explain.

→ Textbook 6B p100

Using a rule 2

Reena has a pile of 5 pence coins.

a) Write the rule for the total value when the number of coins is n.

There are n 5 pence coins. The total value = ☐ pence.

b) Complete the table for different values of n.

Number of coins	Reena's total value
4	5p × 4 = ☐ p
5	
10	
30	
50	

2 To hire a squash court costs 20 pence per minute.

a) Write the rule for hiring the court for n minutes.

____

b) Complete the table.

Time in minutes	Cost
n	20 p × n = ☐ n
10	☐ × 10 = ☐
30	
60	
120	

3 Calculate the result for different values of x by completing the table.

	$x + 30$	$30 - x$	$30x$
$x = 5$			
$x = 10$			
$x = 30$			
$x = 0$			

4 Aki has to substitute $x = 7$ into $10x + 5$.

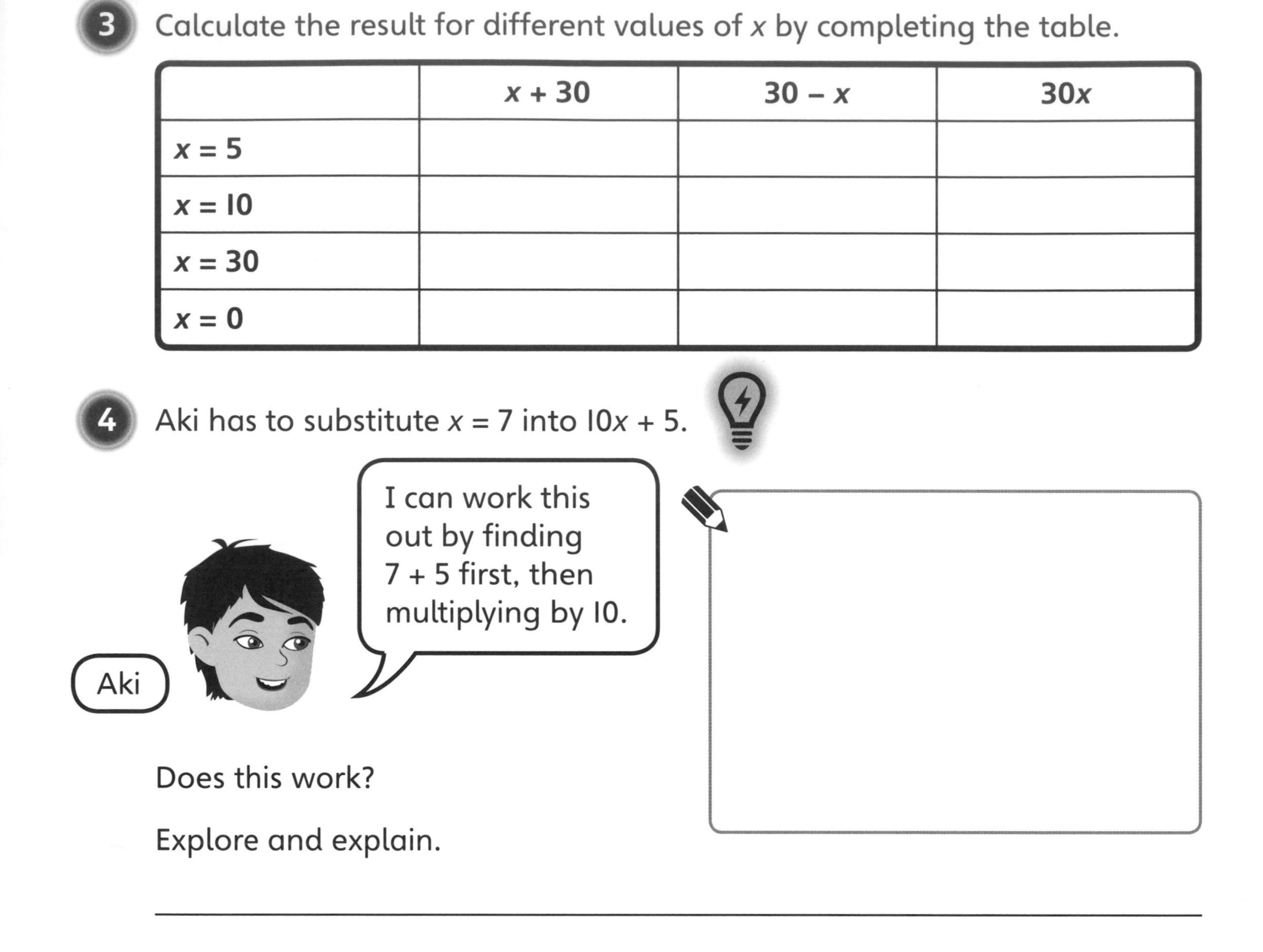

Does this work?

Explore and explain.

____

____

5 Explain how to choose values of y for the following rule, so that the result is a multiple of 10.

$100 - 5y$

____

____

____

____

CHALLENGE

6 Substitute different values for y into the expression $10y - y$.

When $y = 1$, $10y - y =$ ☐.

When $y =$ ☐, $10y - y =$ ☐.

When ______________________________

When ______________________________

When ______________________________

What do you notice? Explain using words and diagrams.

Reflect

Substitute different values for y in the rule $4 + 2y$. Explain why all the results are even.

→ Textbook 6B p104

Using a rule 3

1 a) Toshi cuts 5 equal lengths from 100 cm of ribbon. Each length is y cm.

Write the rule for the length of ribbon he has left.

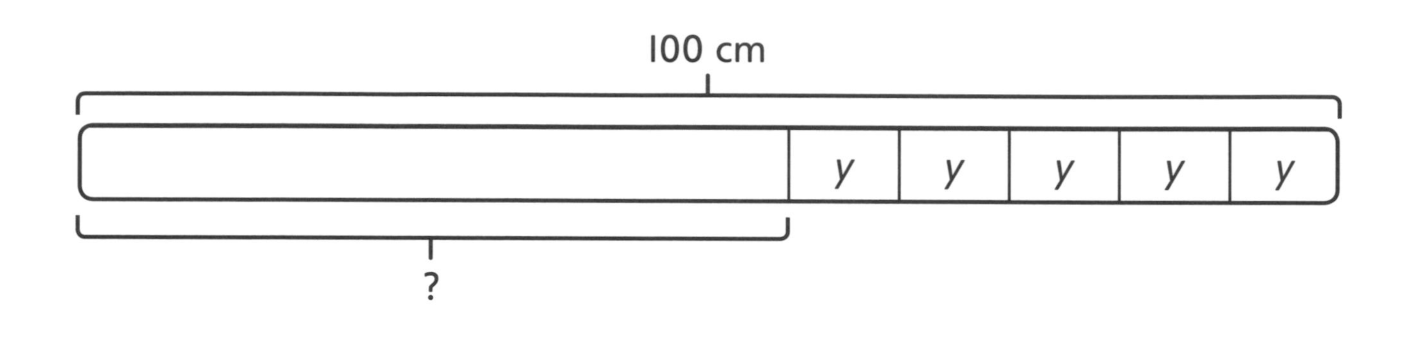

____

b) How much ribbon is left if y = 12 cm?

There is ☐ cm of ribbon left.

2 Amelia stacks n blocks onto the base.

a) Write an expression for the total height of a tower with n blocks.

The total height is ☐ + ☐ n.

b) Calculate the total height when n = 8.

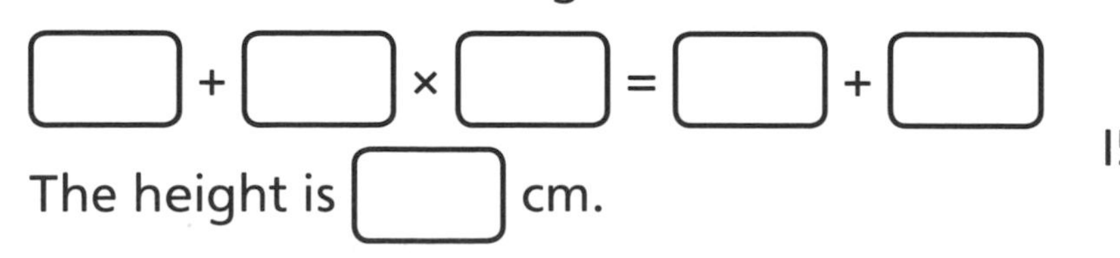

☐ + ☐ × ☐ = ☐ + ☐

The height is ☐ cm.

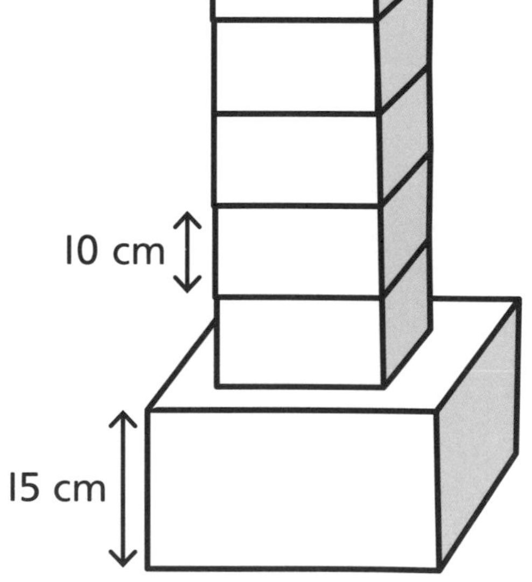

3 **a)** Write the expression in the box for each diagram.

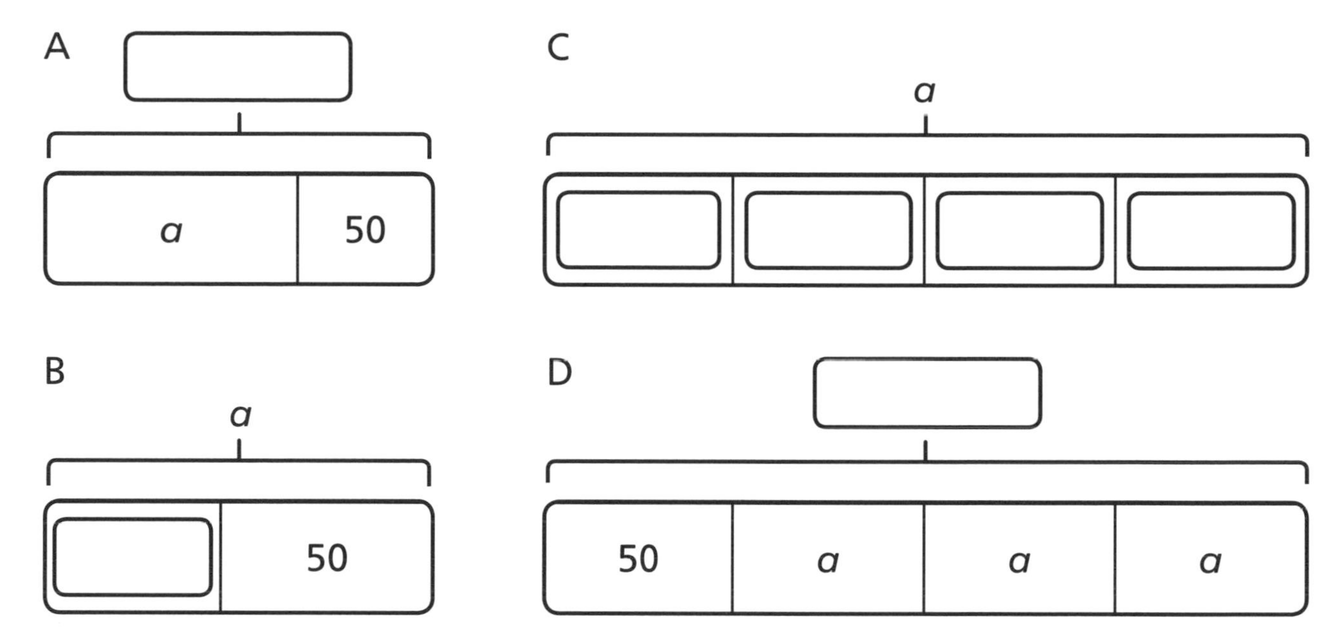

b) Now substitute the value of 75 for a in each expression.

What is the value of the expression for each diagram?

A = ☐ B = ☐ C = ☐ D = ☐

4 Match each expression with the equivalent meaning.

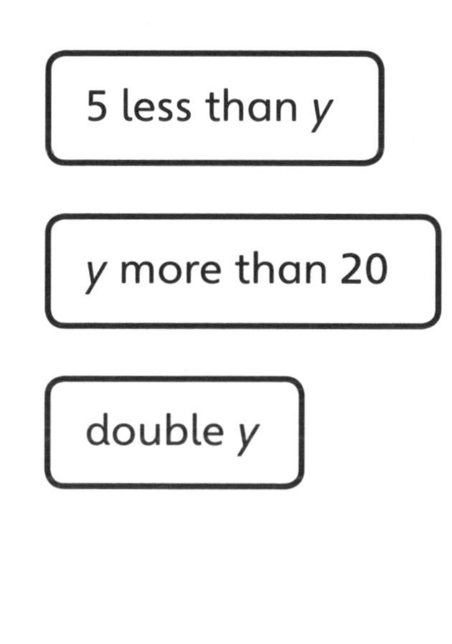

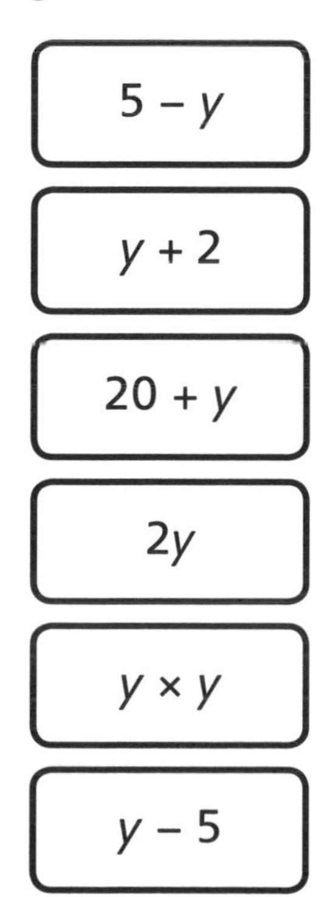

5 Complete the table.

CHALLENGE

	Write an expression for each ?.	Substitute n = 110 into each expression. Calculate the value of ?.
n n n / 20 ?		
n / 10 / ?		
n / 10 / ?		

Reflect

What is the value of 25 – 2y when y equals 3?
Draw a bar model to explain.

→ Textbook 6B p108

Formulae

1 Write an expression for the perimeter of each shape. Then calculate the perimeter by substituting $a = 4$ cm and $b = 5$ cm.

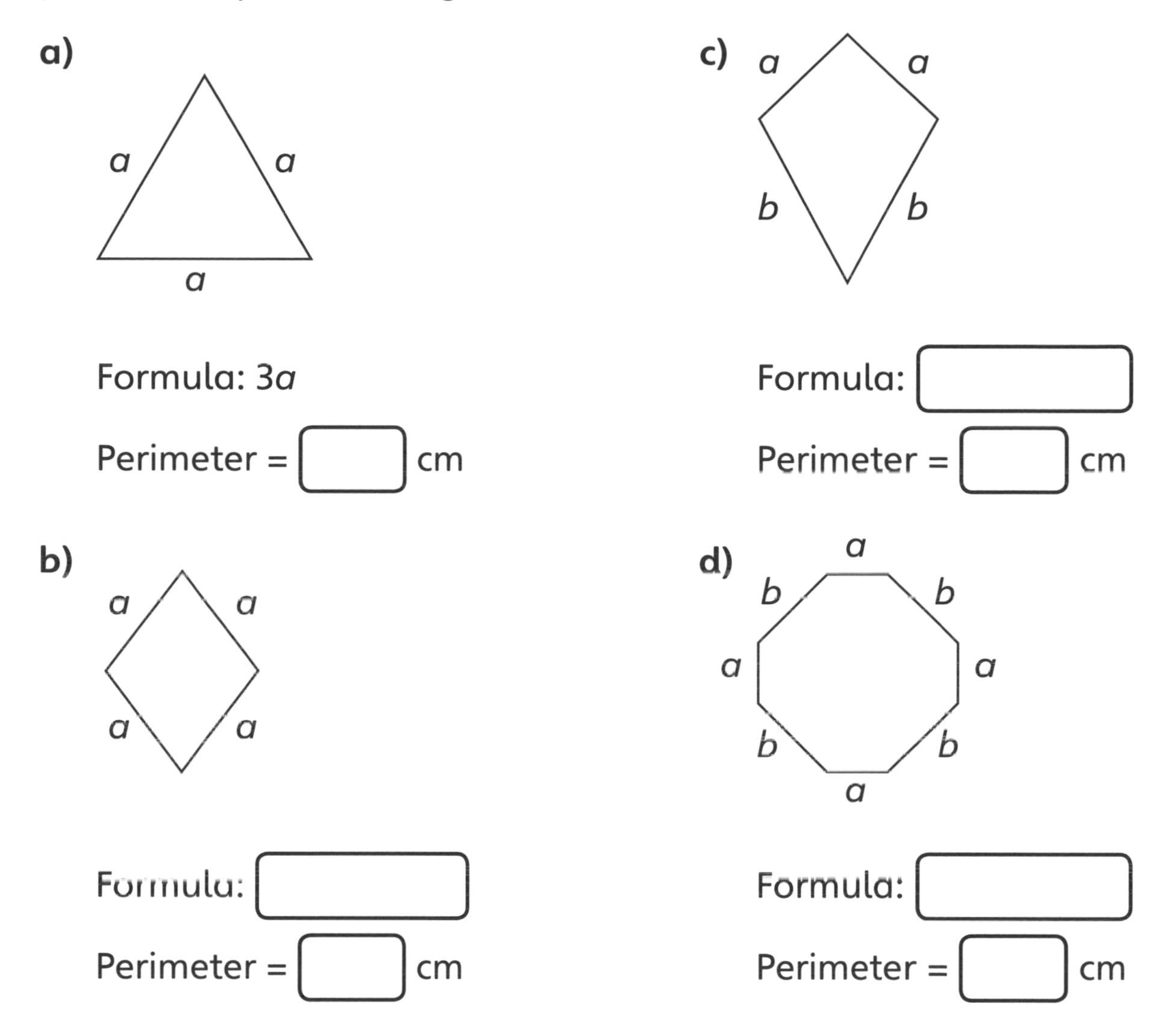

a) Formula: $3a$

Perimeter = ☐ cm

b) Formula: ☐

Perimeter = ☐ cm

c) Formula: ☐

Perimeter = ☐ cm

d) Formula: ☐

Perimeter = ☐ cm

2 A formula to calculate the number of inches in z feet is $12z$.

How many inches tall is each tower?

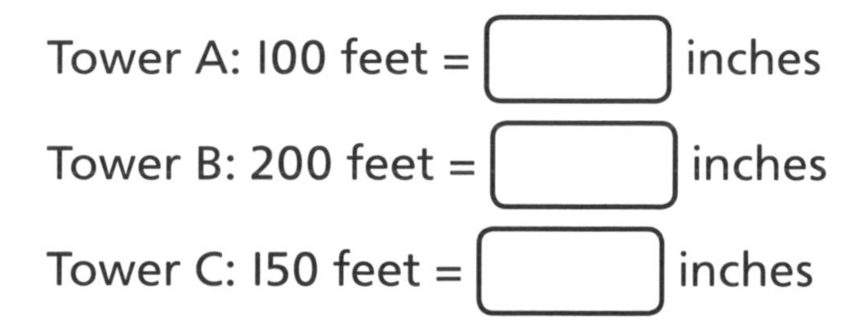

Tower A: 100 feet = ☐ inches

Tower B: 200 feet = ☐ inches

Tower C: 150 feet = ☐ inches

3 A scientist uses the formula distance $= s \times t$ to calculate the distance a rocket has travelled.

Speed is measured in miles per hour (mph).

s stands for the speed in mph.

t stands for the time in hours.

Calculate the distance travelled when the rocket has been moving at a speed of 200 mph for 2 days.

The rocket has travelled ☐ miles.

4 Max joins two of these squares together to make a new shape. What is the perimeter of the new shape?

Do you agree with Max? Explain, and show an example substituting a value for *a*.

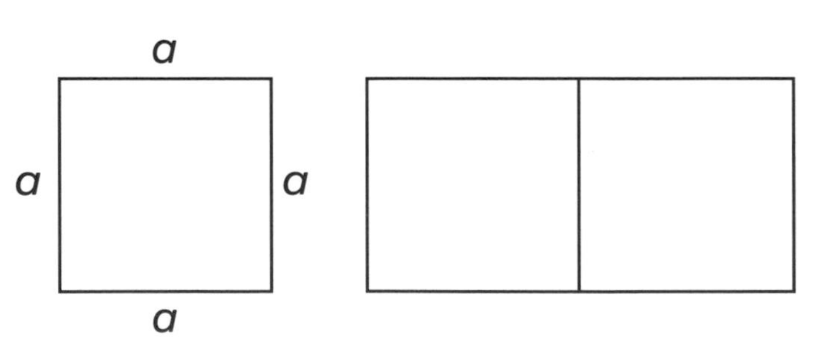

The perimeter of the square is $4a$, so the perimeter of my new shape is $8a$.

Max

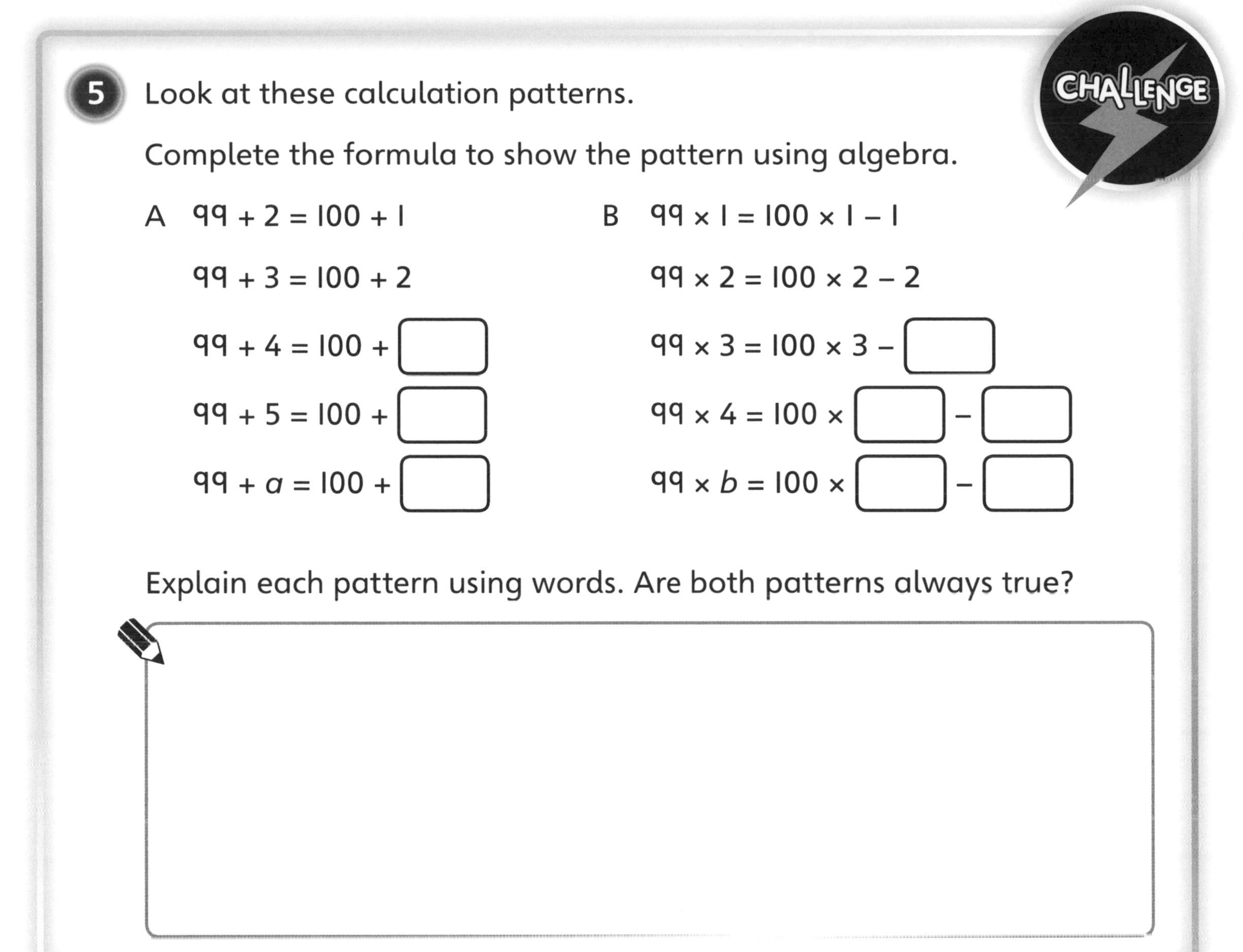

5 Look at these calculation patterns.

Complete the formula to show the pattern using algebra.

A
$99 + 2 = 100 + 1$
$99 + 3 = 100 + 2$
$99 + 4 = 100 + \square$
$99 + 5 = 100 + \square$
$99 + a = 100 + \square$

B
$99 \times 1 = 100 \times 1 - 1$
$99 \times 2 = 100 \times 2 - 2$
$99 \times 3 = 100 \times 3 - \square$
$99 \times 4 = 100 \times \square - \square$
$99 \times b = 100 \times \square - \square$

Explain each pattern using words. Are both patterns always true?

Reflect

Write a formula to show how to calculate the perimeter when $x = 10$ and $y = 8$.

→ Textbook 6B p112

Solving equations 1

a) Substitute different values for a to find a solution to the equation.

$a + 150 =$ ☐

If a is:	Then $a + 150$ is:
100	
200	

b) Substitute different values for b to solve the equation.

☐ $= 150 - b$

If b is:	Then $150 - b$ is:
10	
20	
50	

c) Complete the bar model to represent the equation, then solve it.

$28 + c = 101$

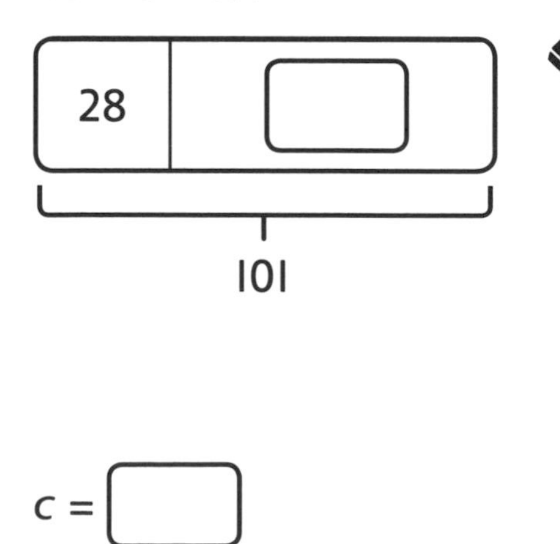

$c =$ ☐

2 **a)** Ambika measured out some flour. She added 50 g of butter, then the mass of these ingredients was $\frac{1}{2}$ kg. Represent the mass of flour as *m*, write an equation and solve.

b) Andy had a bag of raisins. He added 25 g to his pancake. That left 250 g in the bag. Represent the original mass of the bag as *s*, write and solve an equation.

 Solve each equation.

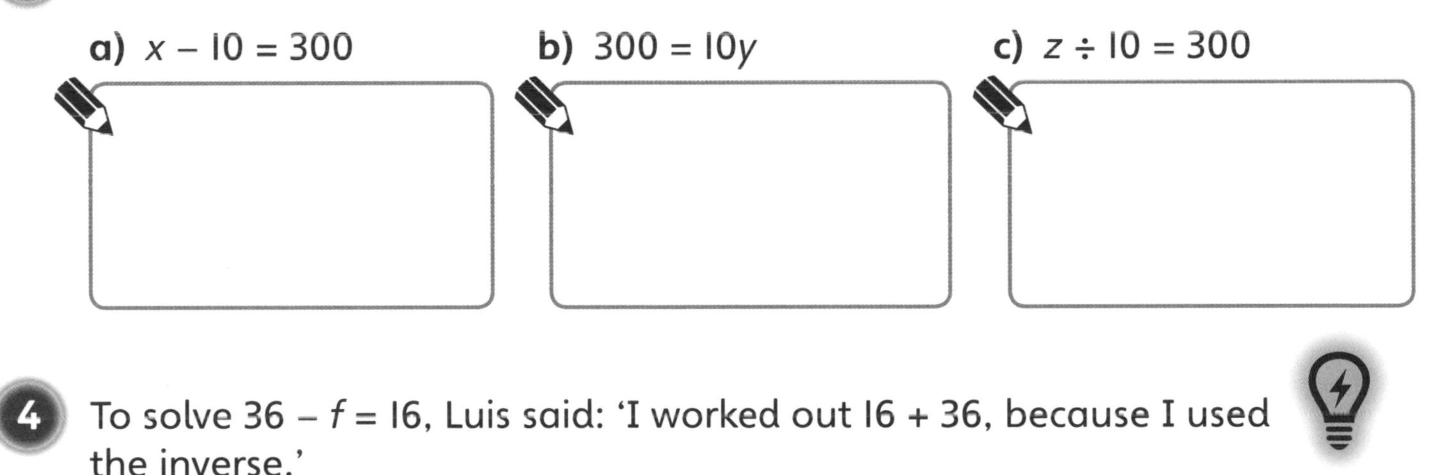

a) $x - 10 = 300$ **b)** $300 = 10y$ **c)** $z \div 10 = 300$

4 To solve $36 - f = 16$, Luis said: 'I worked out 16 + 36, because I used the inverse.'

Is he correct? Show your reasoning using a diagram.

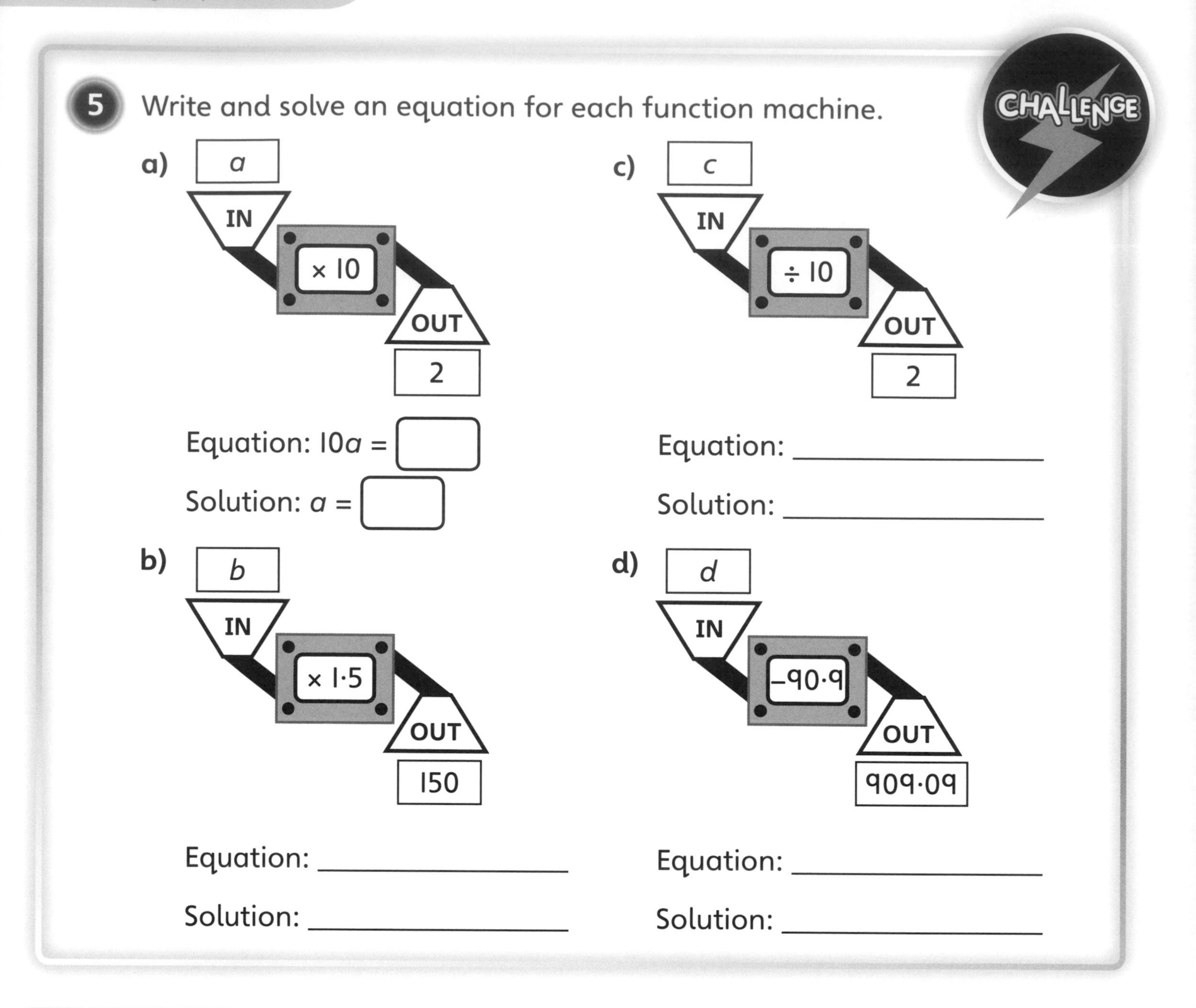

5 Write and solve an equation for each function machine.

a) Equation: $10a = $ ☐

Solution: $a = $ ☐

b) Equation: ______________

Solution: ______________

c) Equation: ______________

Solution: ______________

d) Equation: ______________

Solution: ______________

Reflect

Explain two methods to solve $200 = y + 75$.

→ Textbook 6B p116

Solving equations 2

Complete and solve the equations.

a)

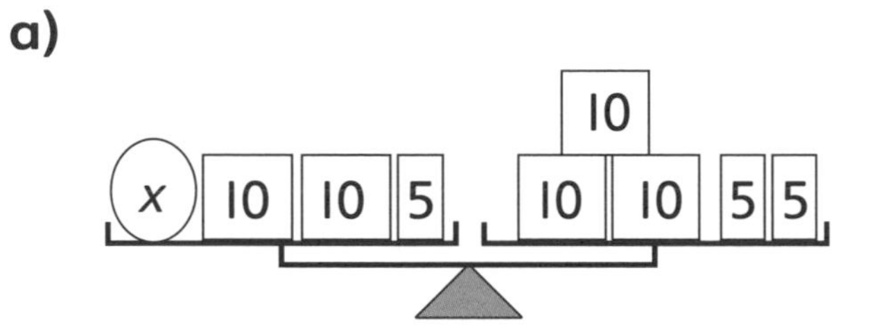

$x + 25 = 40$

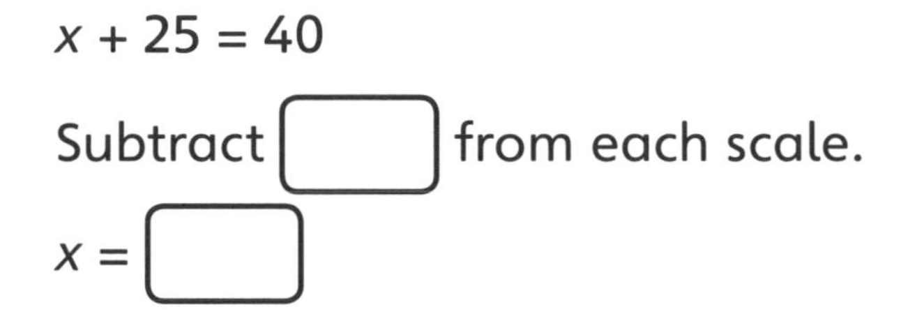

Subtract ☐ from each scale.

$x =$ ☐

b)

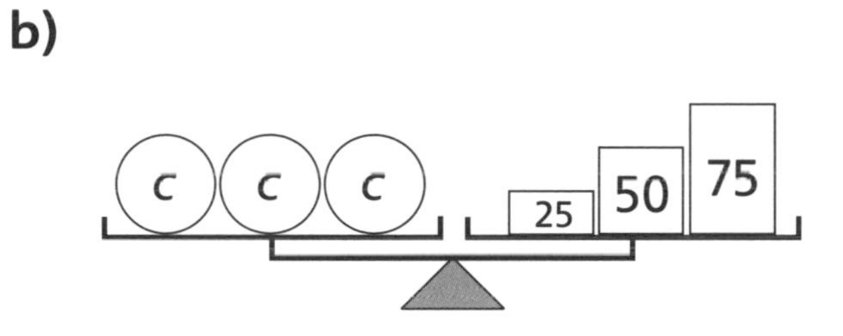

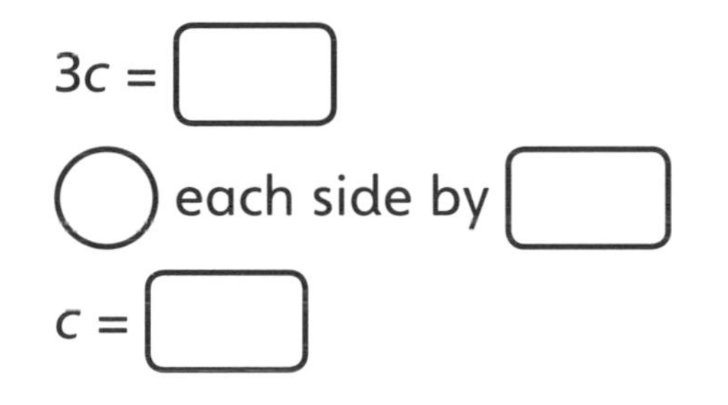

$3c =$ ☐

◯ each side by ☐

$c =$ ☐

c)

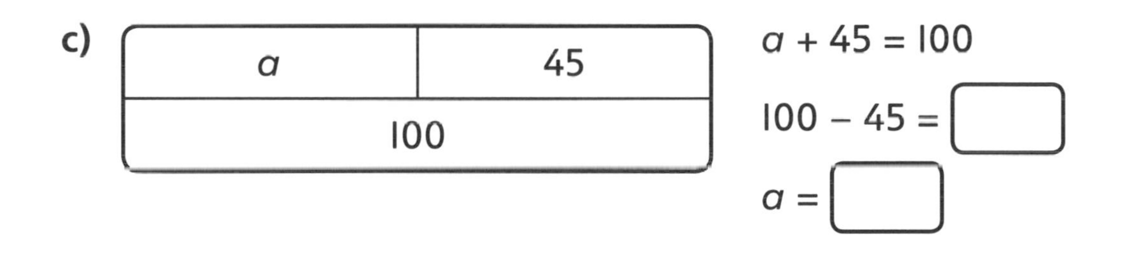

$a + 45 = 100$

$100 - 45 =$ ☐

$a =$ ☐

d)

d	d	d	d	d
150				

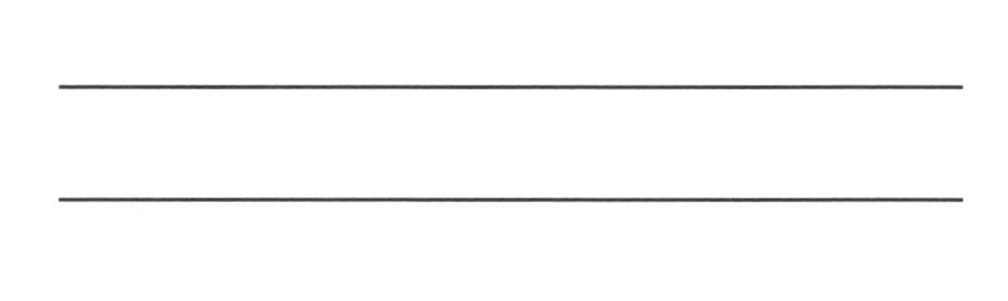

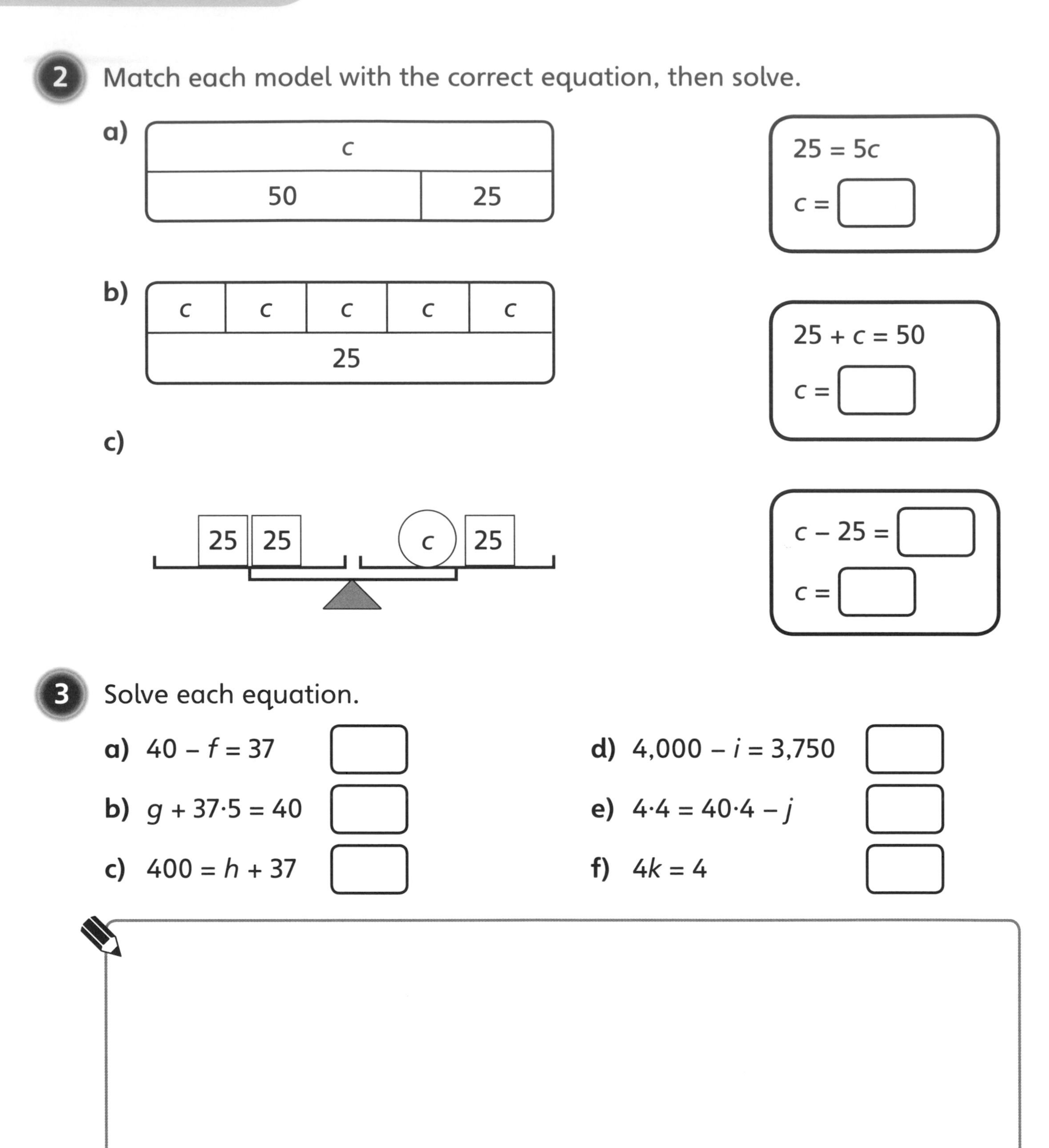

2 Match each model with the correct equation, then solve.

a) Bar model: c on top; 50 and 25 below.

b) Bar model: c, c, c, c, c on top; 25 below.

c) Balance: 25, 25 on one side; c, 25 on the other side.

$25 = 5c$

$c =$ ☐

$25 + c = 50$

$c =$ ☐

$c - 25 =$ ☐

$c =$ ☐

3 Solve each equation.

a) $40 - f = 37$ ☐

b) $g + 37{\cdot}5 = 40$ ☐

c) $400 = h + 37$ ☐

d) $4{,}000 - i = 3{,}750$ ☐

e) $4{\cdot}4 = 40{\cdot}4 - j$ ☐

f) $4k = 4$ ☐

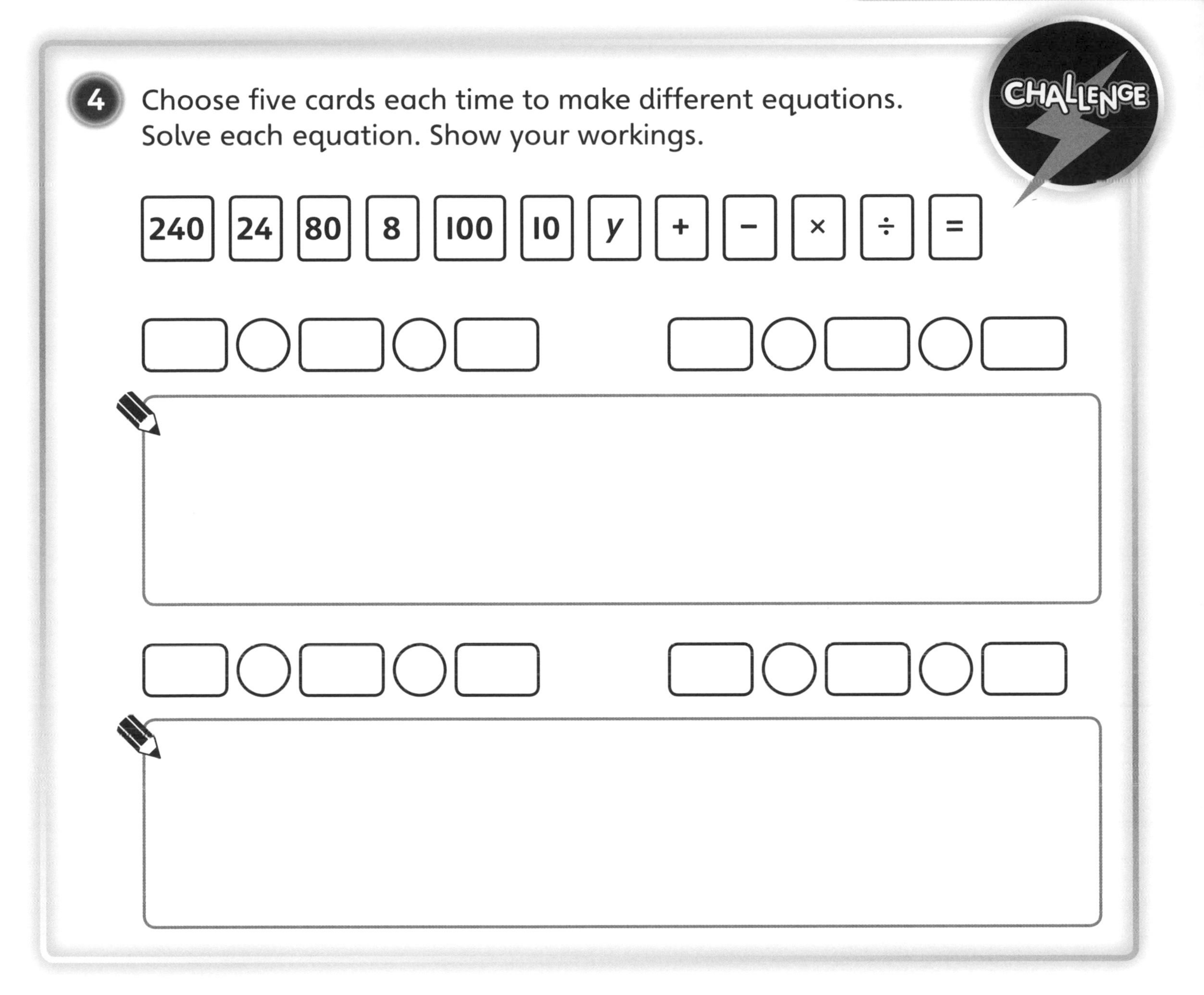

4 Choose five cards each time to make different equations. Solve each equation. Show your workings.

Reflect

Draw a diagram to represent the equation $100 - x = 90$.

→ Textbook 6B p120

Solving equations 3

1 Complete and solve the equation for each mystery number problem.

a) I am thinking of a number. I multiply it by 3 and then add 2. Now I have 17.

Isla

$3a$ + ☐ = ☐

− ☐ − ☐

$3a$ = ☐

÷ ☐ ÷ ☐

a = ☐

b) I am thinking of a number. I multiply it by 4 and then add 80. Now I have 100.

Ebo

b	b	b	b	80
100				

☐ b + ☐ = ☐

b = ☐

2 Solve $50 = 15 + 5c$.

15	
50	

3 Write an equation for the balance scales and solve it.

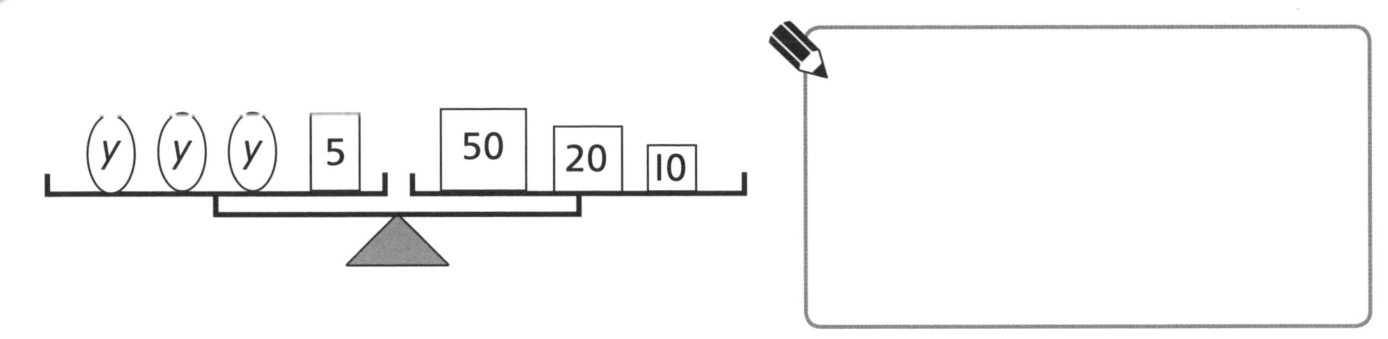

4 Bella has 50 stickers. Max has 6 packets of stickers and 3 more stickers. He has 1 more sticker than Bella.

Use n to represent the number of stickers in a packet.

Write an equation and solve n.

5 Solve each equation.

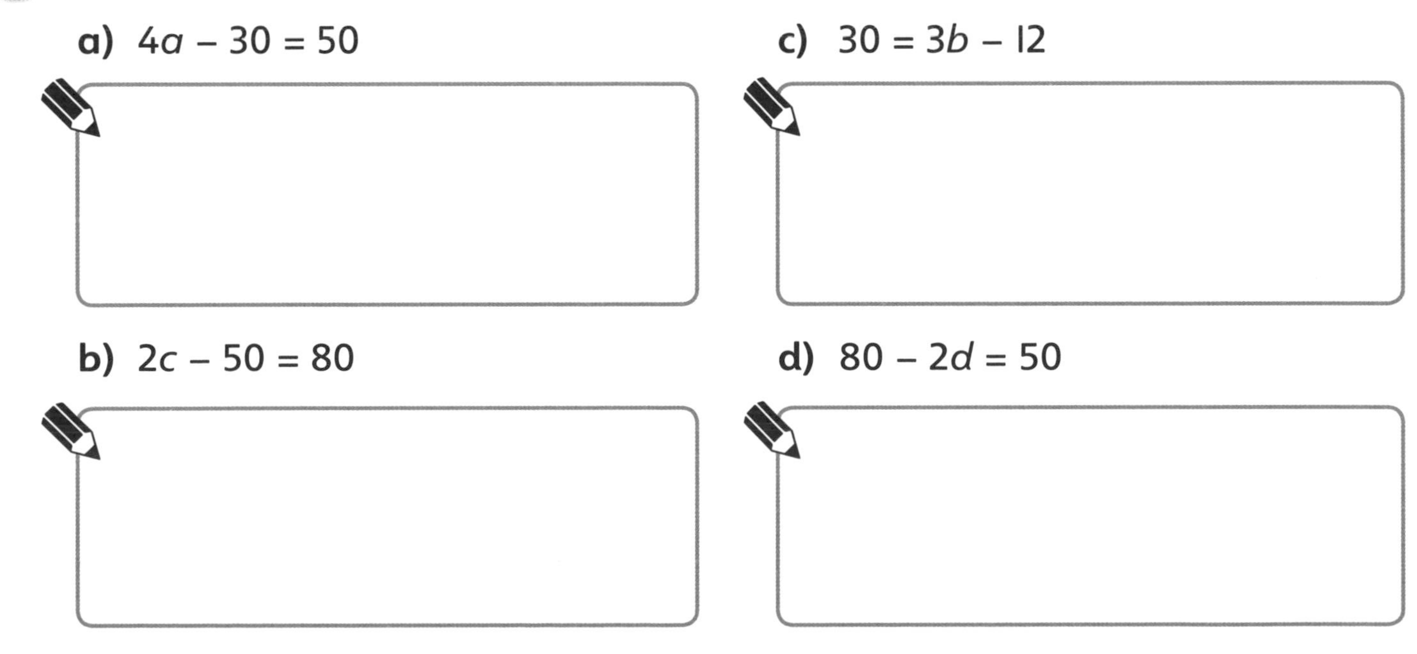

a) $4a - 30 = 50$

b) $2c - 50 = 80$

c) $30 = 3b - 12$

d) $80 - 2d = 50$

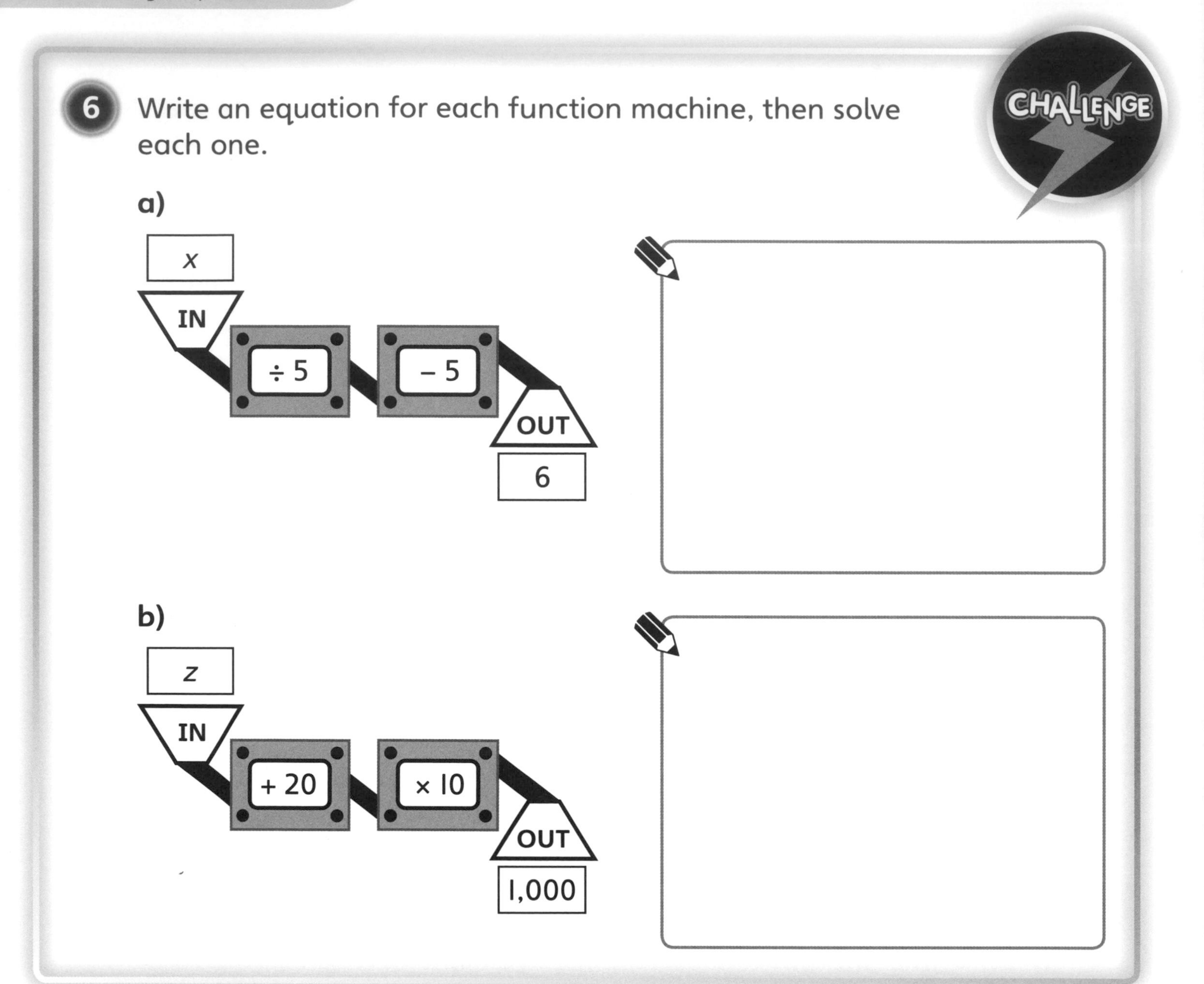

Reflect

Draw a bar model to represent the equation $5x + 5 = 25$.

→ Textbook 6B p124

Solving equations 4

a) A rectangle has a perimeter of 12 cm. Each side is a whole number of centimetres. Find all of the solutions.

Perimeter	j = ?	k = ?
12 cm		
12 cm		
12 cm		

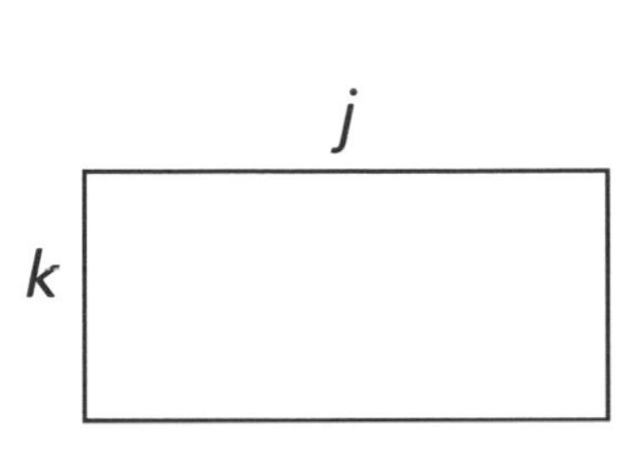

b) Which solution has the greatest area?

Write an equation to show the balance, and then find five different solutions.

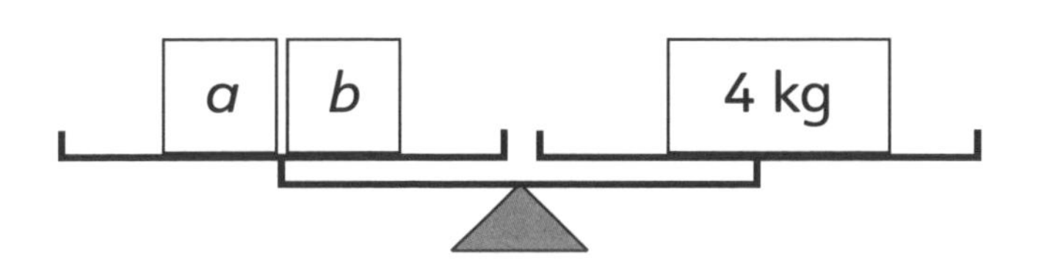

a = ?	b = ?

3 A rectangular playground has an area of 100 m^2. Each side is a whole number of metres.

Write an equation and find all the possible measurements.

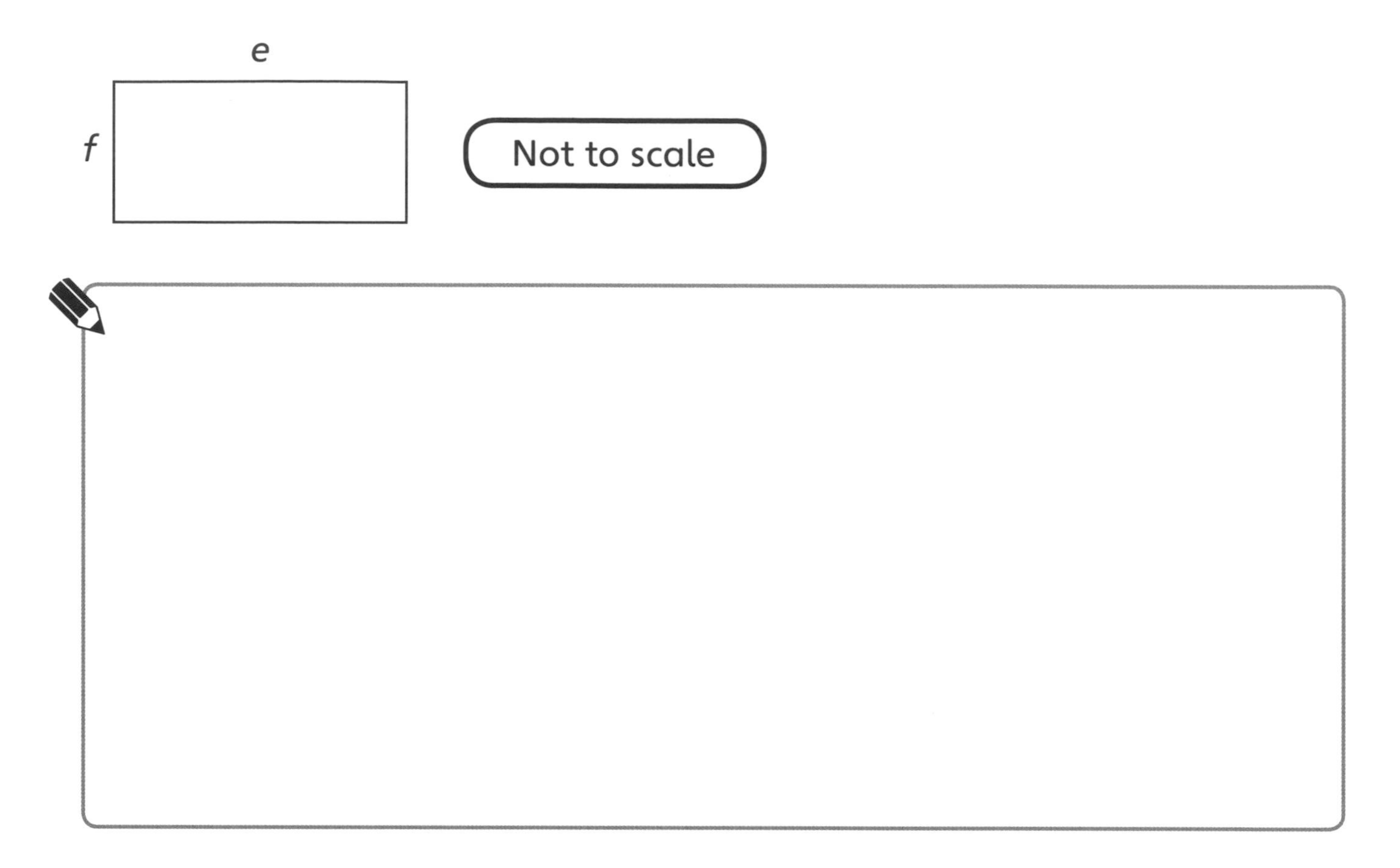

4 Plot solutions to each equation on the grid. Use a different colour for each equation.

a) $x + y = 9$

b) $x + y = 6$

c) $y - x = 2$

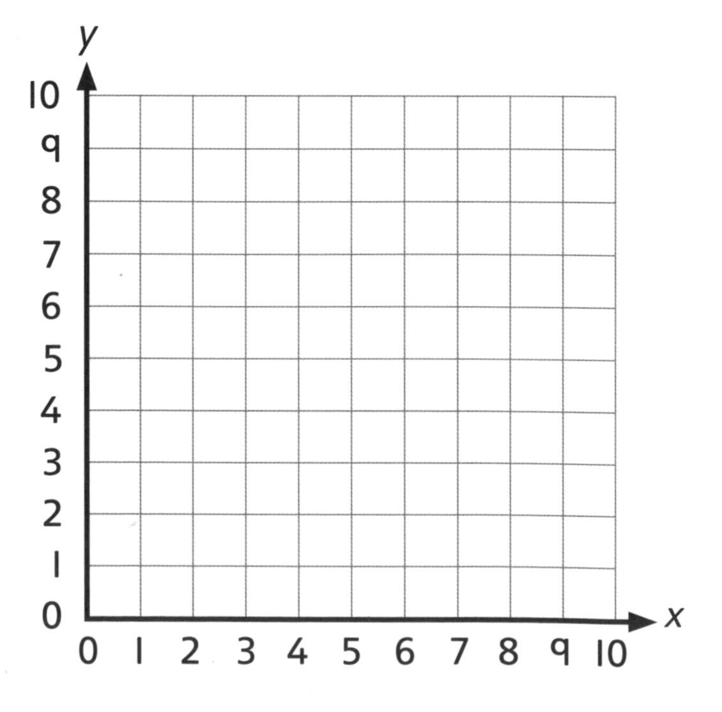

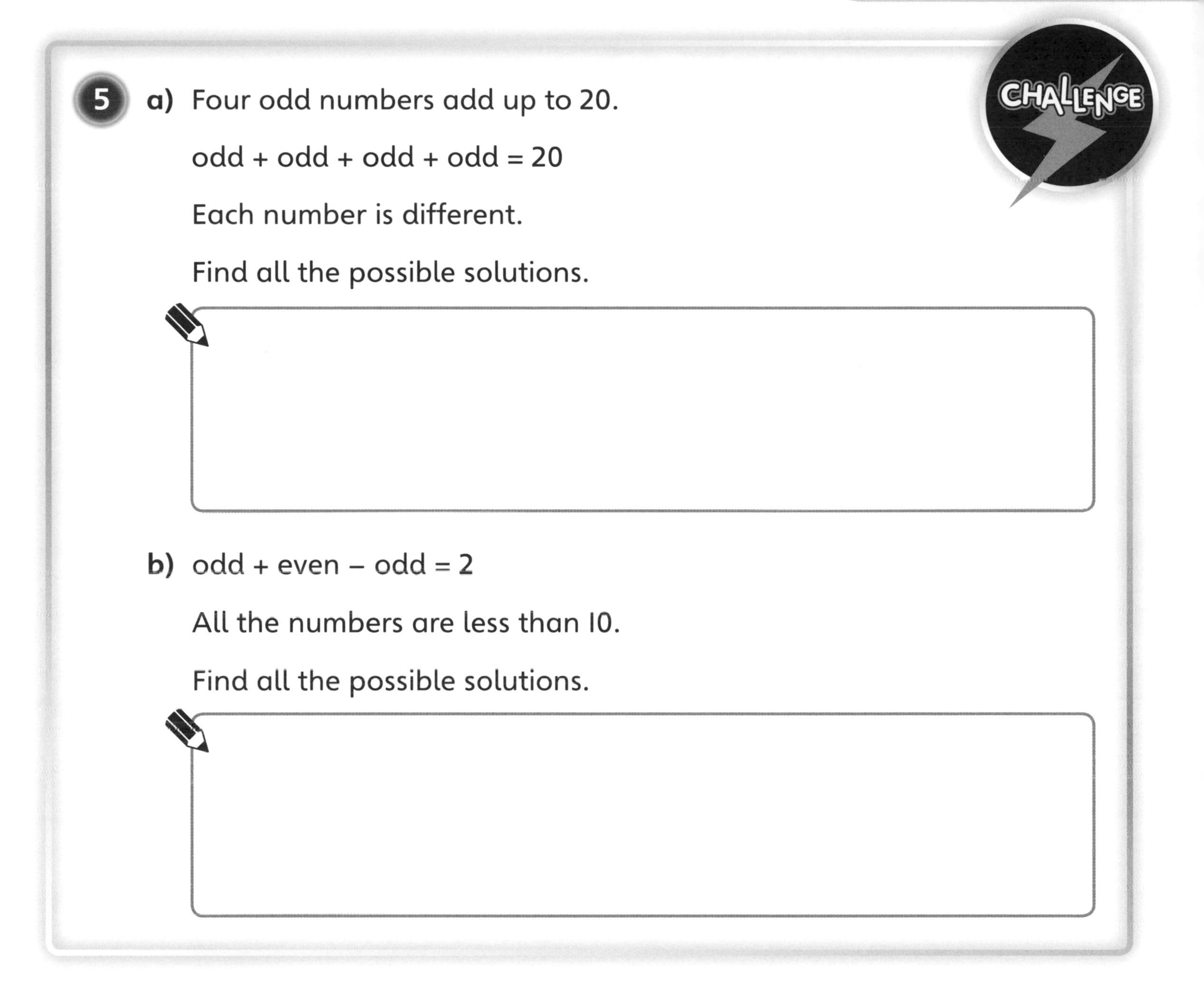

5 a) Four odd numbers add up to 20.

odd + odd + odd + odd = 20

Each number is different.

Find all the possible solutions.

b) odd + even – odd = 2

All the numbers are less than 10.

Find all the possible solutions.

Reflect

Describe a strategy for finding all possible solutions to an equation.

→ Textbook 6B p128

Solving equations 5

1 Alex has some 2p coins and some 5p coins. In total she has 25p. How many of each coin could she have?

Find all possible solutions.

2 A rectangle has a perimeter of 24 cm and an area less than 30 cm^2. Both the length and the width are whole numbers. Find all possible solutions.

3 There are some fish in a tank. Blue fish have 4 spots. Red fish have 8 spots. In total there are 32 spots.

Use b for the number of blue fish and r for the number of red fish. Write an equation and find all possible solutions.

4 Find five different **whole number** solutions to each of the equations. Describe any patterns you notice.

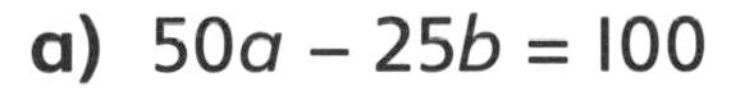

a) $50a - 25b = 100$

b) $50 + c = d - 150$

5 Bella and Danny each choose two numbers less than 20.

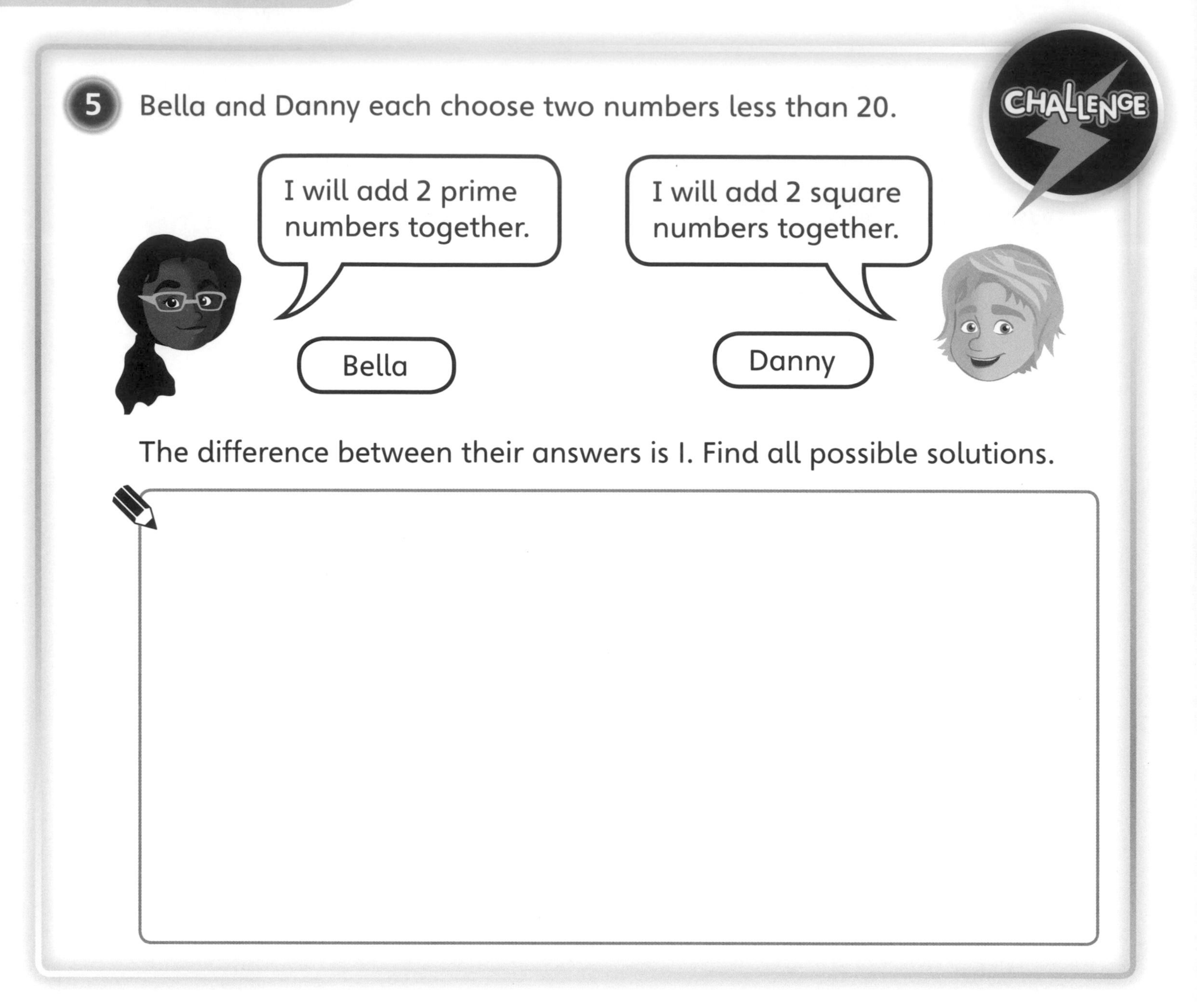

The difference between their answers is 1. Find all possible solutions.

Reflect

Write an equation that has more than three solutions.

→ Textbook 6B p132

End of unit check

My journal

1 **a)** Write and solve an equation which can be represented by this bar model. Then write a story problem for it.

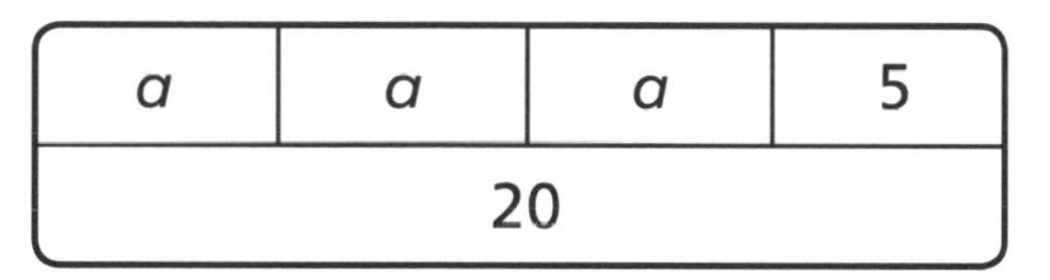

b) Now write and solve an equation represented by this bar model.
Write another story problem to go with it.

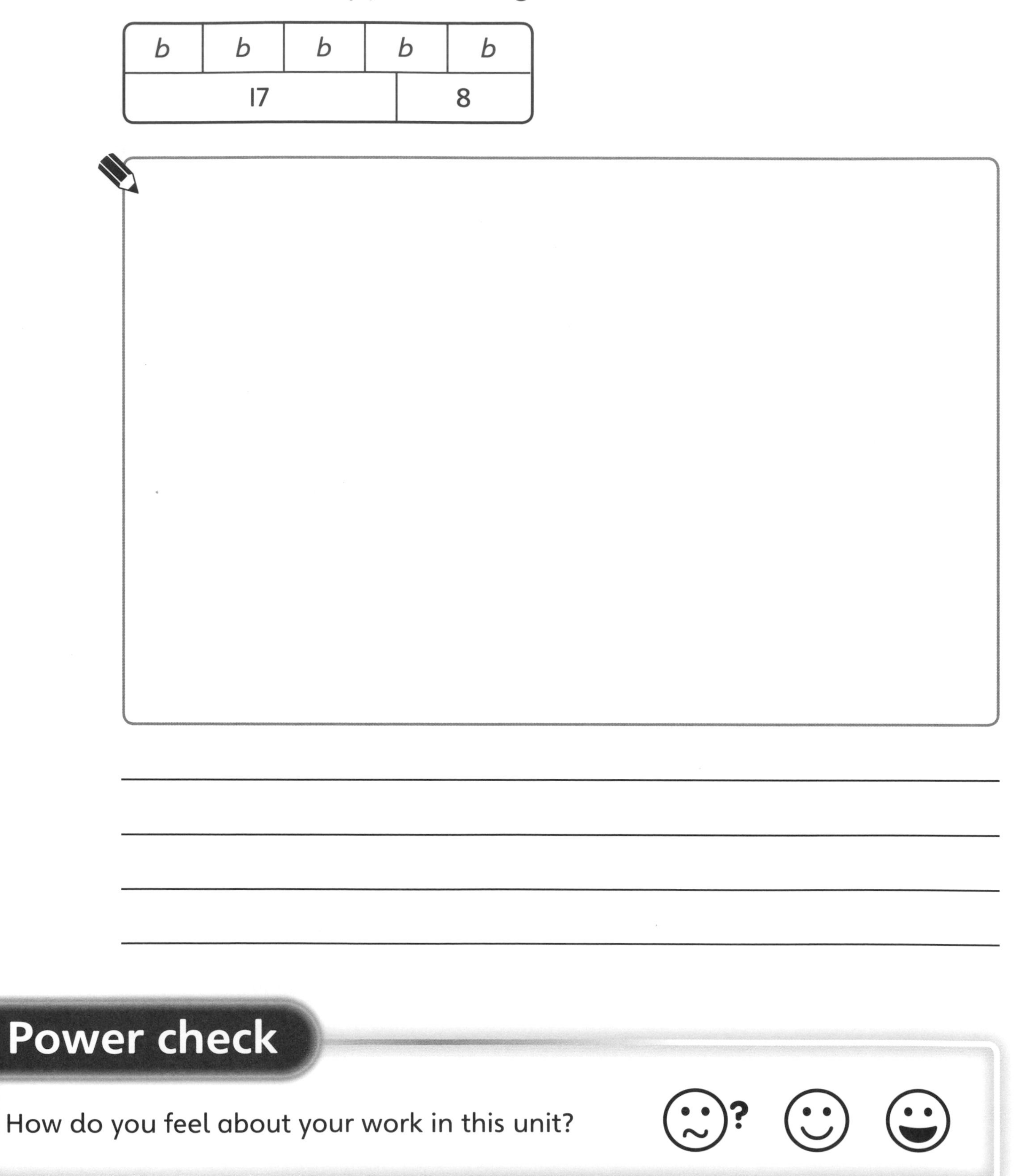

Power check

How do you feel about your work in this unit?

Power puzzle

How many rectangles can you see in this grid?

Can you find all the possible rectangles hidden in the grid?

Show your strategy for finding them all.

Investigate this for different-sized grids. Can you predict how many you can find, based on the size of the grid?

→ Textbook 6B p136

Metric measures

1 Circle the most appropriate unit of measurement for:

a) the distance between two towns mm cm km

b) the mass of a slipper g kg

c) the length of a key km m mm

d) the capacity of a pond l ml

e) the height of a giraffe m cm km

2 A bottle of juice holds 330 ml.

Do you think these containers hold more than, less than or about the same as the bottle?

Tick one column for each container.

	More than	**Less than**	**About the same as**
Yoghurt pot			
Drinking glass			
Cereal bowl			
Carton of milk			
Watering can			
Tin of soup			

3 Give at least two metric units of measure for each category.

a) Length is measured in ____________________ .

b) Mass is measured in ____________________ .

c) Volume / capacity is measured in ____________________ .

4 Circle the best estimate for each measurement.

a) the height of a door	2 m	20 cm
b) the mass of an adult dog	25 g	25 kg
c) the length of a pencil sharpener	21 mm	21 cm
d) the capacity of a small carton of juice	2 ml	200 ml
e) the mass of a loaf of bread	80 g	800 g

5 Are these statements true or false? Tick one column for each statement.

	True	**False**
The length of a pencil is about the same as the length of a toothbrush.		
The most appropriate unit of measure for the distance between two countries is metres.		
A bag of crisps should be labelled in kilograms.		
Centimetres are a longer unit of measurement than millimetres.		
1 litre is less liquid than 1 millilitre.		

6 Luis has a cold and his mum gives him a Vitamin C tablet.

CHALLENGE

The packet says that one tablet contains 80 milligrams (mg) of Vitamin C.

a) Do you think a milligram is more or less than a gram?

More than a gram ☐ Less than a gram ☐

b) Explain why you think this.

____

____

____

____

Look carefully at this shopping list:

1,000 ml milk
0·25 kg flour
$\frac{1}{2}$ m shoelaces

Do you think that the most appropriate units of measurement have been used for each item? Explain your answer.

→ Textbook 6B p140

Converting metric measures

1 Complete the calculations.

Use a place value grid to help with the calculations.

a) Convert 8·5 kilograms into grams.

kilograms → grams

larger unit → smaller unit, so multiply

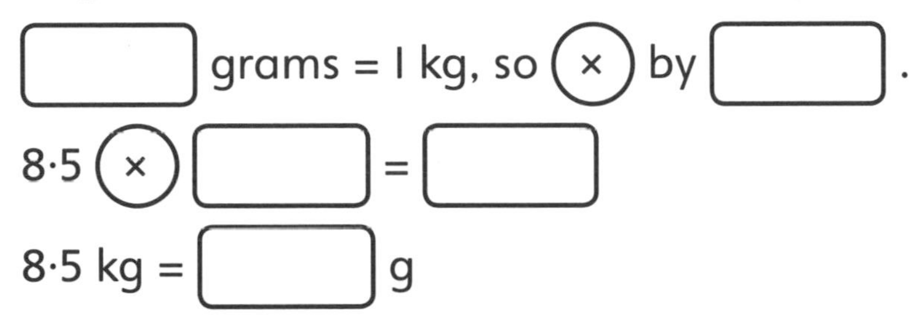

___ grams = 1 kg, so (×) by ___ .

8·5 (×) ___ = ___

8·5 kg = ___ g

b) Convert 4,200 metres into kilometres.

metres → kilometres

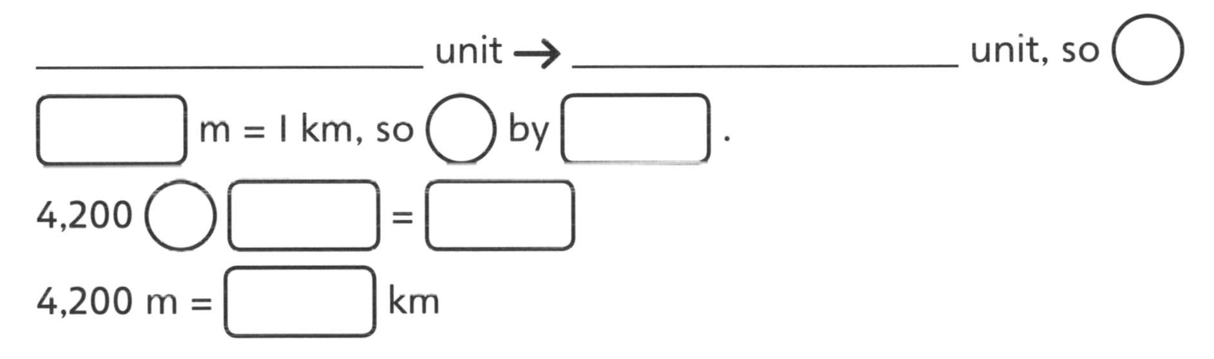

___ unit → ___ unit, so ( )

___ m = 1 km, so ( ) by ___ .

4,200 ( ) ___ = ___

4,200 m = ___ km

2 **a)** Convert from litres to millilitres.

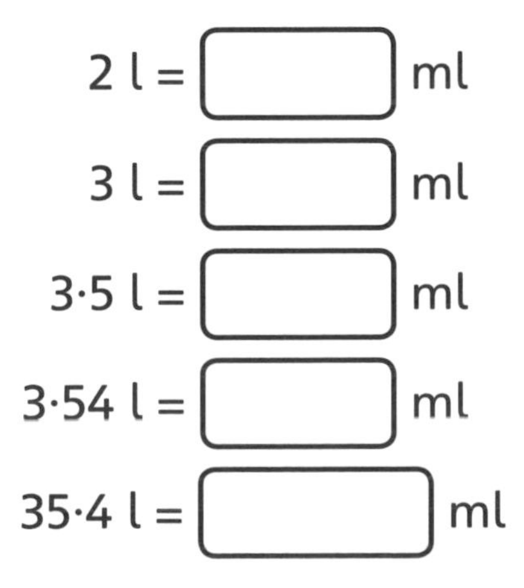

2 l = ___ ml

3 l = ___ ml

3·5 l = ___ ml

3·54 l = ___ ml

35·4 l = ___ ml

b) Convert from grams to kilograms.

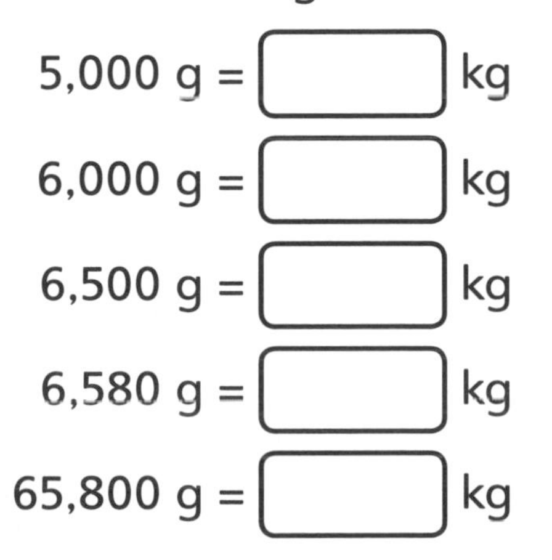

5,000 g = ___ kg

6,000 g = ___ kg

6,500 g = ___ kg

6,580 g = ___ kg

65,800 g = ___ kg

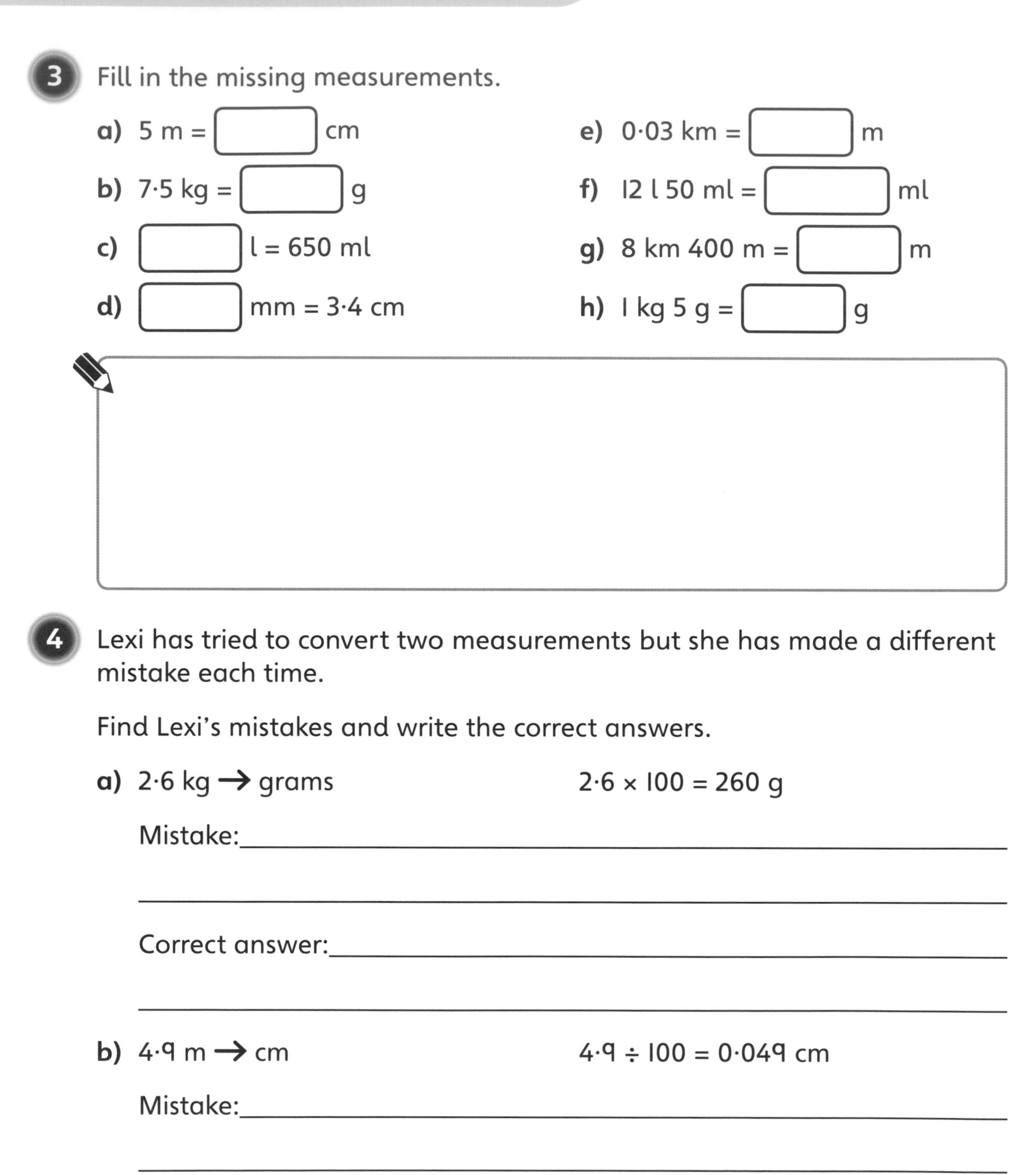

3 Fill in the missing measurements.

a) 5 m = ☐ cm

b) 7·5 kg = ☐ g

c) ☐ l = 650 ml

d) ☐ mm = 3·4 cm

e) 0·03 km = ☐ m

f) 12 l 50 ml = ☐ ml

g) 8 km 400 m = ☐ m

h) 1 kg 5 g = ☐ g

4 Lexi has tried to convert two measurements but she has made a different mistake each time.

Find Lexi's mistakes and write the correct answers.

a) 2·6 kg → grams   2·6 × 100 = 260 g

Mistake: ____________________

____

Correct answer: ____________________

____

b) 4·9 m → cm   4·9 ÷ 100 = 0·049 cm

Mistake: ____________________

____

Correct answer: ____________________

____

CHALLENGE

5 Isla is converting between six metric units.

To convert between A and B, she divides by 1,000.

To convert between C and D, she multiplies by 100.

To convert between E and F, she multiplies by 10.

a) Which units of measure could each letter stand for?

A ________ B ________ C ________ D ________ E ________ F ________

b) Is it possible for D and E to be the same unit of measurement? Explain your answer.

____

____

____

Reflect

57 metres is converted to a different metric unit of measurement.

Danny thinks that the answer could have any digits in it because he does not know what the other unit is. Alex does not agree with Danny and she says that the answer can only contain the digits 5, 7 and 0.

Who do you agree with? Tick the box. Danny ☐ Alex ☐

I think this because ____

____

____

____.

→ Textbook 6B p144

Problem solving – metric measures

a) A Fun Run is 3 km long.

Isla has run 900 m.

How many metres has she got left to run?

b) The height of a bush is 2·5 m.

The fence next to it is 205 cm tall.

Will you be able to see the bush over the top of the fence? Why?

c) A bag contains 2·4 kg of frozen peas.

How many servings of 50 g can be taken from the bag?

2

A book weighs 1·5 kg.
A second book weighs 880 g.
What do the two books weigh altogether?

Aki has made a mistake. What is it? What is the correct answer?

____

____

____

3 A jug holds 1·5 litres of orange squash. The squash is poured equally into 5 glasses.

a) How many millilitres of squash are in each glass?

b) Every 100 ml of squash contains 20 ml of orange juice. How many millilitres of orange juice are in each glass of squash?

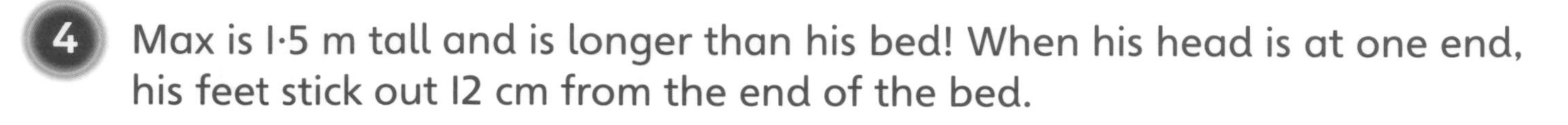

4 Max is 1·5 m tall and is longer than his bed! When his head is at one end, his feet stick out 12 cm from the end of the bed.

Find the length of Max's bed.

____

____

CHALLENGE

5 + = 500 g

+ = 1·2 kg

Calculate the mass of each piece of fruit.

One banana weighs ☐.   One apple weighs ☐.

Reflect

Write your own word problem based on metric measures for a partner to solve. Make sure that the units of measure need to be converted to find the answer.

____

____

____

→ Textbook 6B p148

Miles and km

A speedometer shows a car's speed in miles per hour (mph).

5 miles is about the same as 8 kilometres.

Convert each speed into kilometres per hour (km/h).

The first one has been done for you.

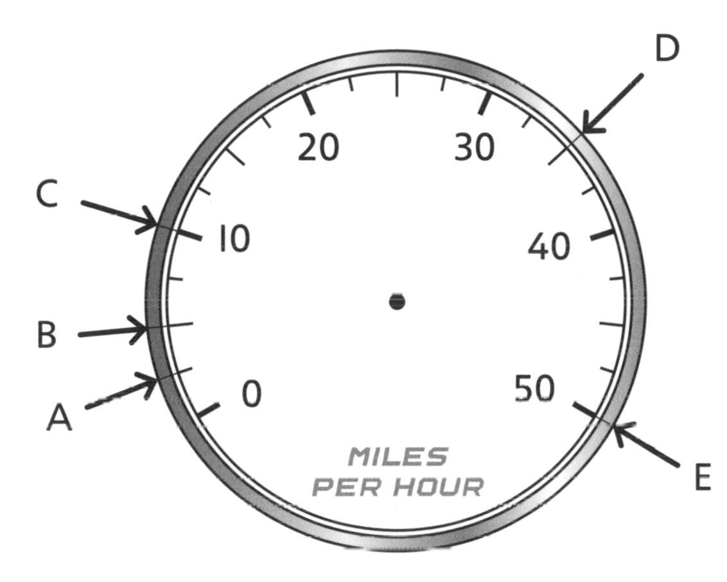

	Speed (mph)	Speed (km/h)
A	2·5	4
B		
C		
D		
E		

2 How many miles are the same as 72 km?

Complete the bar model to work out the answer.

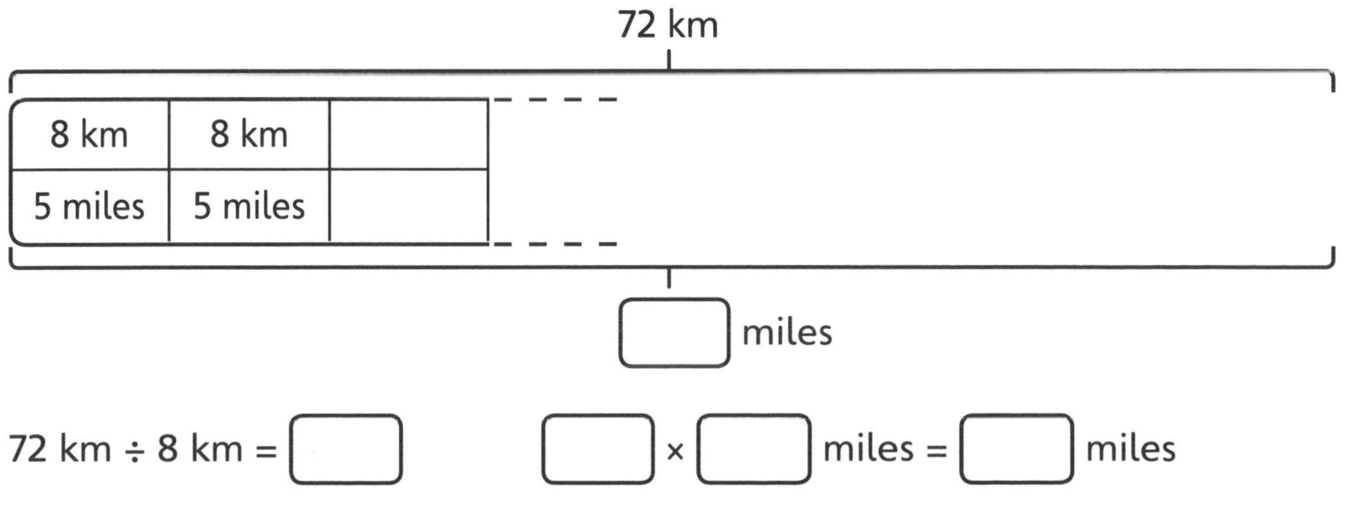

72 km ÷ 8 km = ☐   ☐ × ☐ miles = ☐ miles

3 Complete the table of lengths and use it to find the longest river.

The longest river is the

______________________________ .

Name of river	Length (miles)	Length (km)
River Mersey	70	
River Tamar		80
River Severn	220	
River Clyde		176

4 Aki and Ambika are working out what 100 miles is in kilometres.

Aki: I know that 1 mile is about 1·6 km, so I am going to work out 100 × 1·6.

Ambika: 5 miles are about 8 km. I am going to find out how many 5s are in 100 and then multiply by 8.

Whose method will give the correct answer? Circle your choice:

Aki   Ambika   Both

What is the correct answer? 100 miles is about ☐ km.

CHALLENGE

5 Toshi is returning home by train. There are two trains he can choose from.

Train A travels 60 miles every hour.

Train B travels 80 kilometres every hour.

Tick the train Toshi should take to get home as quickly as possible.

Explain your answer.

____

____

____

____

Write five facts that you can work out from the following sentence:

If I know that 5 miles is about the same as 8 km, I also know

____

____

____

____

____.

→ Textbook 6B p152

Imperial measures

Use this conversion graph to convert between inches and centimetres.

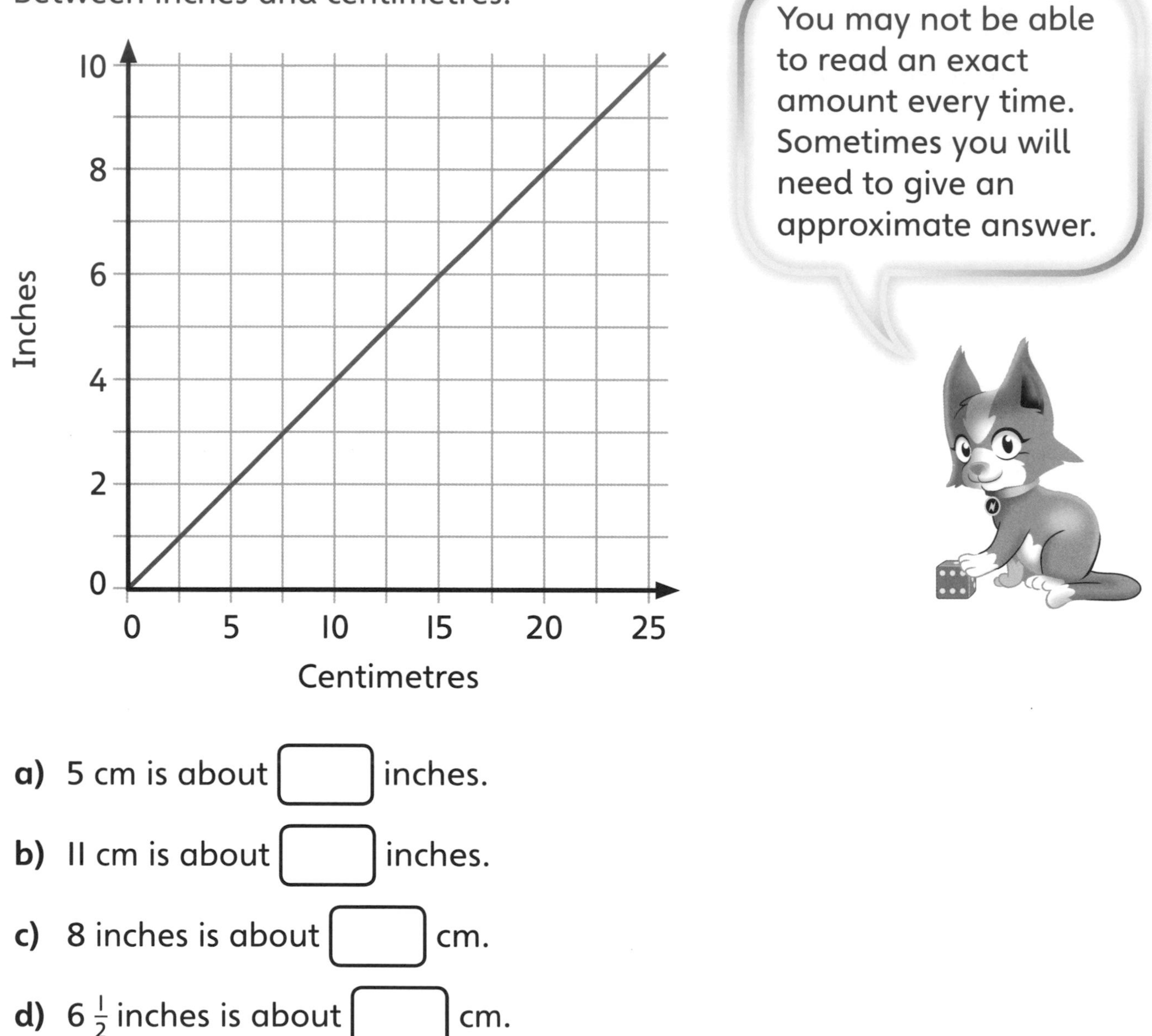

a) 5 cm is about ☐ inches.

b) 11 cm is about ☐ inches.

c) 8 inches is about ☐ cm.

d) $6\frac{1}{2}$ inches is about ☐ cm.

e) Explain how to use the graph to find out how many inches are in 50 cm.

____

____

____

____

2 Complete this conversion table.

Kilograms	1	2	3			50	
Pounds	2·2			11	22		220

3 Which of these is not an example of an imperial unit of measure? Put a tick in the correct box.

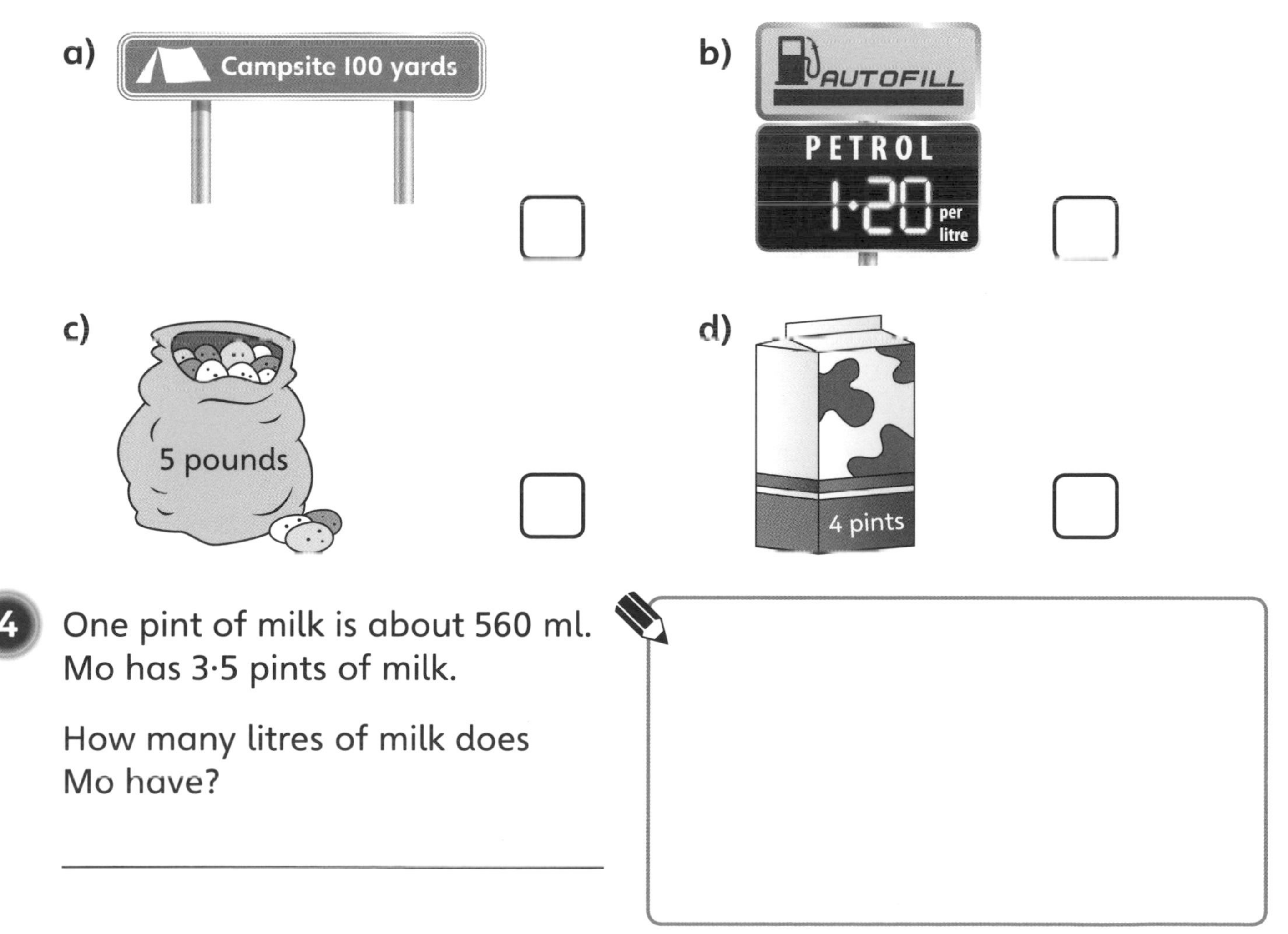

4 One pint of milk is about 560 ml. Mo has 3·5 pints of milk.

How many litres of milk does Mo have?

____

5 I inch is about 2·5 cm. There are I2 inches in I foot.

CHALLENGE

These children have measured their height in different ways.

Name	Height
Aki	I45 cm
Lee	50 inches
Jamilla	5 feet
Ambika	I,390 mm
Max	I·48 m

Write their names in order from shortest to tallest.

_______ _______ _______ _______ _______

Shortest Tallest

Now that you have used both metric and imperial units of measure, which do you prefer? Explain why.

→ Textbook 6B p156

End of unit check

My journal

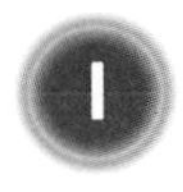

1. The children have each made a mistake. Find each mistake and then give the correct answer.

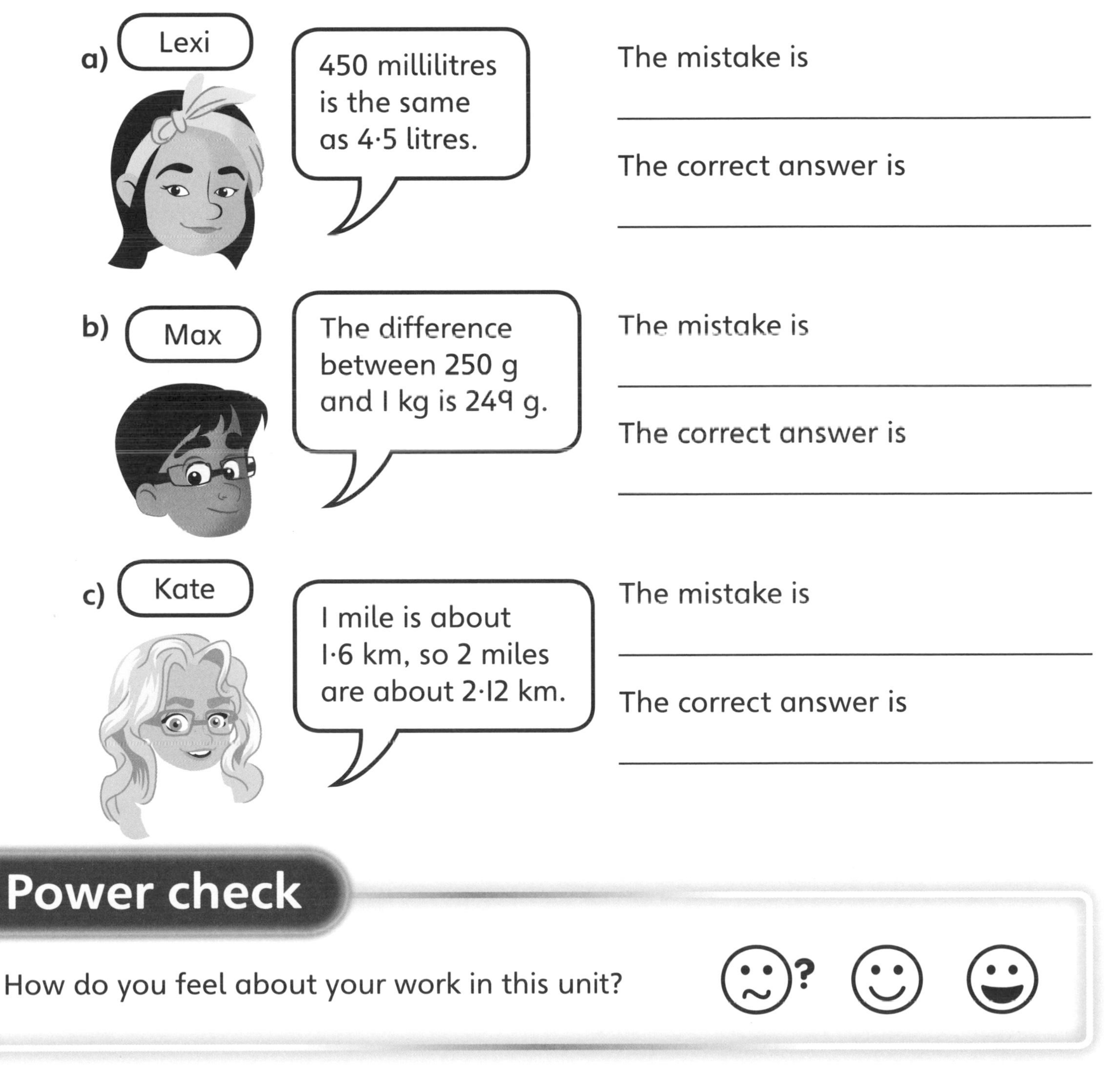

a) The mistake is

____

The correct answer is

____

b) The mistake is

____

The correct answer is

____

c) The mistake is

____

The correct answer is

____

Power check

How do you feel about your work in this unit?

Power puzzle

The answer to each of these conversions is linked to a letter.

The letters spell out things people can eat. Crack the code to find out what they are. Be careful – the item in part b) is two words!

KEY:

56,000	5,600	470	39	2·1	0·21	0·47
P	L	S	I	E	T	A

a)

	Number	Letter
56 km = ? m		
470 g = ? kg		
47 cm = ? mm		
210 g = ? kg		
390 mm = ? cm		
2,100 ml = ? l		
0·47 l = ? ml		

b)

	Number	Letter
47 cm = ? m		
56 kg = ? g		
560 m = ? cm		
5·6 kg = ? g		
0·21 cm = ? mm		
56 l = ? ml		
3,900 cm = ? m		
2,100 g = ? kg		

Now invent your own conversion code for your partner to crack!

You could use imperial and metric conversions.

Shapes with the same area

1 Calculate the area of each rectangle. Do both the rectangles in each pair have the same area? Tick the correct box.

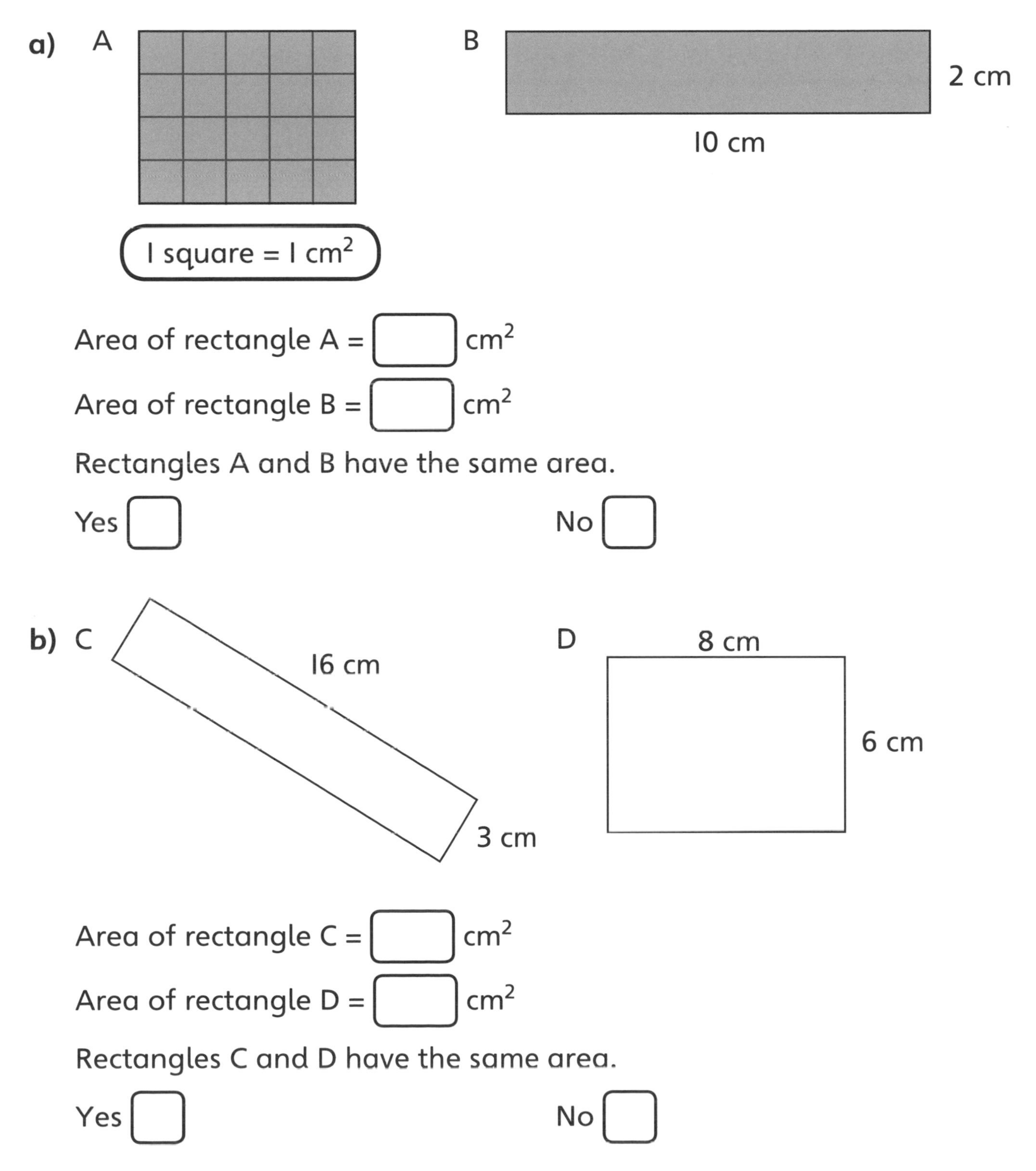

a)

Area of rectangle A = ☐ cm^2

Area of rectangle B = ☐ cm^2

Rectangles A and B have the same area.

Yes ☐ No ☐

b)

Area of rectangle C = ☐ cm^2

Area of rectangle D = ☐ cm^2

Rectangles C and D have the same area.

Yes ☐ No ☐

2 Use these clues to draw three shapes that each have an area of 36 cm^2.

	Shape A	Shape B	Shape C
Clue 1	Square	Rectangle	Compound shape
Clue 2		Length is 4 × width	

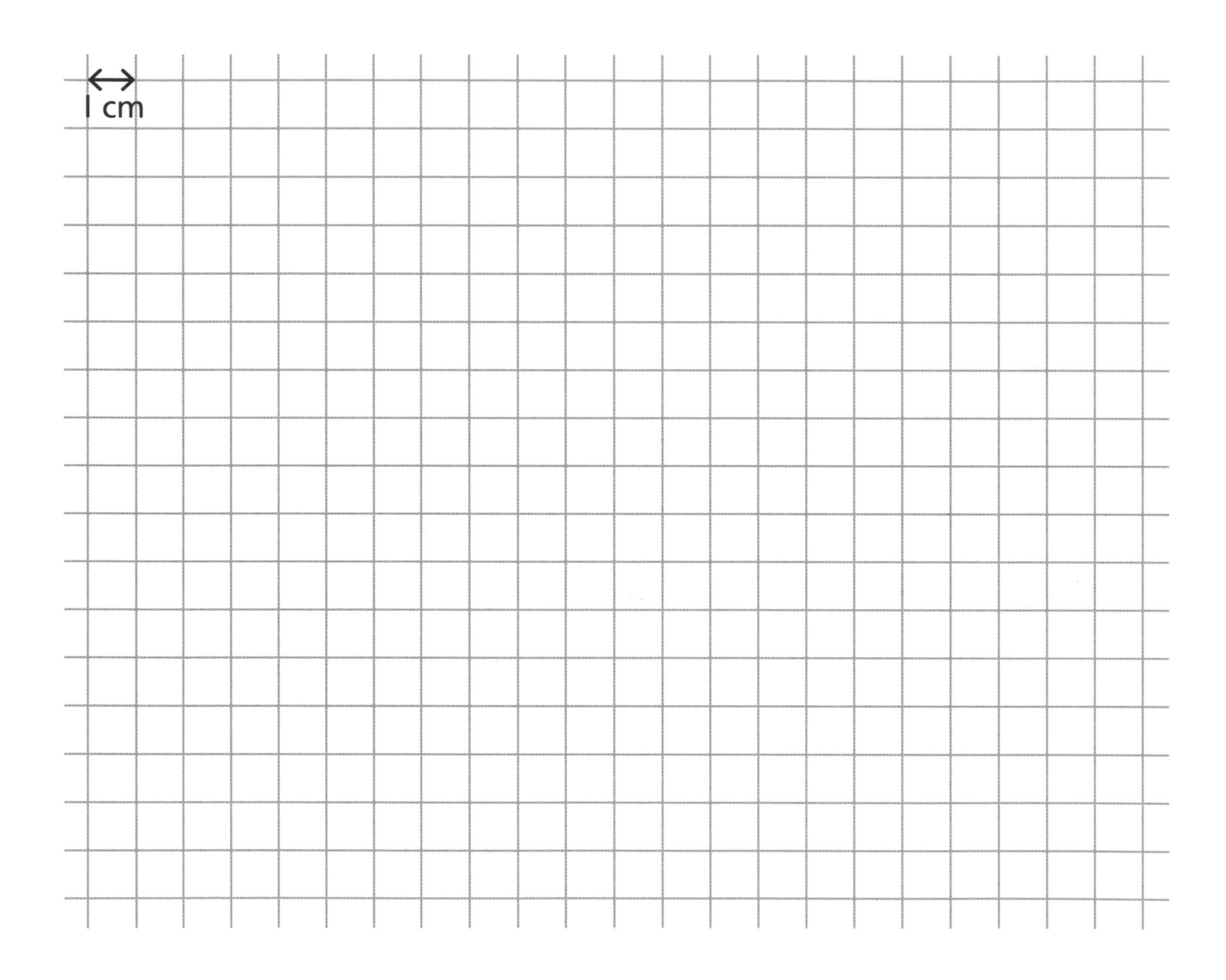

What other shapes with the same area can you draw?

___

___

___

3 All of these shapes have the same area. Calculate the missing measurements.

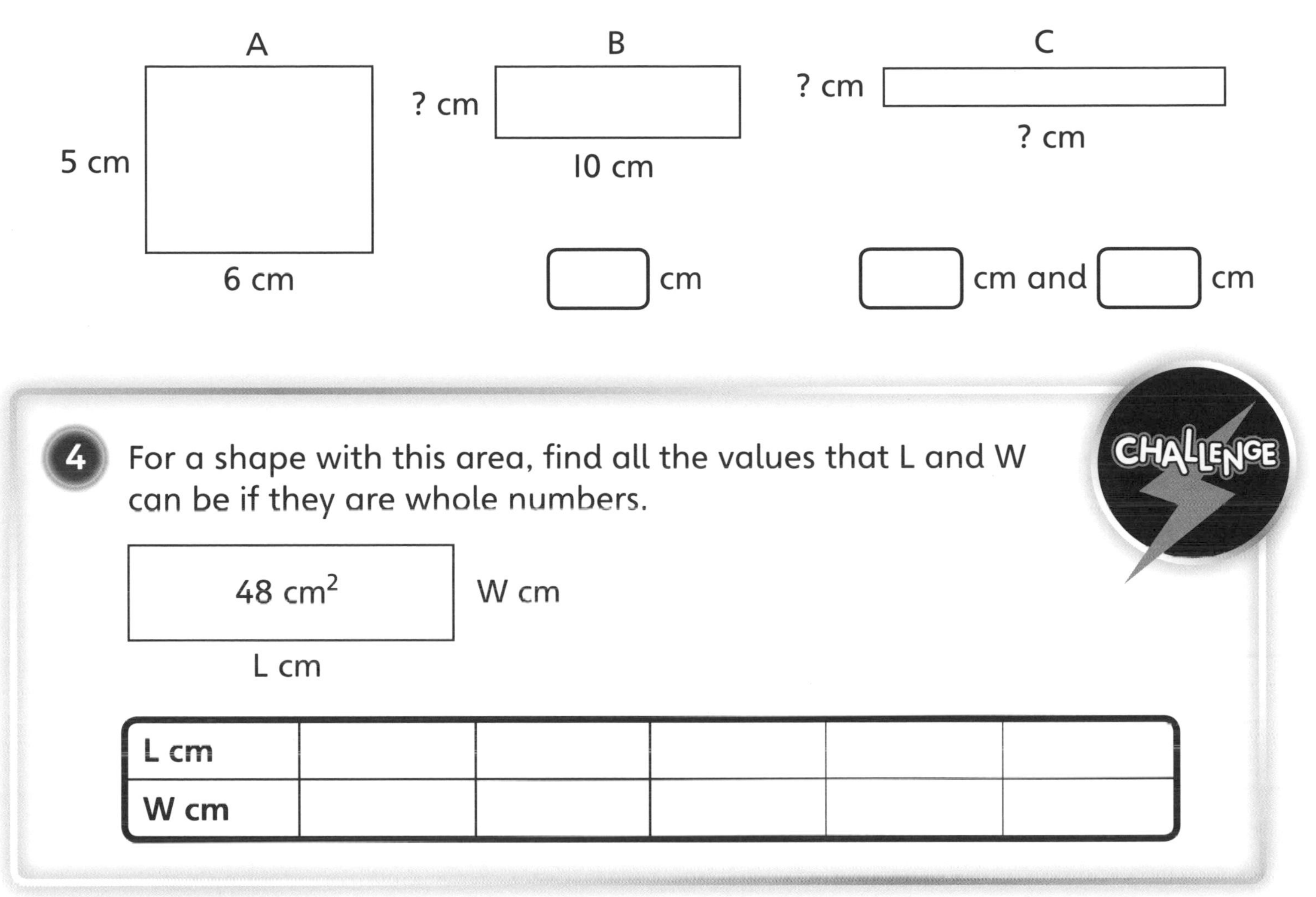

☐ cm

☐ cm and ☐ cm

4 For a shape with this area, find all the values that L and W can be if they are whole numbers.

48 cm^2

W cm

L cm

L cm					
W cm					

Reflect

Max draws a plan of his room on squared paper. Every square represents 1 metre. His room is 4 m wide and 3 m long. How can Max find the area of his room without counting every single square on the plan?

→ Textbook 6B p164

Area and perimeter 

1 **a)** Calculate the perimeter and area of shapes A, B and C. Then complete the table.

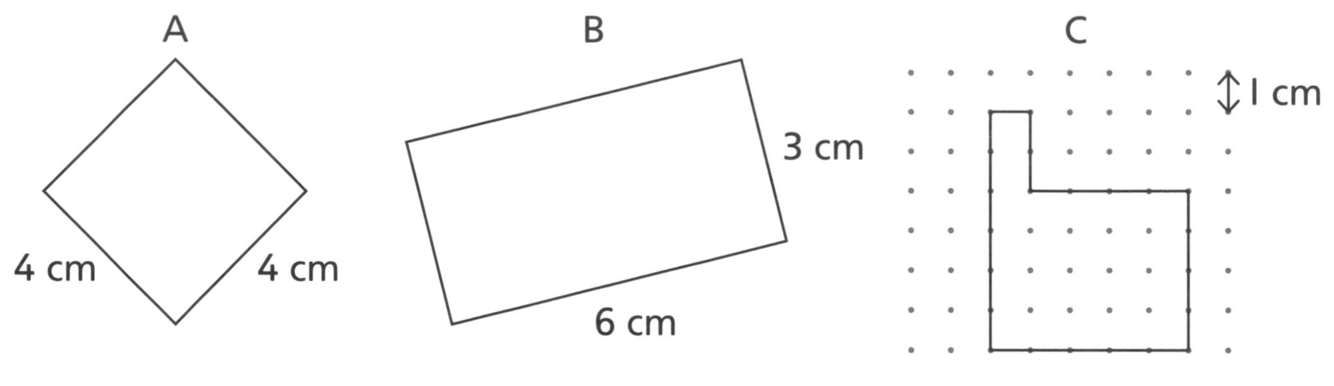

Shape	Perimeter (cm)	Area (cm²)
A		
B		
C		

b) What do shapes A, B and C have in common?

____

____

2 **a)** Draw a different shape with the same area as the shaded square.

b) Draw a different shape with the same perimeter as the shaded square.

c) Draw a shape with the same area as the shaded square, but with a greater perimeter.

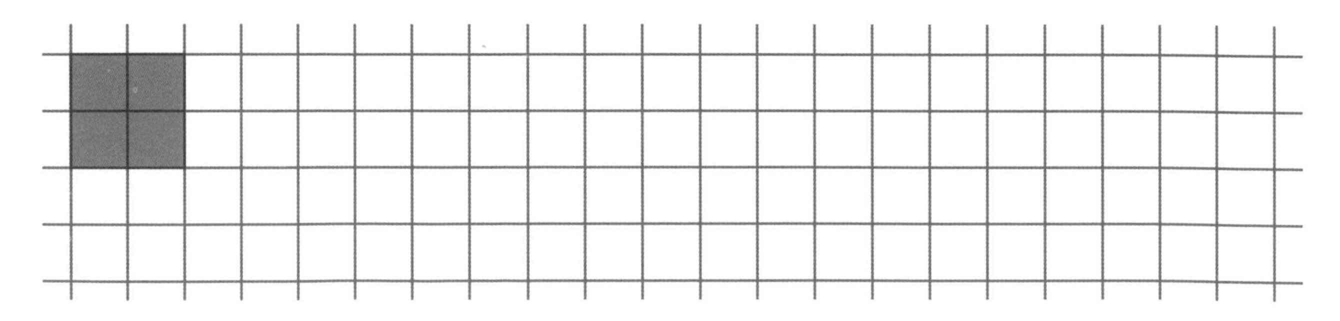

3 Calculate the area and perimeter of each shape below. Which shapes have equal areas?

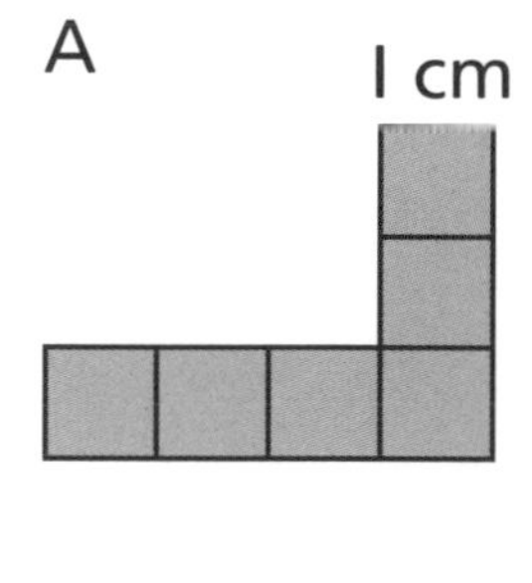

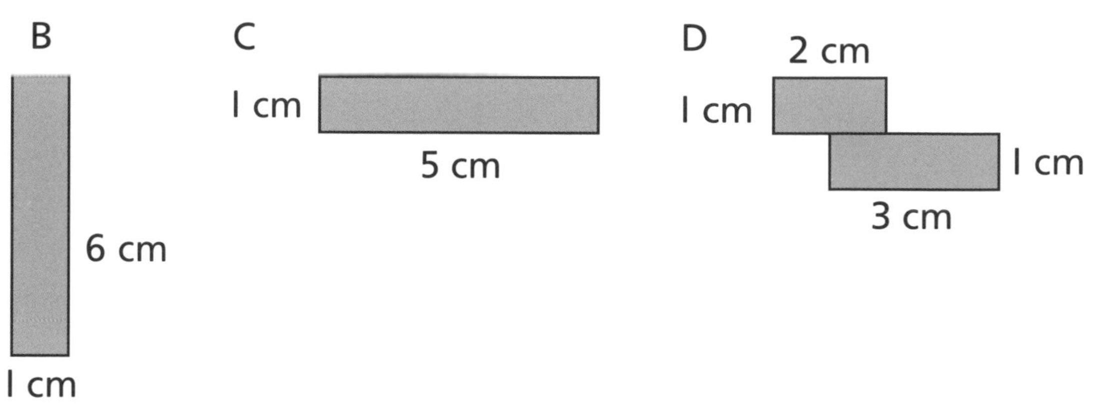

Shape	Area (cm^2)	Perimeter (cm)
A		
B		
C		
D		

The shapes with equal areas are: ____________________

4 What do you notice about the areas and perimeters of these shapes? What is the same? What is different about these shapes?

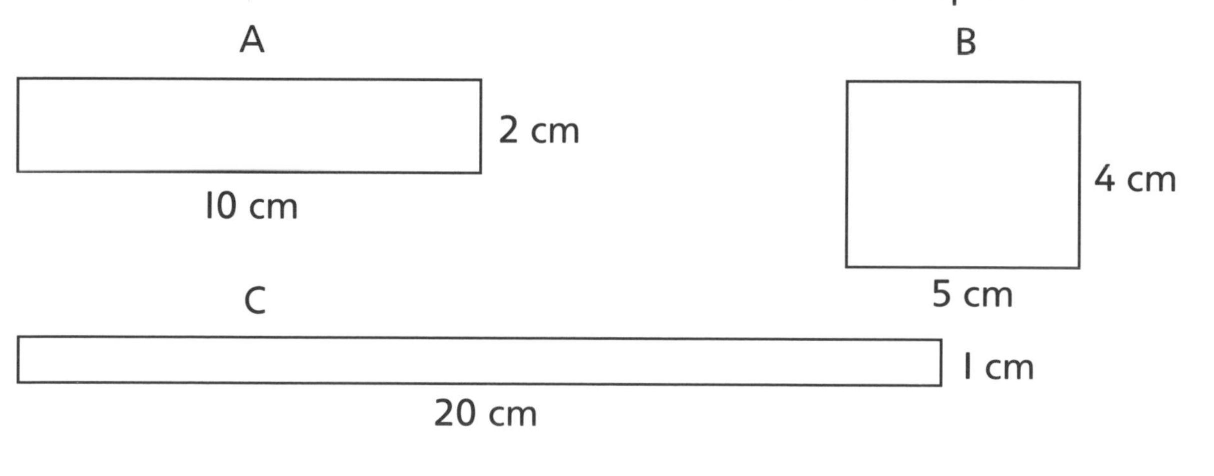

____

____

____

5

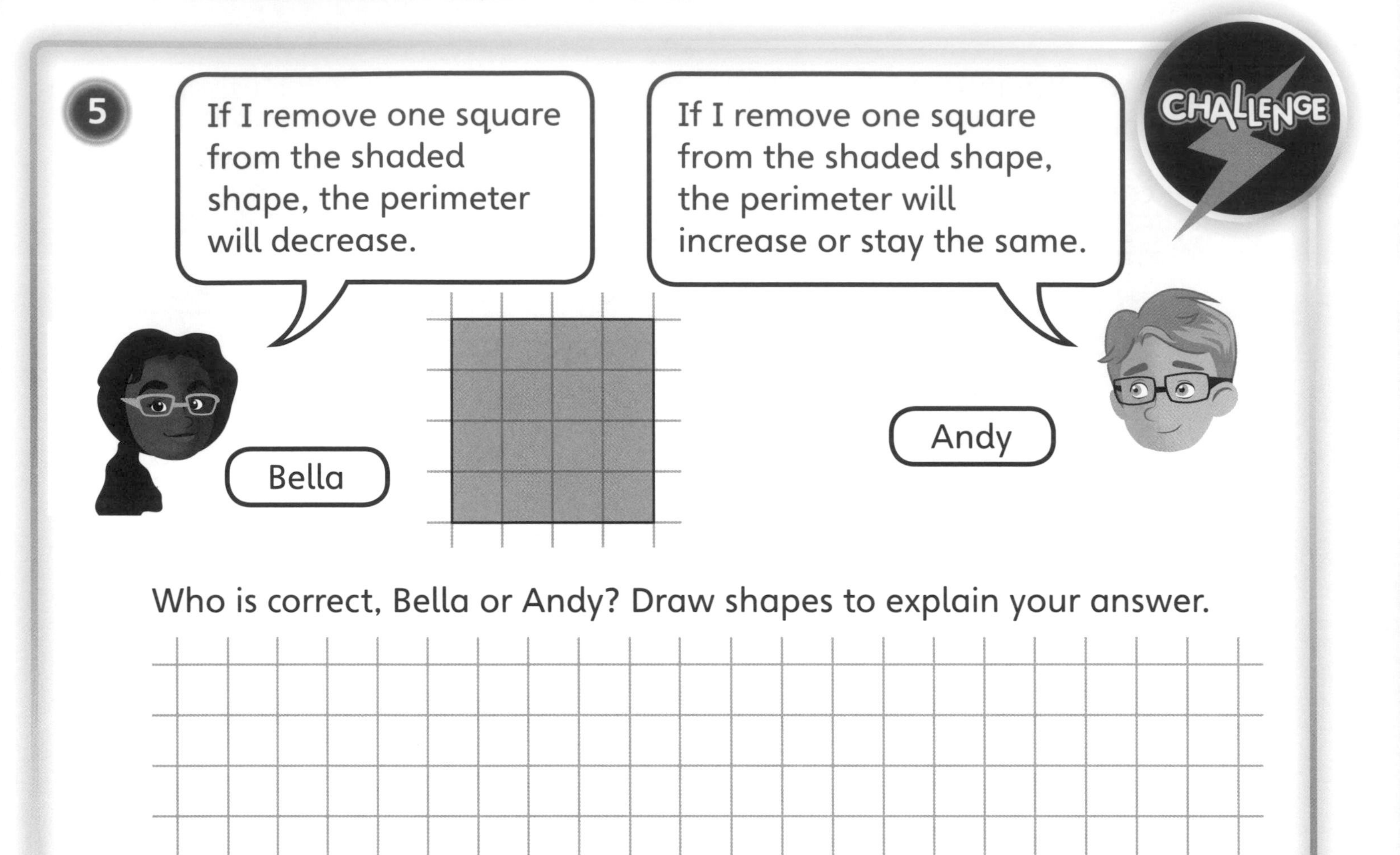

Who is correct, Bella or Andy? Draw shapes to explain your answer.

____

____

Reflect

Amy says: 'If two shapes have equal areas, their perimeters must be equal too.' Explain why Amy is not correct.

____

____

____

→ Textbook 6B p168

Area and perimeter 2

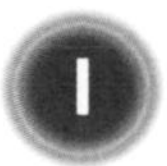

a) Calculate the perimeter and area of each shape.

1 cm

A B C D

Shape	Perimeter (cm)	Area (cm²)
A		
B		
C		
D		

b) What do you notice about the shapes?

I notice that ______________________________

______________________________.

Find the missing numbers. What do you notice about the numbers?

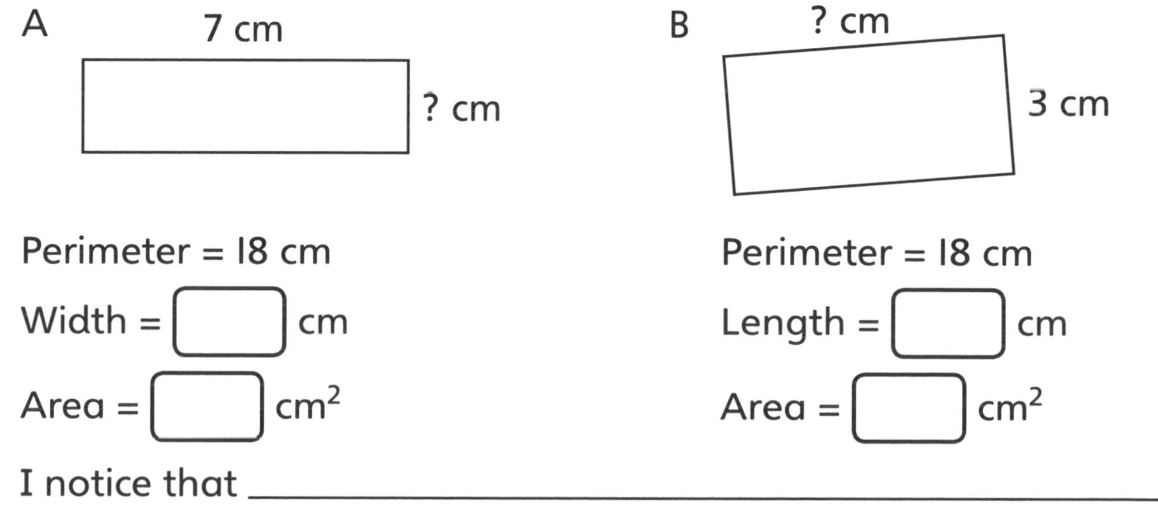

Perimeter = 18 cm

Width = [ ] cm

Area = [ ] cm^2

Perimeter = 18 cm

Length = [ ] cm

Area = [ ] cm^2

I notice that ______________________________.

3 Three shapes each have a perimeter of 12 cm. The area of shape A is 9 cm^2, the area of shape B is 5 cm^2 and the area of shape C is 8 cm^2.

Draw the three shapes.

1 cm

4 Two gardens each have a perimeter of 30 m. The area of garden A is 4 times greater than the area of garden B. Work out the dimensions of each garden.

A

B

5 The shape below is made of square tiles. Which of the tiles can be removed without changing the perimeter?

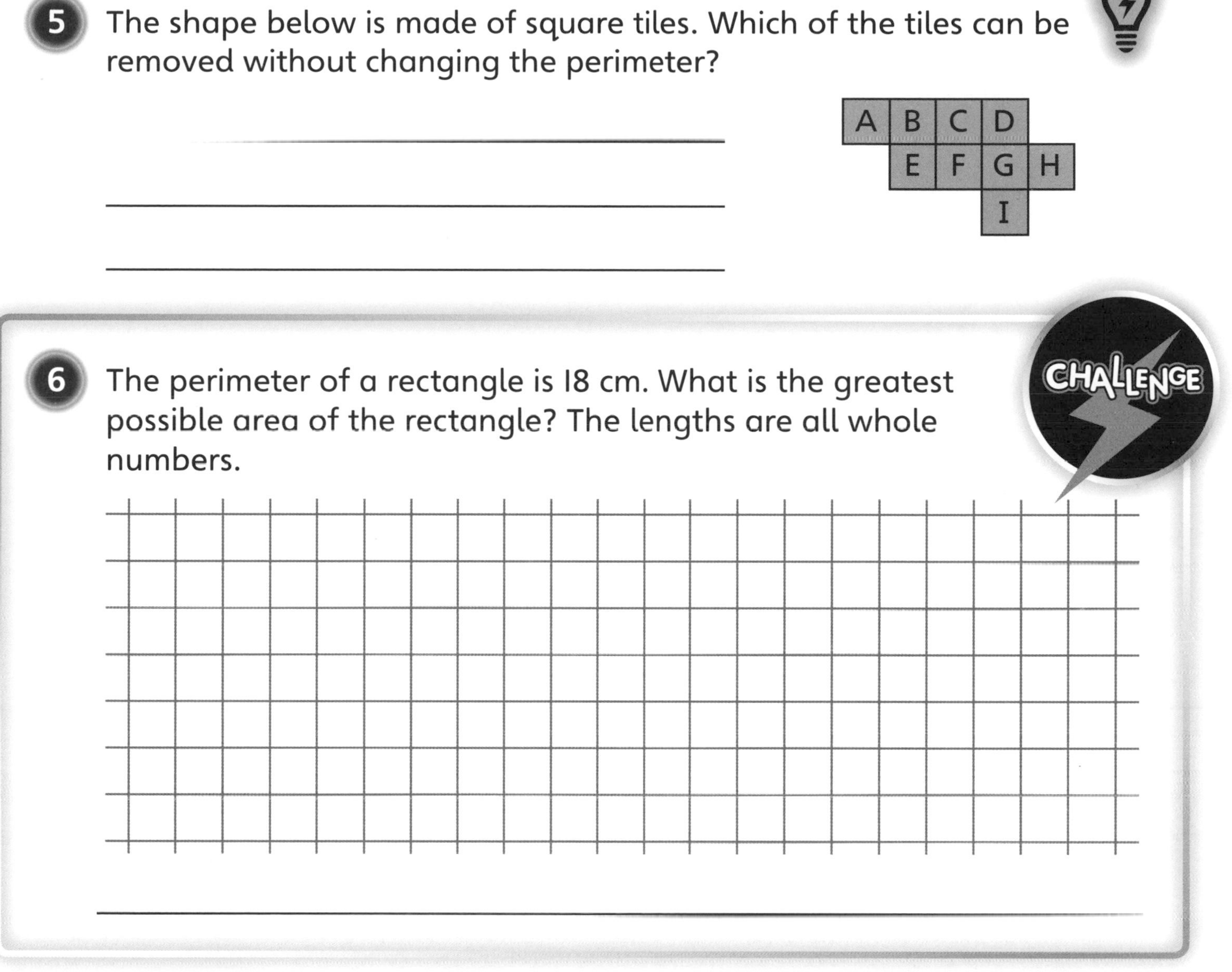

6 The perimeter of a rectangle is 18 cm. What is the greatest possible area of the rectangle? The lengths are all whole numbers.

Reflect

Olivia says: 'Shapes with the same perimeter have the same area.' Use your knowledge from this lesson to say whether you agree or disagree with her.

→ Textbook 6B p172

Area of a parallelogram

1 Calculate the area of each parallelogram by turning it into a rectangle.

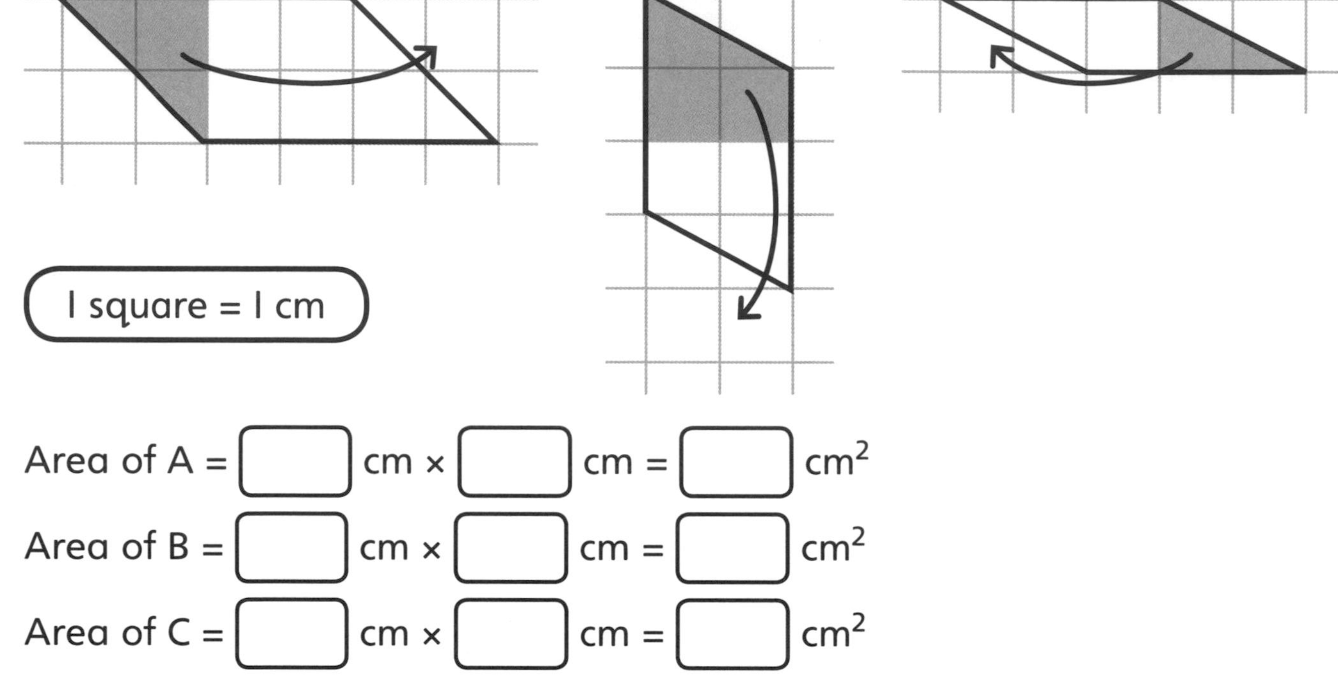

Area of A = ☐ cm × ☐ cm = ☐ cm^2

Area of B = ☐ cm × ☐ cm = ☐ cm^2

Area of C = ☐ cm × ☐ cm = ☐ cm^2

2 Find the area of each parallelogram. Which of them is the odd one out?

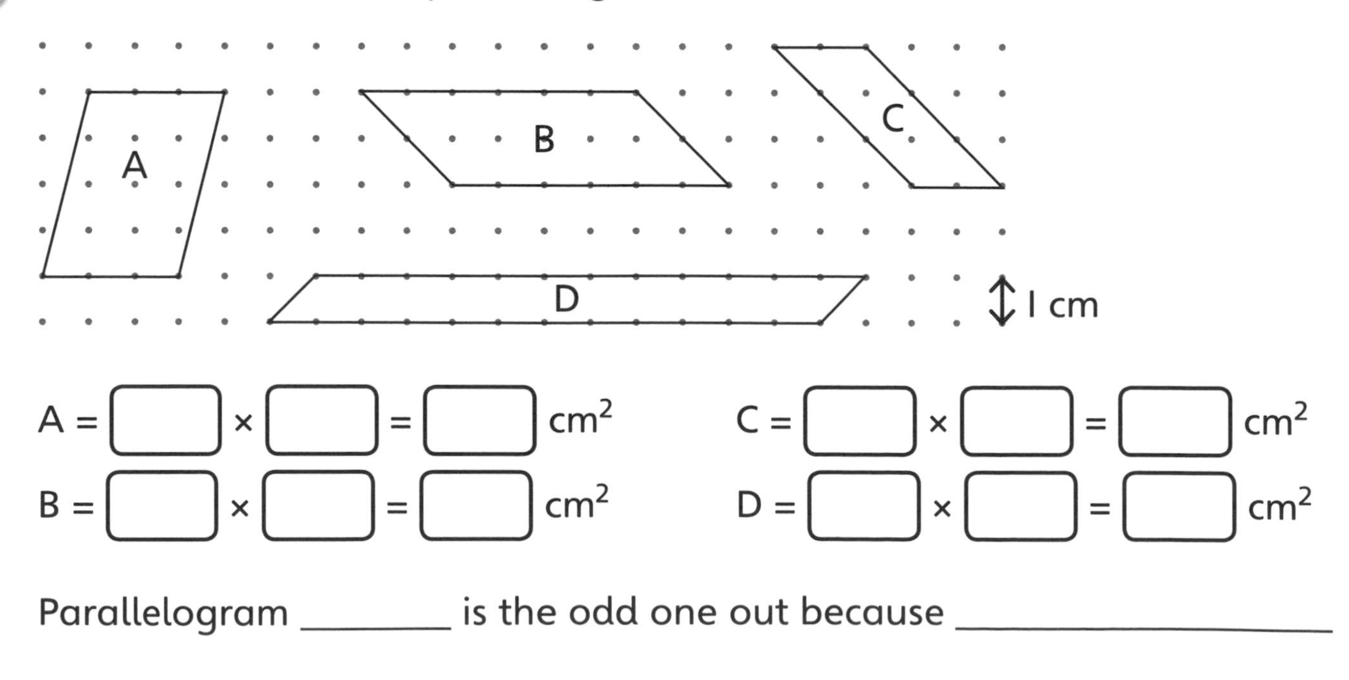

A = ☐ × ☐ = ☐ cm^2

B = ☐ × ☐ = ☐ cm^2

C = ☐ × ☐ = ☐ cm^2

D = ☐ × ☐ = ☐ cm^2

Parallelogram _______ is the odd one out because ____________________

____.

3 **a)** Find the area of each parallelogram.

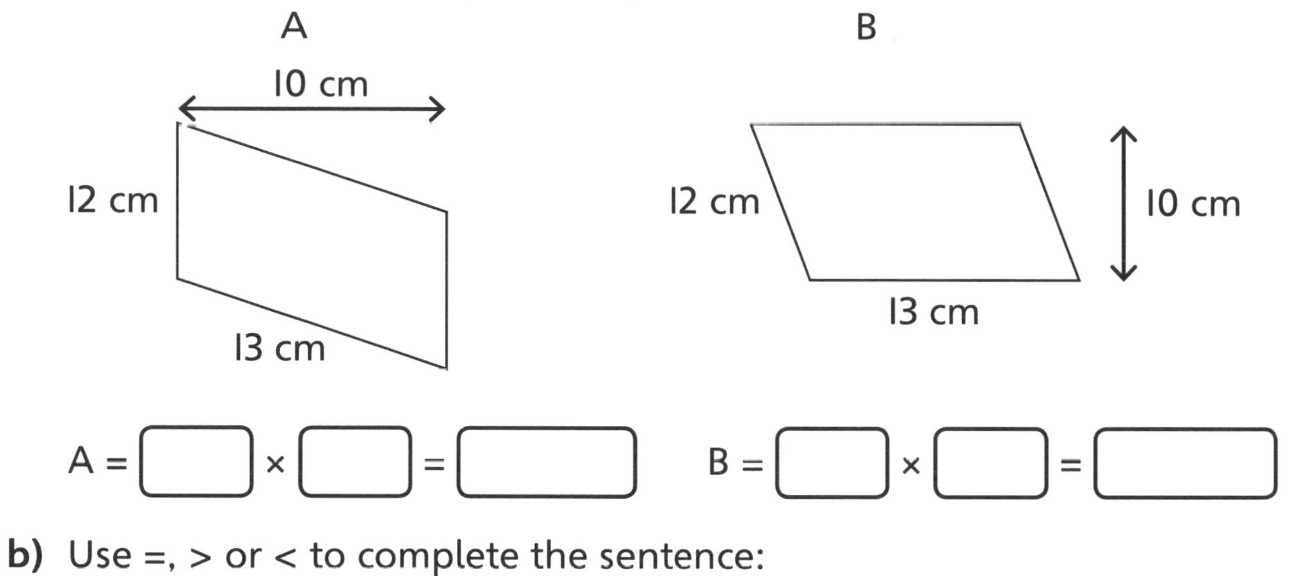

A = ☐ × ☐ = ☐   B = ☐ × ☐ = ☐

b) Use =, > or < to complete the sentence:

Area of parallelogram A ◯ area of parallelogram B.

4 Use the facts that are given in the diagrams to find lengths *a*, *b* and *c*.

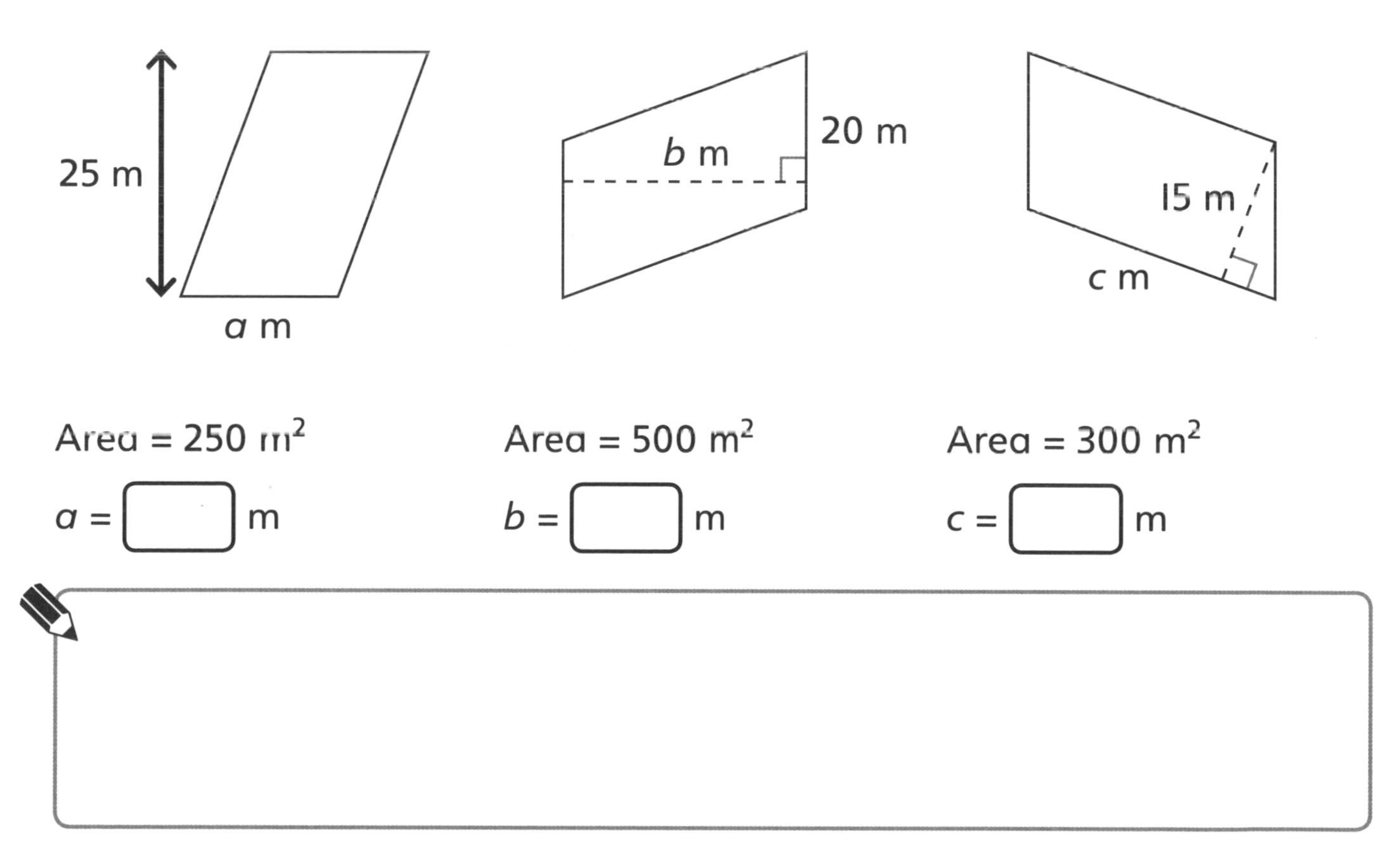

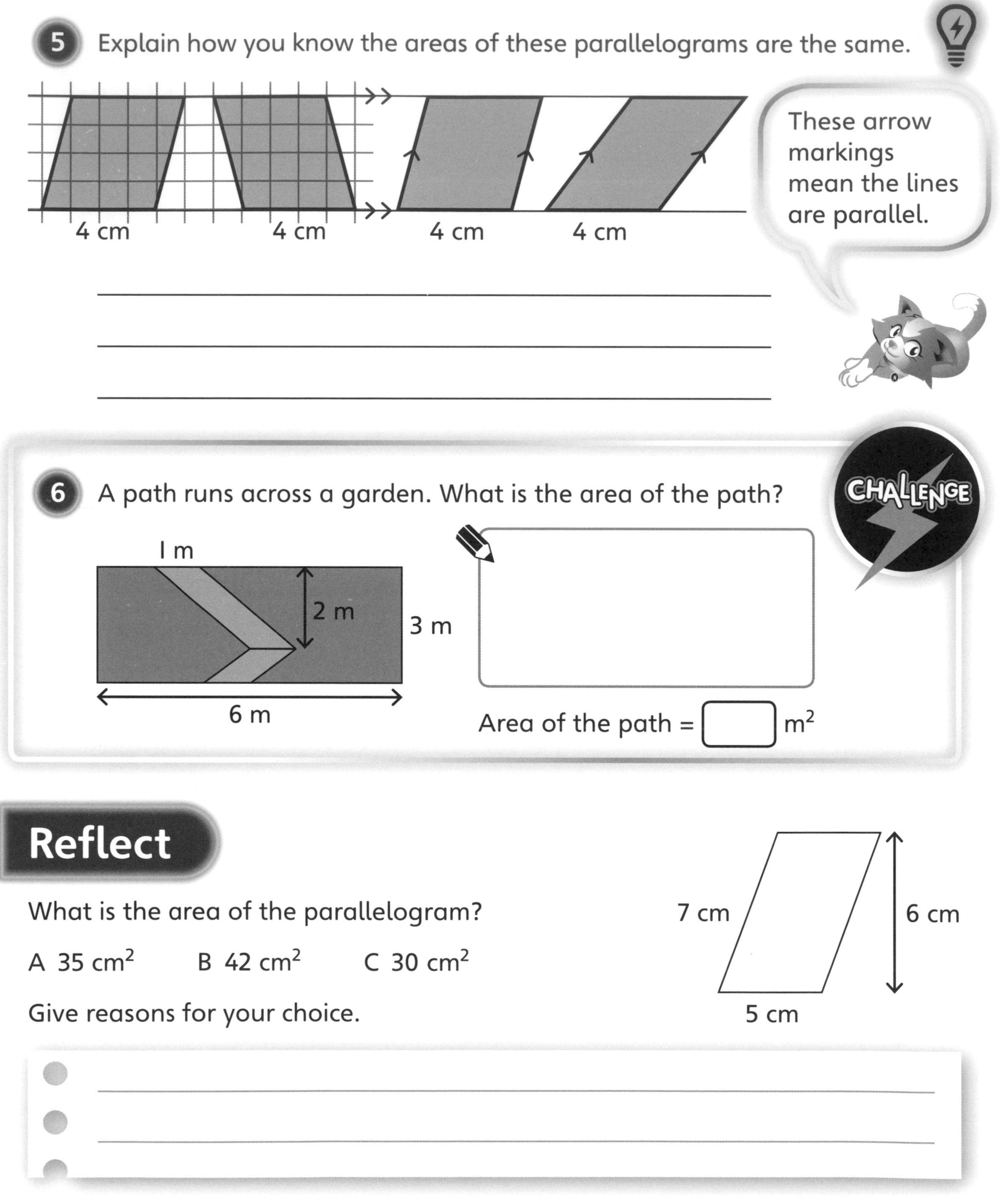

5 Explain how you know the areas of these parallelograms are the same.

____

____

____

6 A path runs across a garden. What is the area of the path?

Area of the path = ☐ m^2

Reflect

What is the area of the parallelogram?

A 35 cm^2 B 42 cm^2 C 30 cm^2

Give reasons for your choice.

____

____

→ Textbook 6B p176

Area of a triangle 1

Remember, the area of a rectangle = width × length.

1 Calculate the area of each triangle by turning it into a rectangle.

1 square = 1 cm^2

a) [ ] rows in the rectangle formed.

[ ] squares in each row.

[ ] × [ ] = [ ]

Total number of squares = [ ]

Area: [ ] cm × [ ] cm = [ ] cm^2

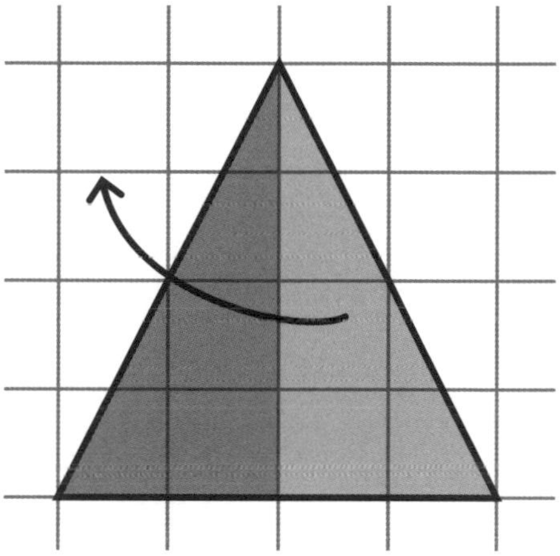

b) [ ] rows in the rectangle.

[ ] squares in each row.

[ ] × [ ] = [ ]

Total number of squares = [ ]

Area: [ ] cm × [ ] cm = [ ] cm^2

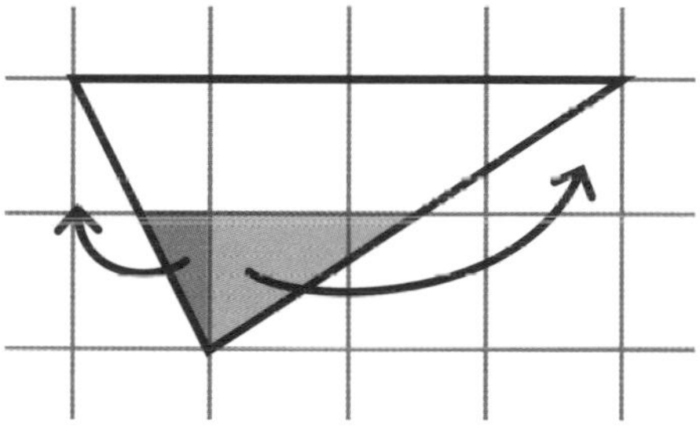

c)

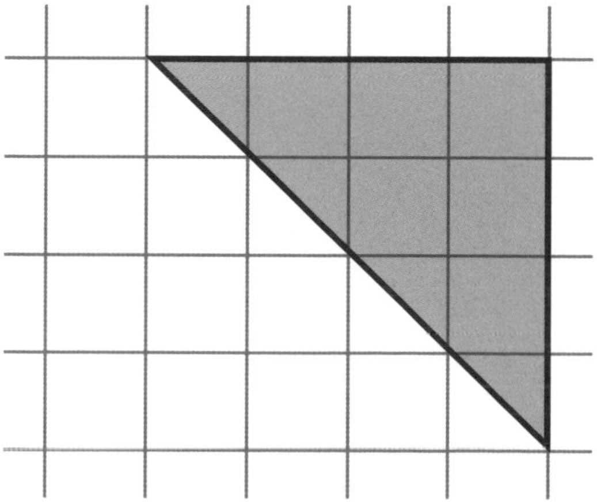

Area = [ ] cm^2

2 Estimate the area of each triangle by counting the squares.

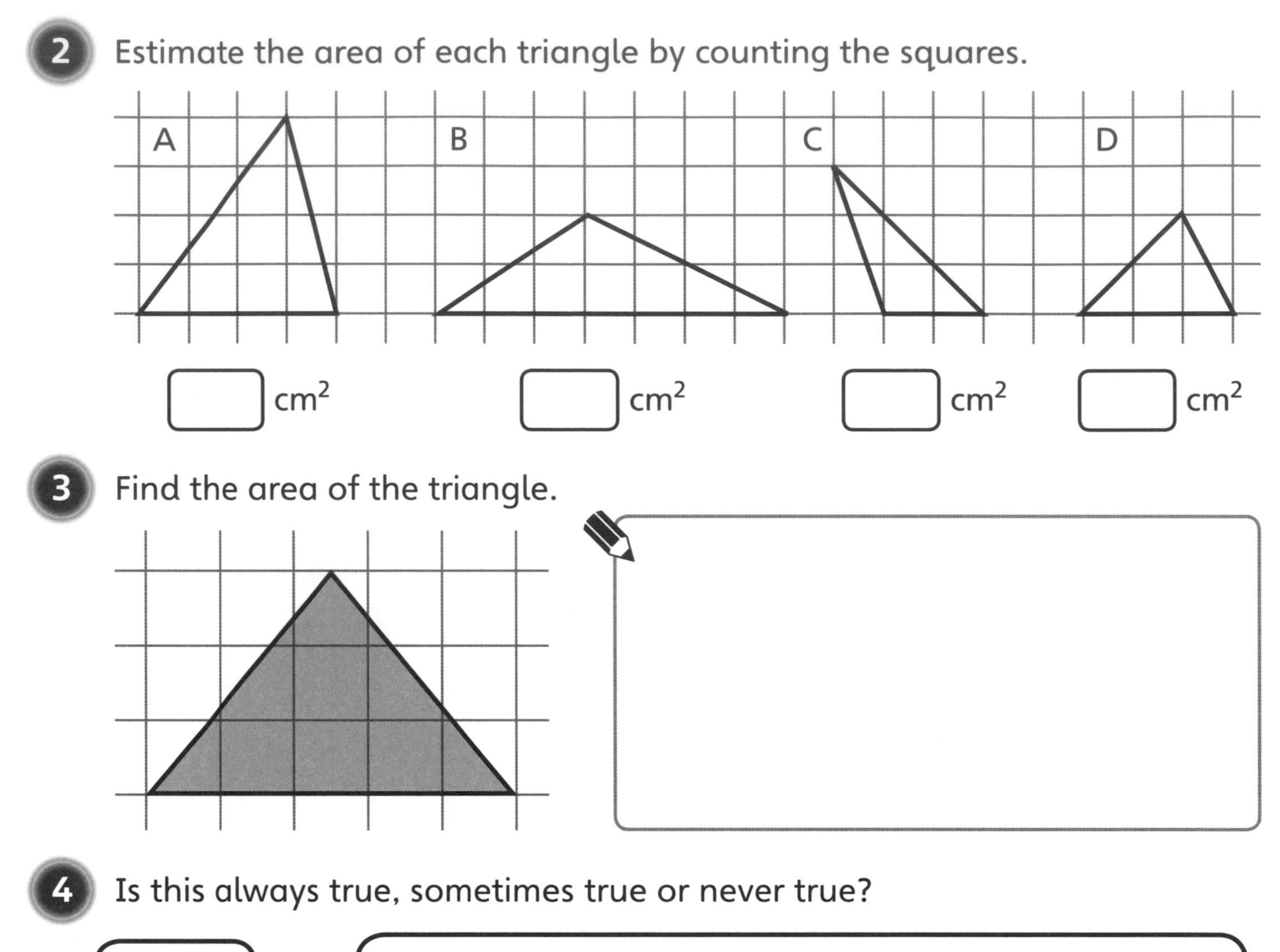

3 Find the area of the triangle.

4 Is this always true, sometimes true or never true?

Draw examples to explain your answer.

5 Triangle A has an area of 6 cm^2. Jess thinks that the area of triangle B is twice the area of triangle A. Is she correct?

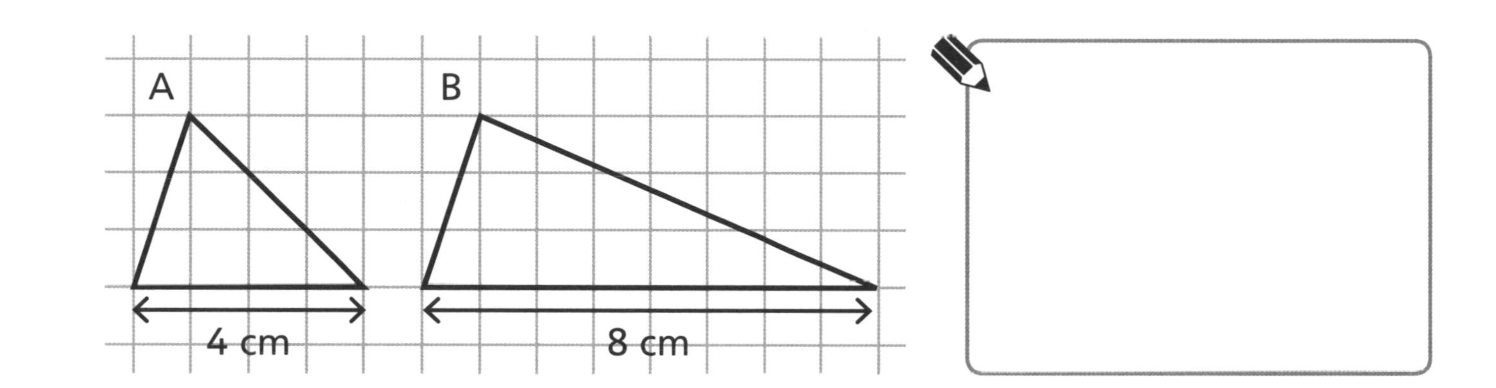

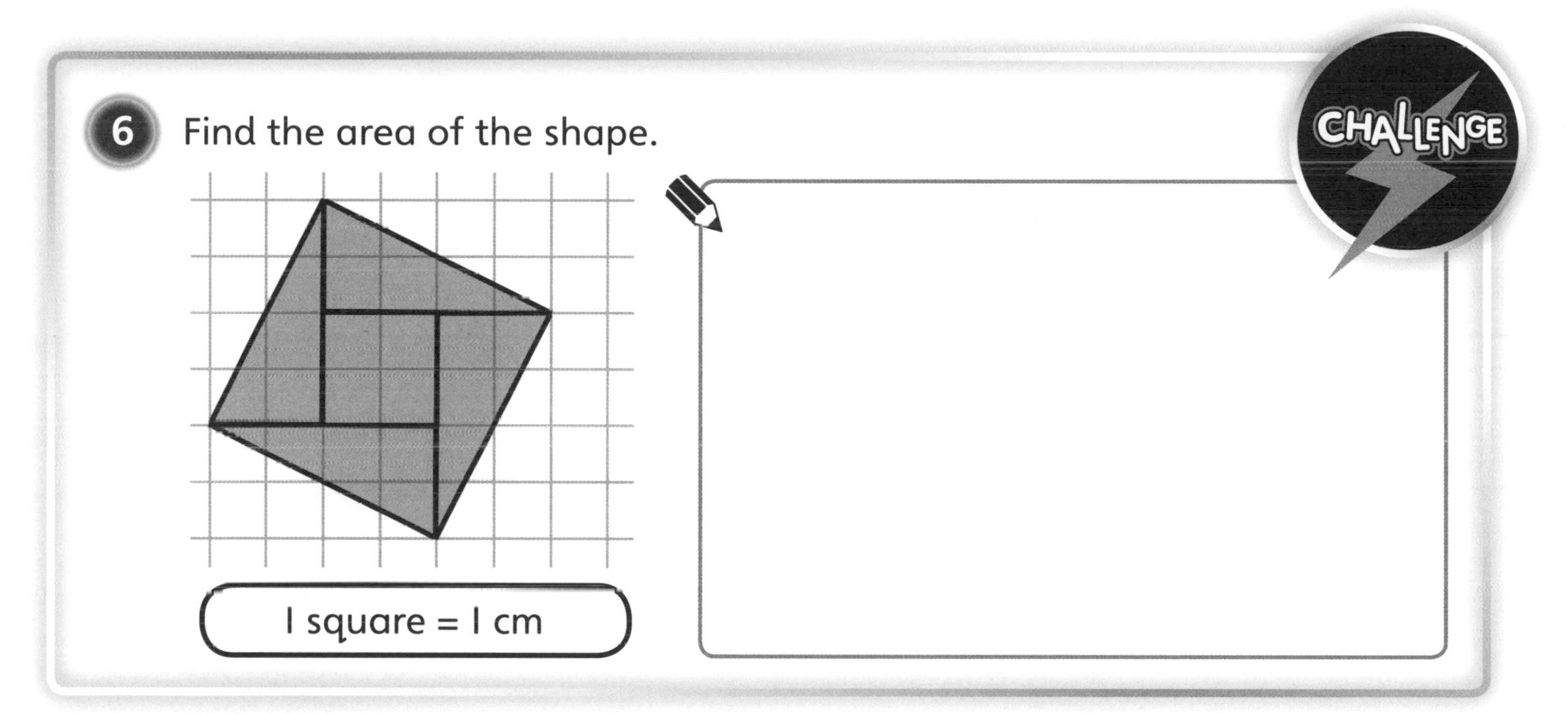

6 Find the area of the shape.

I square = I cm

Reflect

Explain how to find the area of a triangle in two different ways.

→ Textbook 6B p180

Area of a triangle 2

1 Find the area of each shaded right-angled triangle.

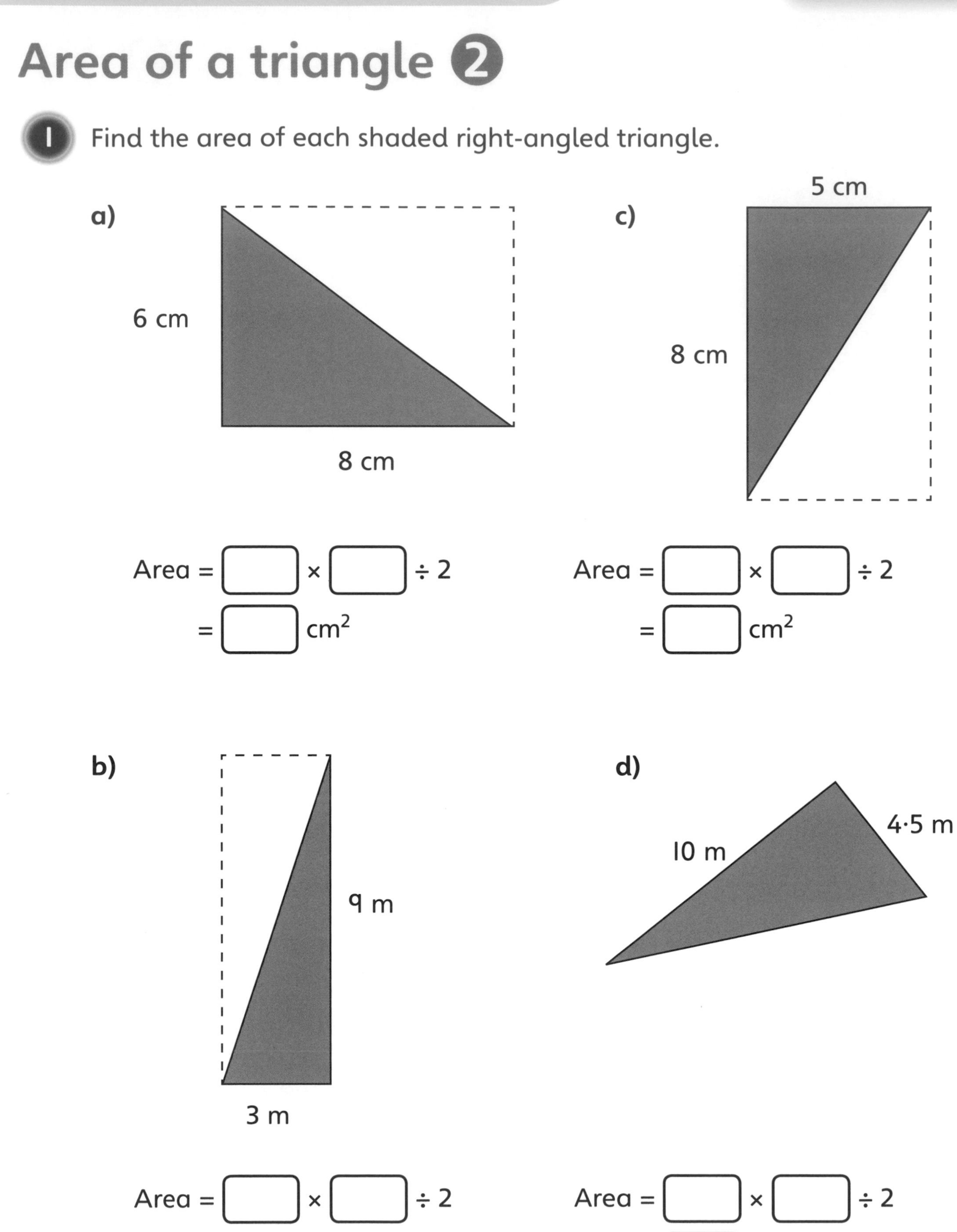

a) Area = ☐ × ☐ ÷ 2
= ☐ cm^2

c) Area = ☐ × ☐ ÷ 2
= ☐ cm^2

b) Area = ☐ × ☐ ÷ 2
= ☐ m^2

d) Area = ☐ × ☐ ÷ 2
= ☐ m^2

2 Lexi thinks that the two triangles below have the same area. Explain why Lexi is wrong.

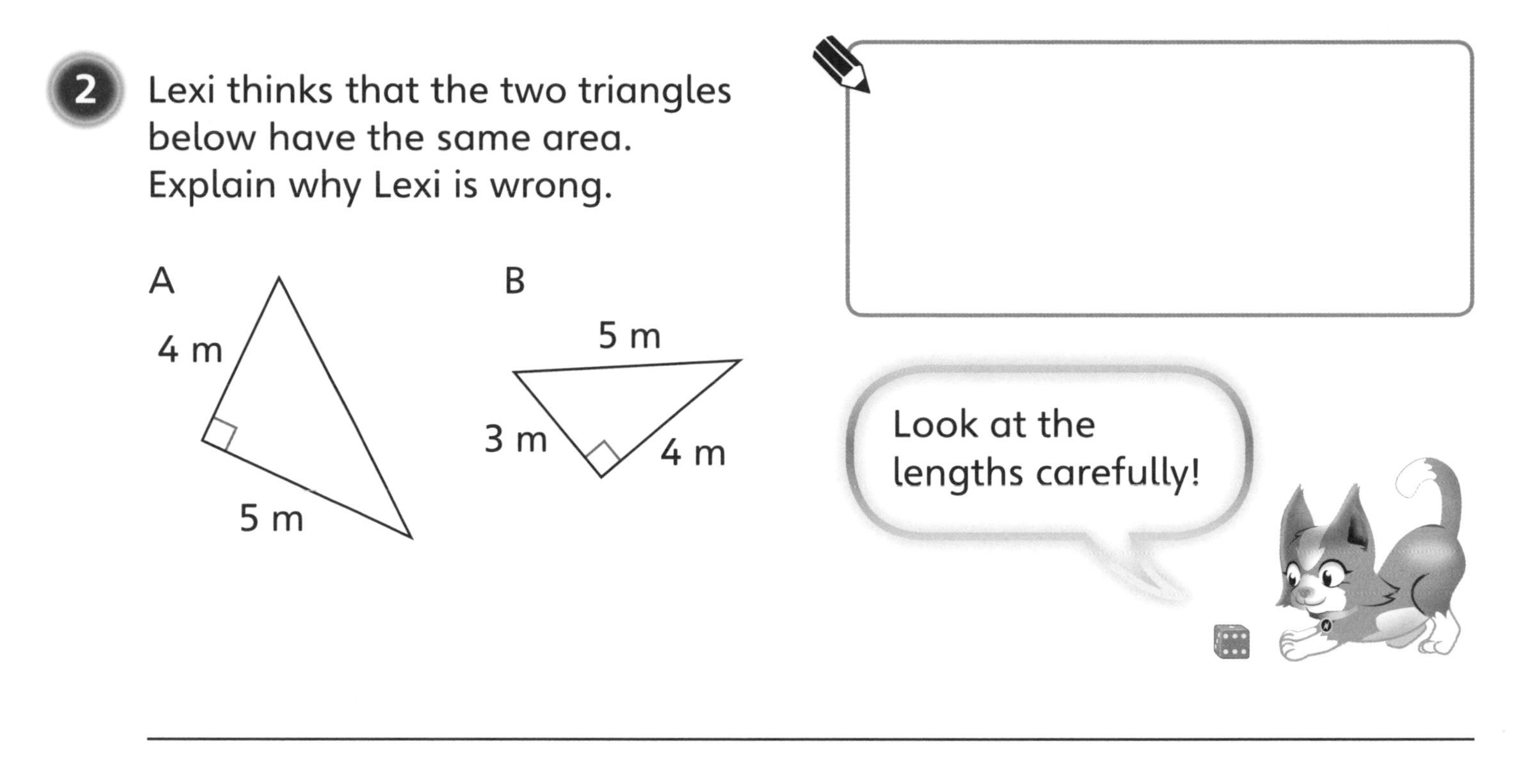

3 Look at the triangles below. Circle the triangle with the greatest area.

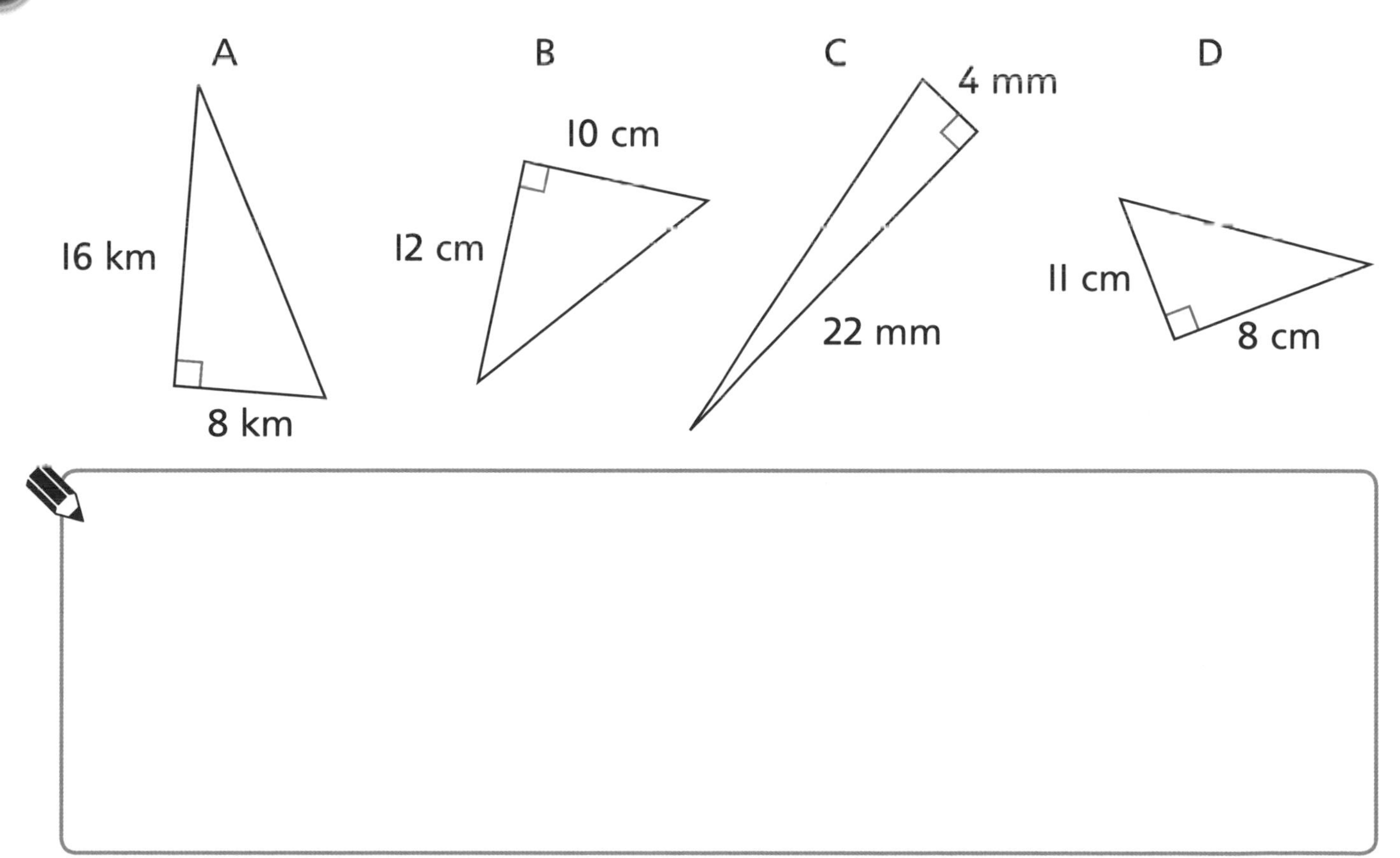

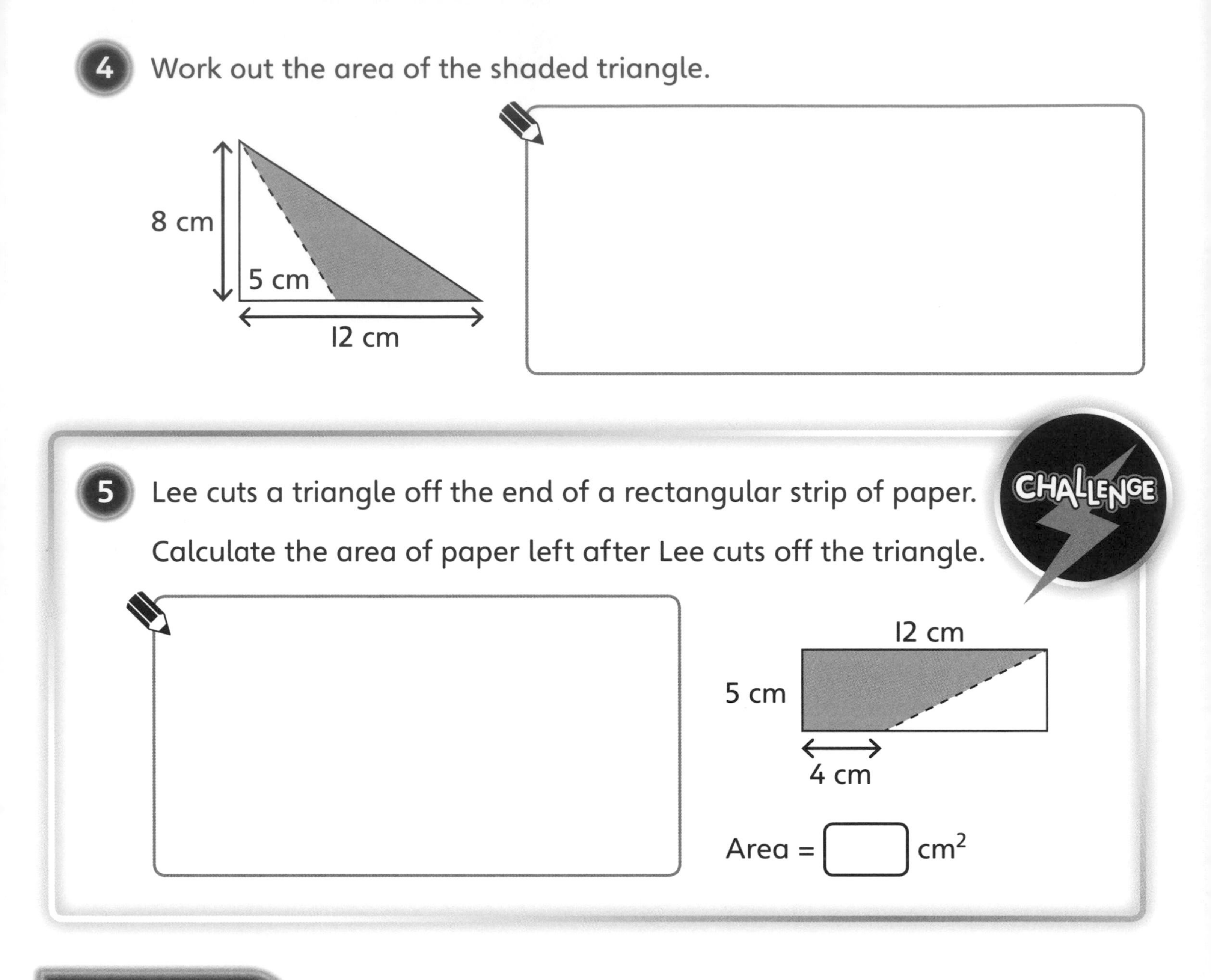

4 Work out the area of the shaded triangle.

5 Lee cuts a triangle off the end of a rectangular strip of paper.

Calculate the area of paper left after Lee cuts off the triangle.

Area = ☐ cm^2

Reflect

Explain how you can use the area of a rectangle to find the area of a right-angled triangle.

→ Textbook 6B p184

Area of a triangle 3

1 Find the area of each triangle below.

Not drawn to scale

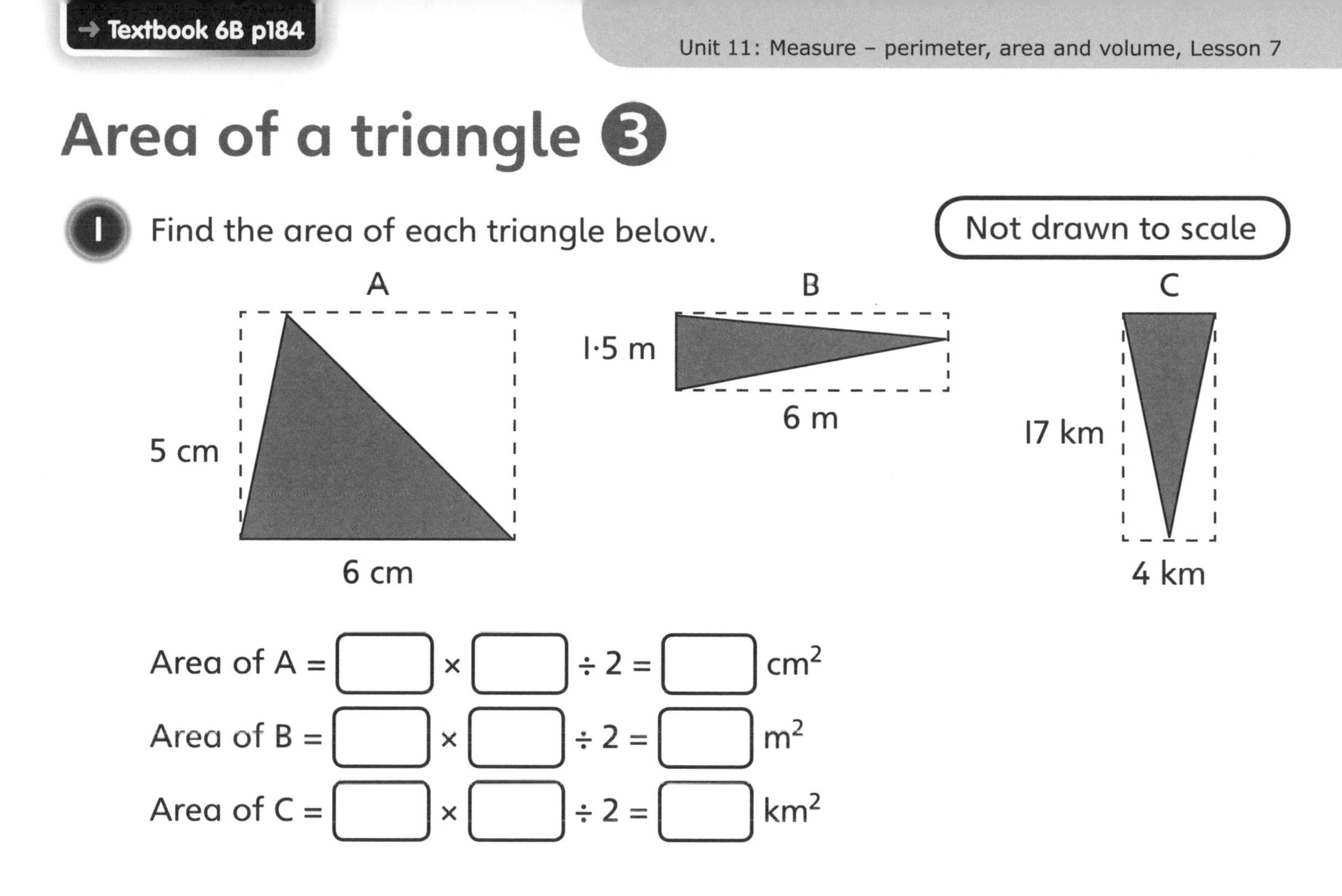

Area of A = ☐ × ☐ ÷ 2 = ☐ cm^2

Area of B = ☐ × ☐ ÷ 2 = ☐ m^2

Area of C = ☐ × ☐ ÷ 2 = ☐ km^2

2 Draw three triangles with a base of 4 cm and an area of 8 cm^2. What do the triangles have in common?

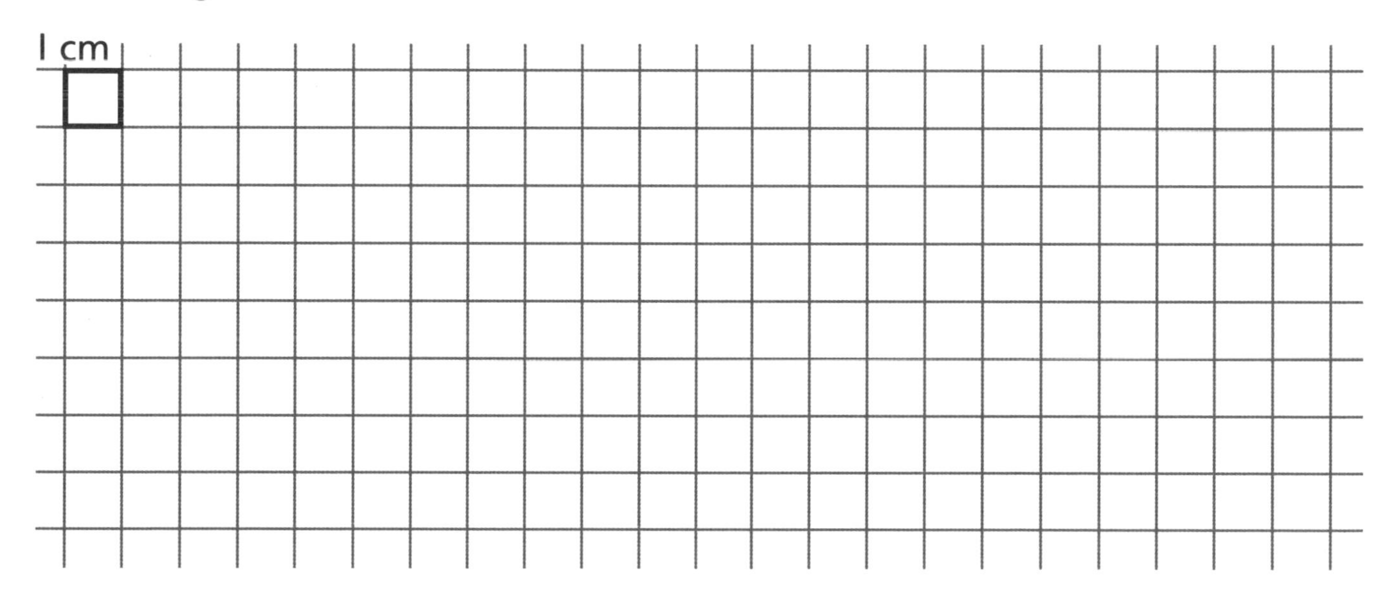

____

____

3

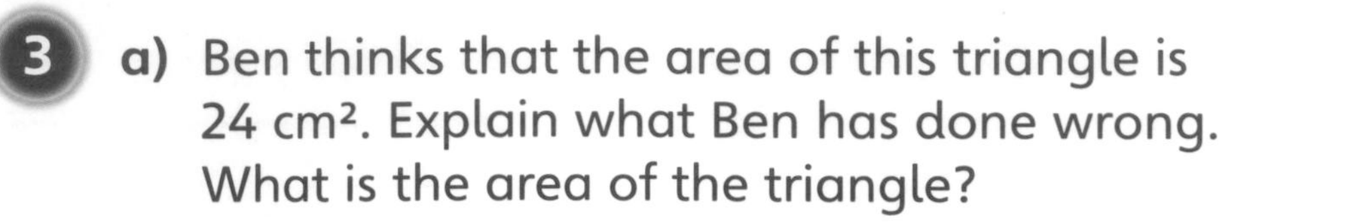

a) Ben thinks that the area of this triangle is 24 cm². Explain what Ben has done wrong. What is the area of the triangle?

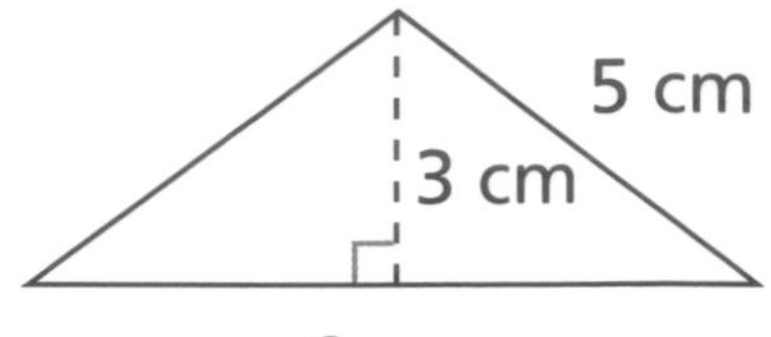

b) Alex thinks that the area of this triangle is 60 cm². Is Alex correct? Explain why.

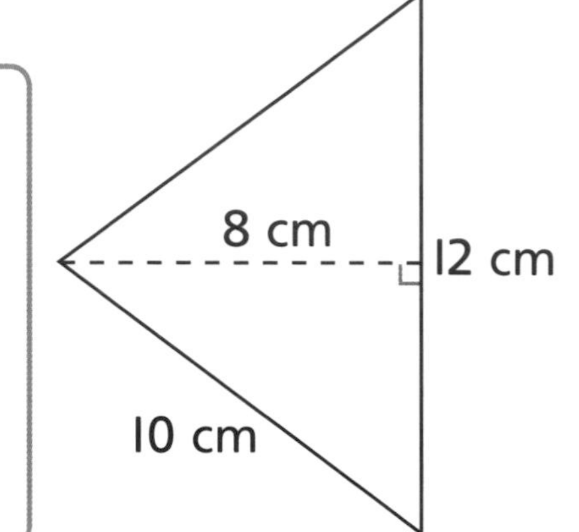

4 Find the area of each triangle.

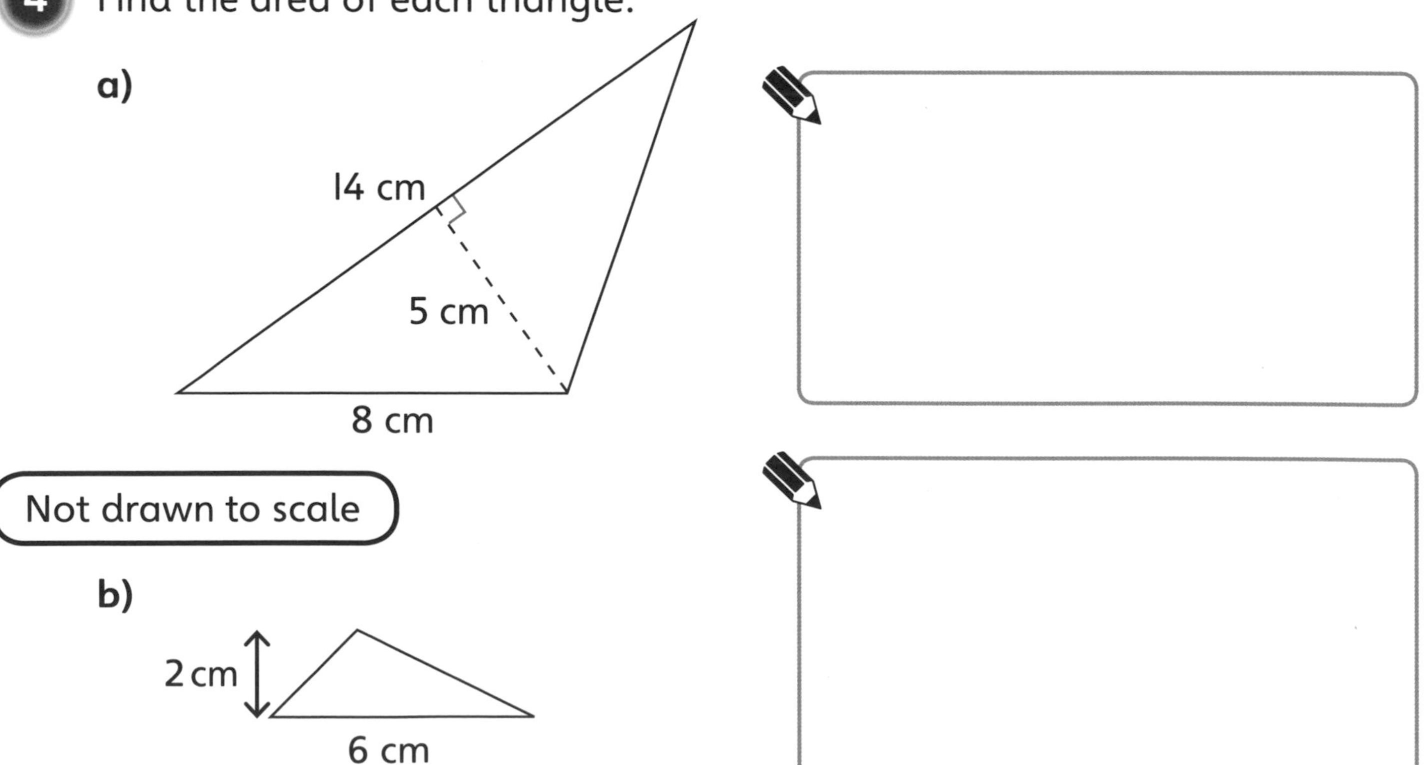

5 To find the area of each triangle, Max put them together to make a parallelogram.

How can you use the area of the parallelogram to work out the area of the triangle?

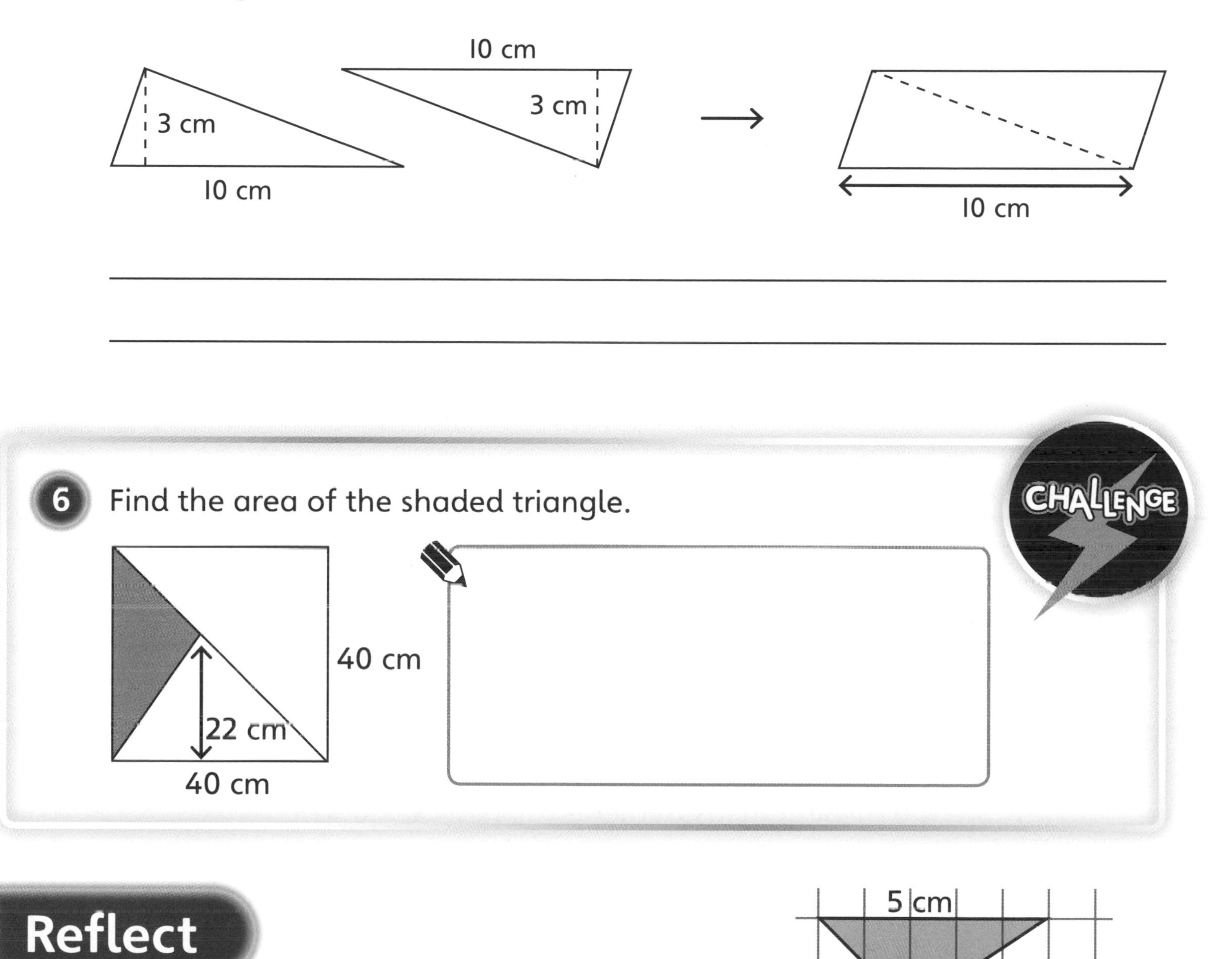

6 Find the area of the shaded triangle.

Reflect

Explain how to find the area of the shaded triangle.

→ Textbook 6B p188

Problem solving – area

1 Calculate the areas of the shapes below.

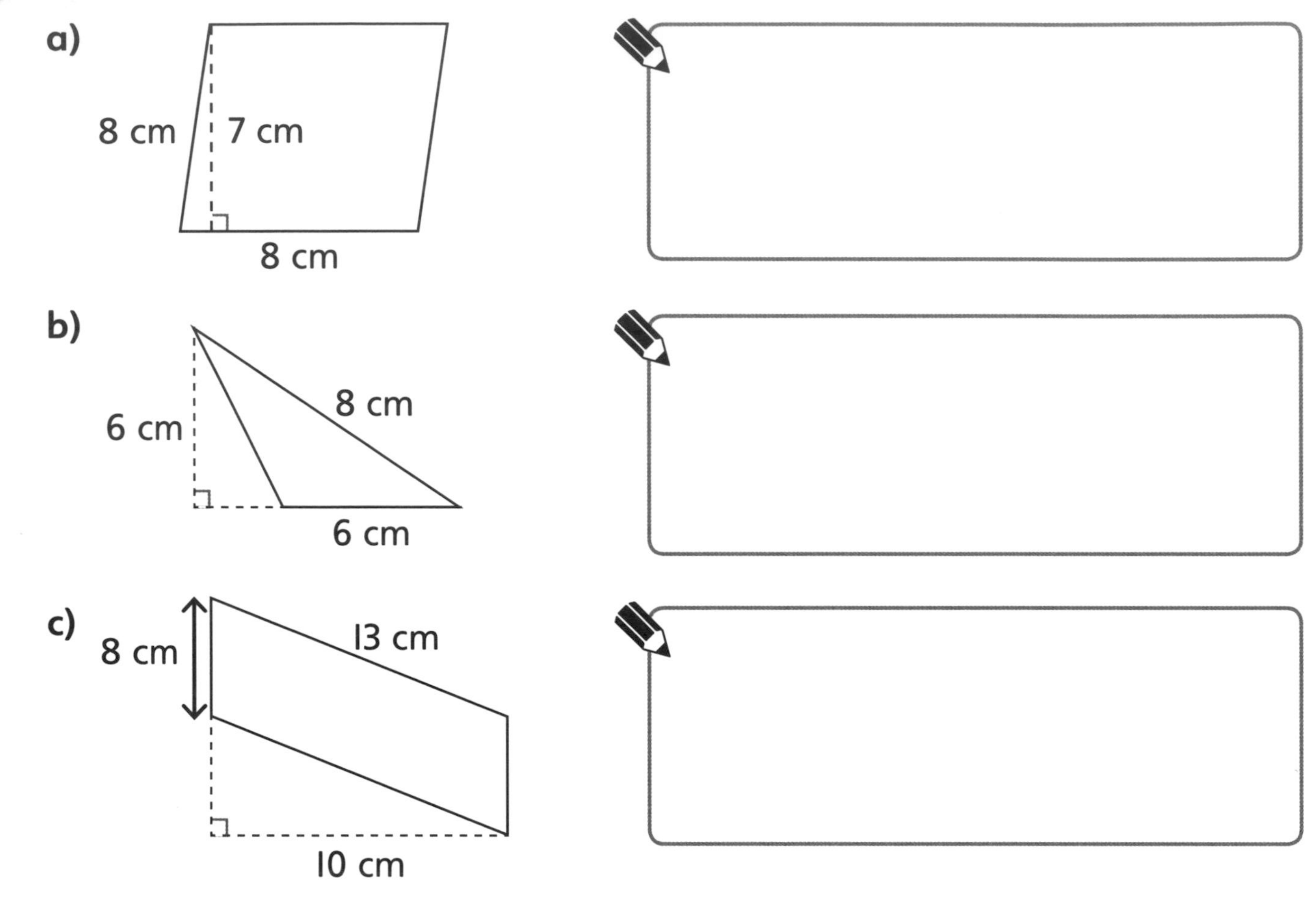

2 These shapes have the same area.

What are the missing measurements?

Not drawn to scale

a

6 cm

b

12 cm

c

12 cm

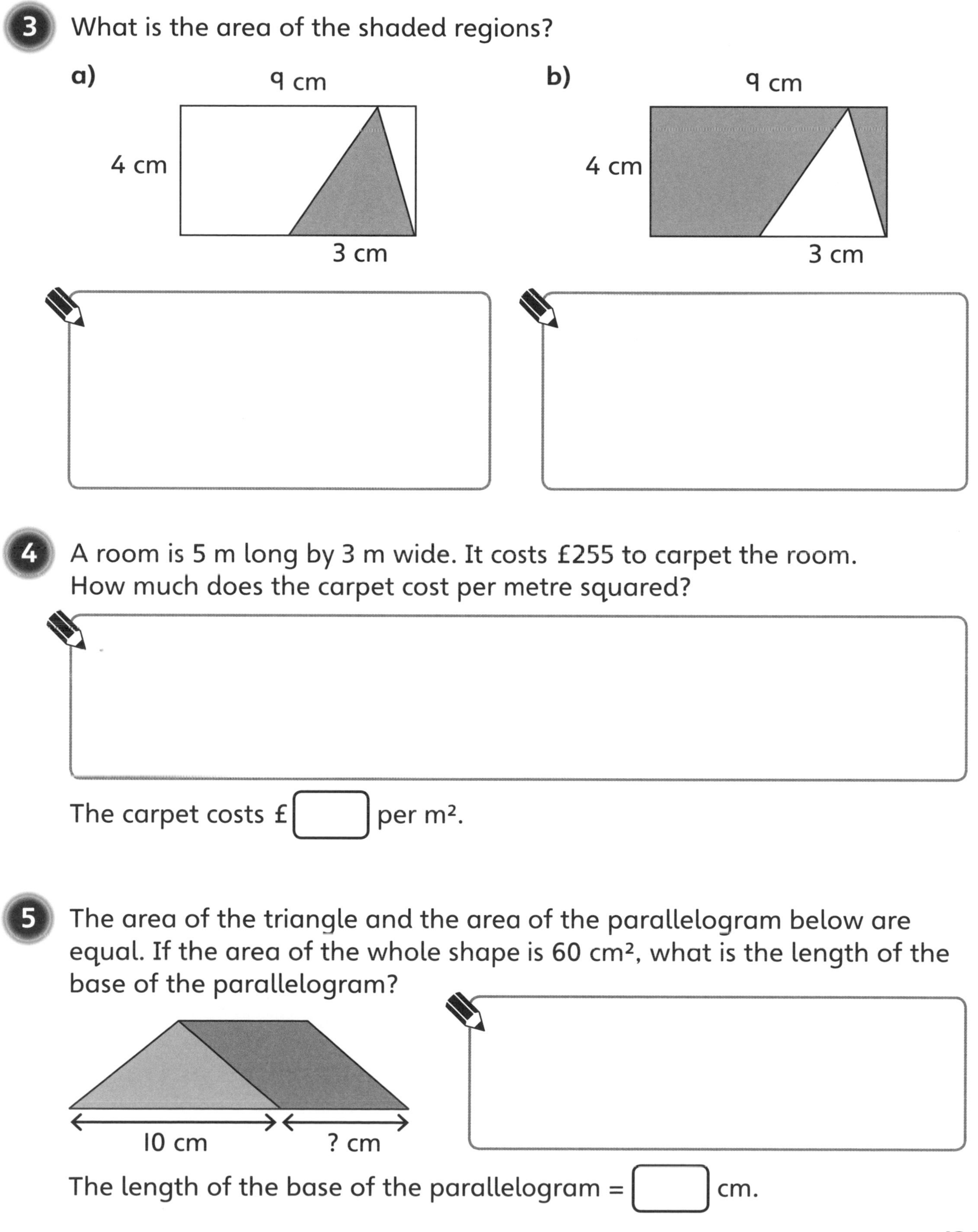

3 What is the area of the shaded regions?

a) 9 cm, 4 cm, 3 cm

b) 9 cm, 4 cm, 3 cm

4 A room is 5 m long by 3 m wide. It costs £255 to carpet the room. How much does the carpet cost per metre squared?

The carpet costs £ ☐ per m^2.

5 The area of the triangle and the area of the parallelogram below are equal. If the area of the whole shape is 60 cm^2, what is the length of the base of the parallelogram?

10 cm, ? cm

The length of the base of the parallelogram = ☐ cm.

CHALLENGE

6 Twelve identical rectangles are arranged to make a square frame. Calculate the area of one of the rectangles.

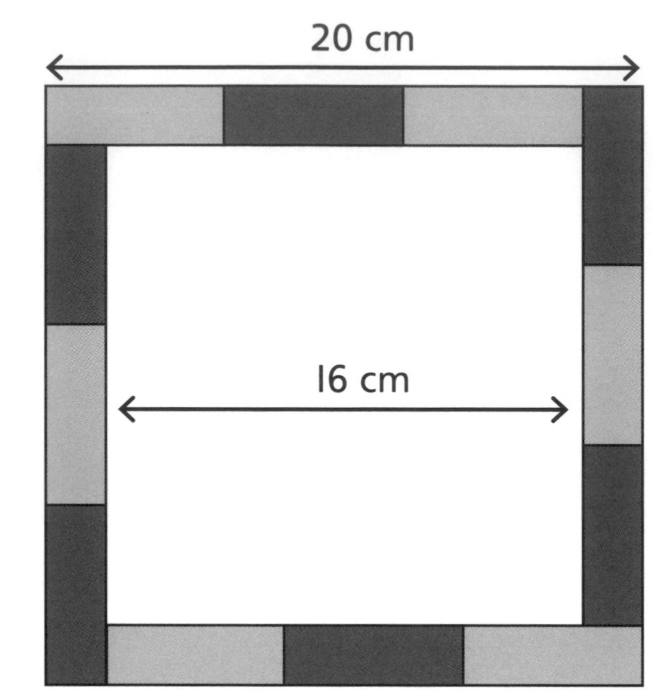

Reflect

Write down three facts you have learnt about area in the last few lessons.

→ Textbook 6B p192

Problem solving – perimeter

Max is competing in two running races. Using the information below, work out which race is longer.

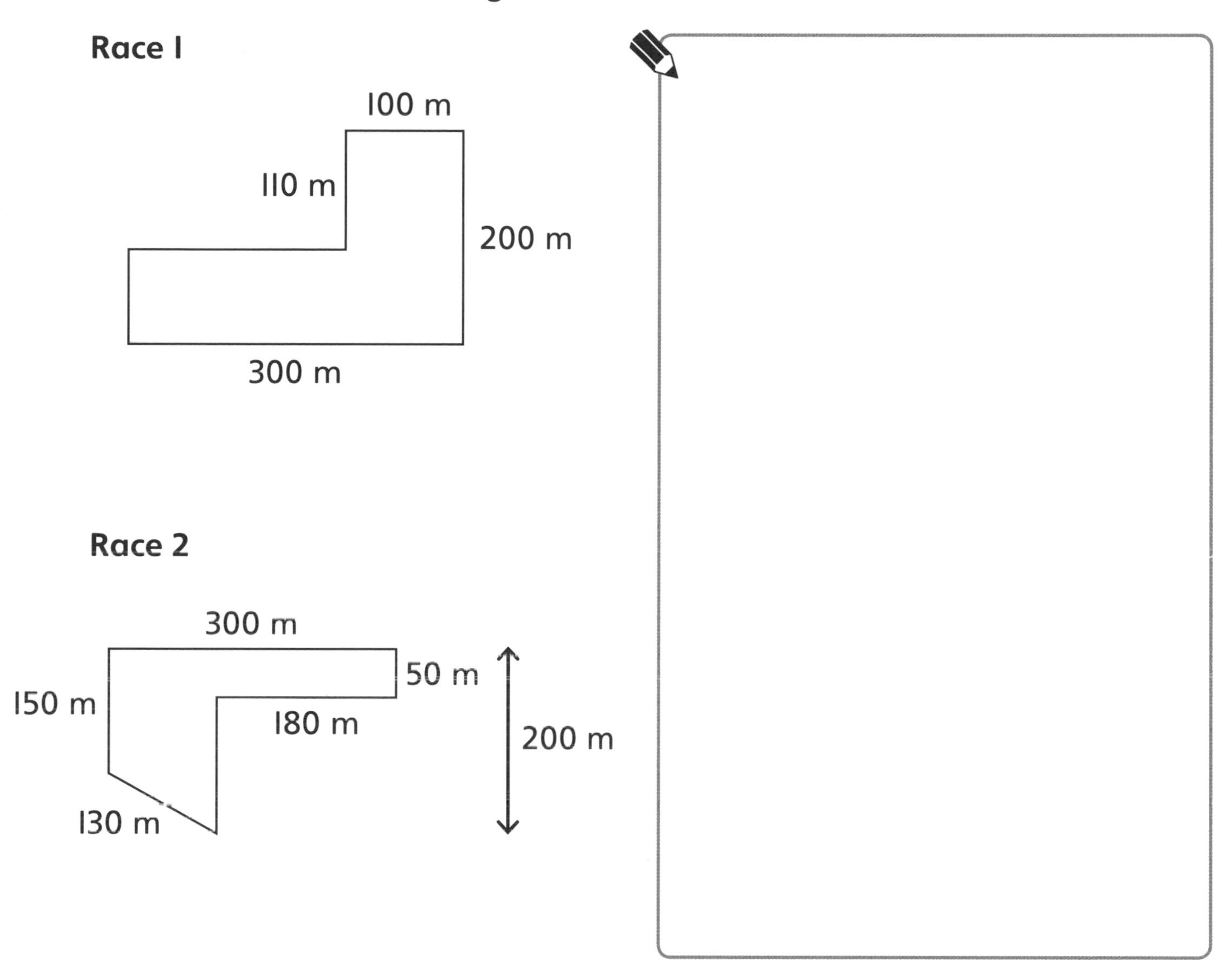

2 Ebo joins squares to make a shape with an area of 63 cm^2. Find the perimeter of the shape.

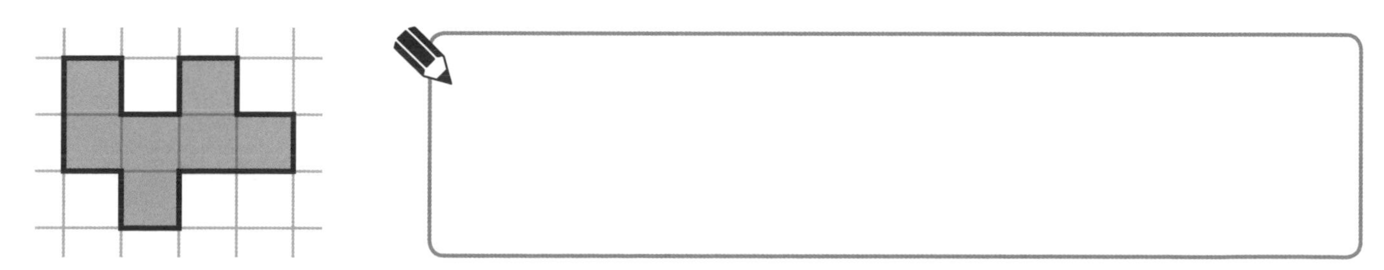

3 A rectangle has an area of 60 cm^2. Its length is 11 cm more than its width. What is the perimeter of the rectangle?

4 Look at the plans for two areas in a park below. Which area has the longer perimeter?

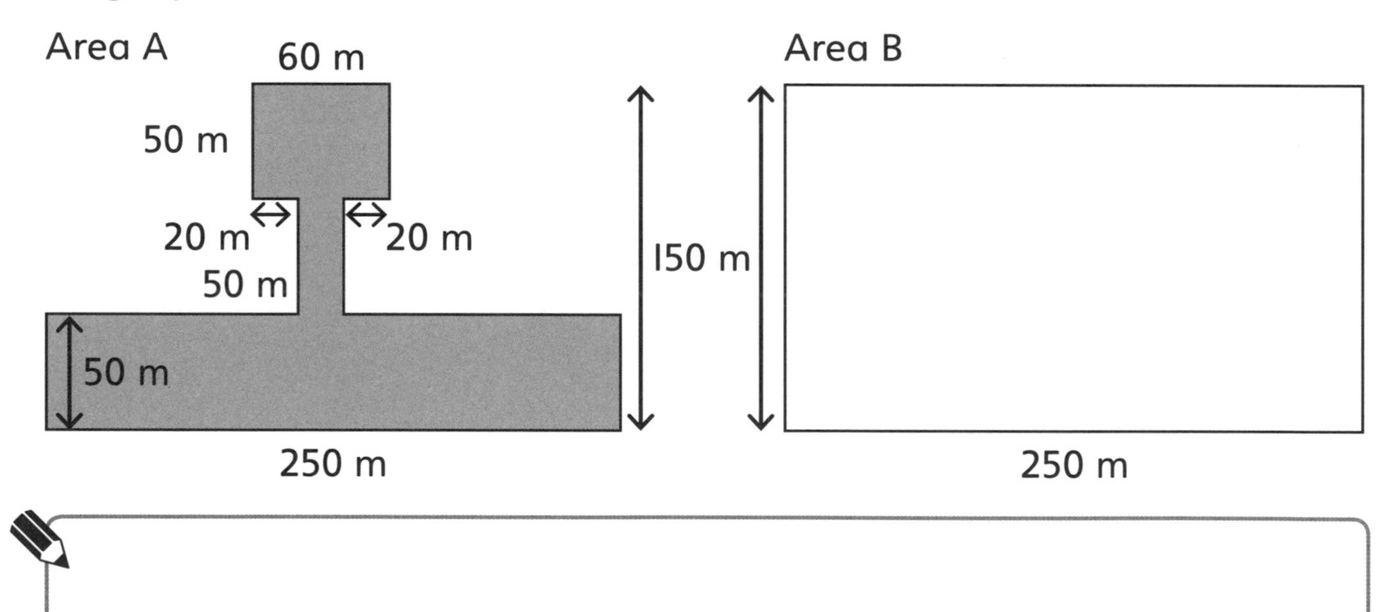

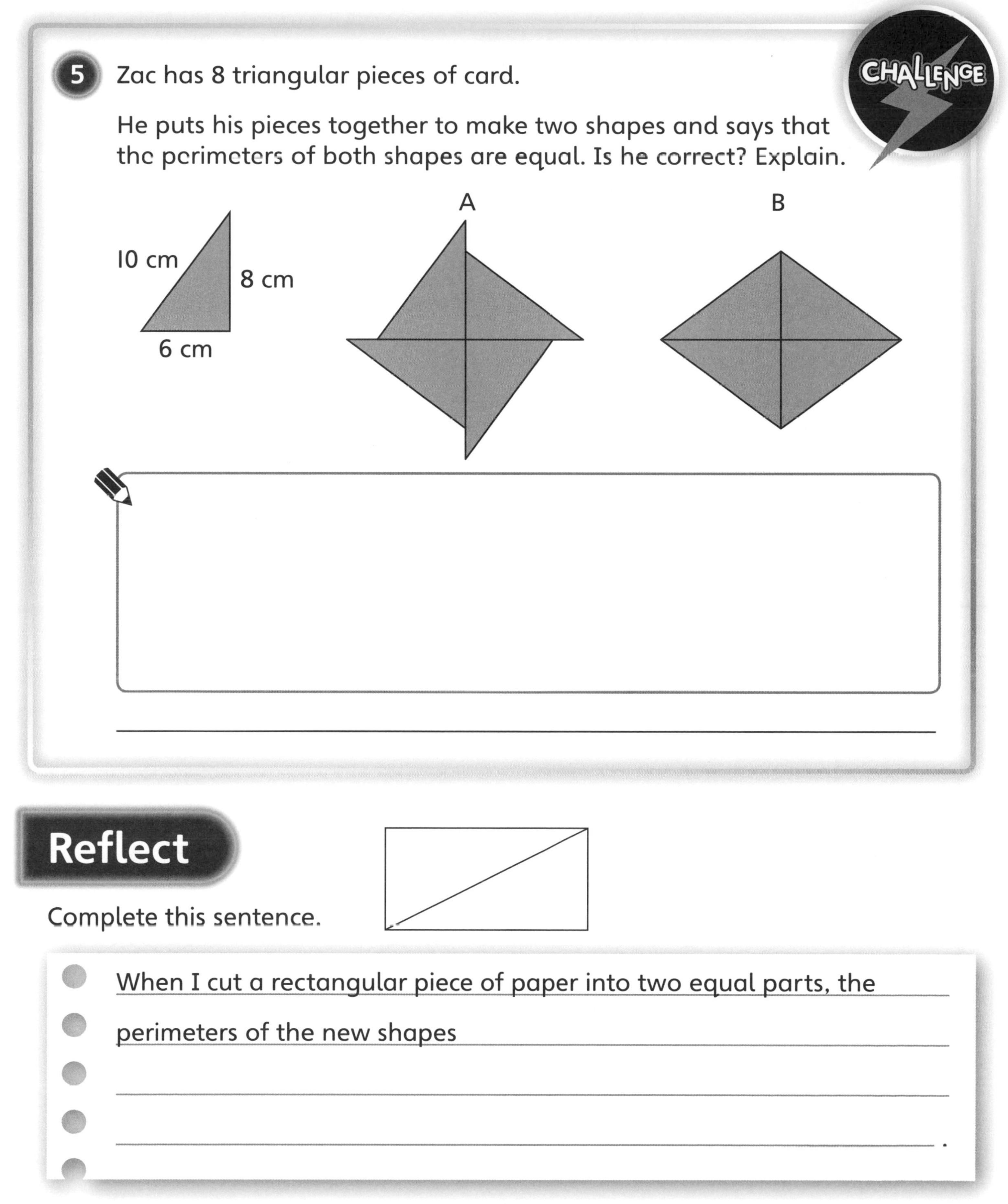

5 Zac has 8 triangular pieces of card.

CHALLENGE

He puts his pieces together to make two shapes and says that the perimeters of both shapes are equal. Is he correct? Explain.

Reflect

Complete this sentence.

When I cut a rectangular piece of paper into two equal parts, the perimeters of the new shapes ____.

→ Textbook 6B p196

Volume of a cuboid 1

 Each small cube has a volume of $1\ cm^3$.

Find the number of cubes and the volume of each solid.

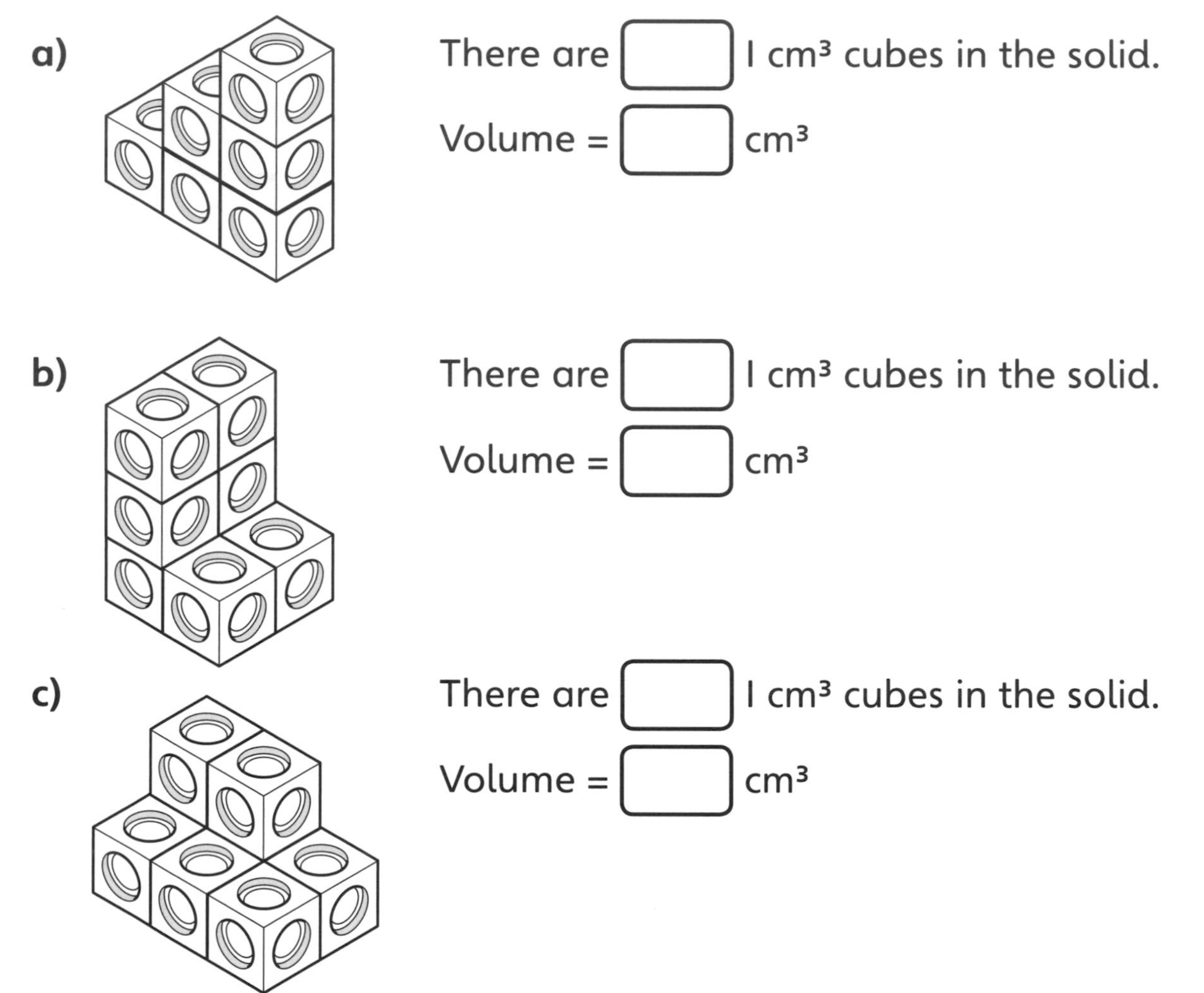

a) There are ☐ $1\ cm^3$ cubes in the solid.

Volume = ☐ cm^3

b) There are ☐ $1\ cm^3$ cubes in the solid.

Volume = ☐ cm^3

c) There are ☐ $1\ cm^3$ cubes in the solid.

Volume = ☐ cm^3

 Circle the shapes that have a volume of $10\ cm^3$.

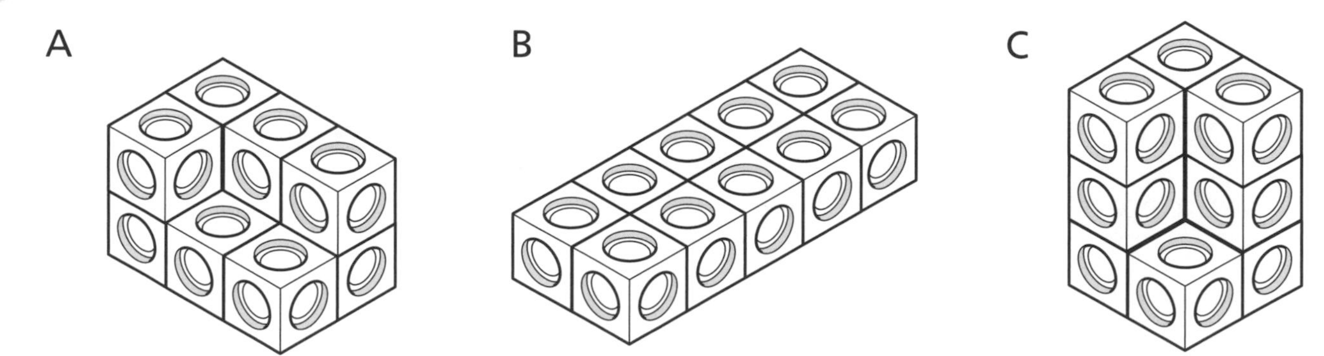

3 Match the 3D shapes that have the same volume.

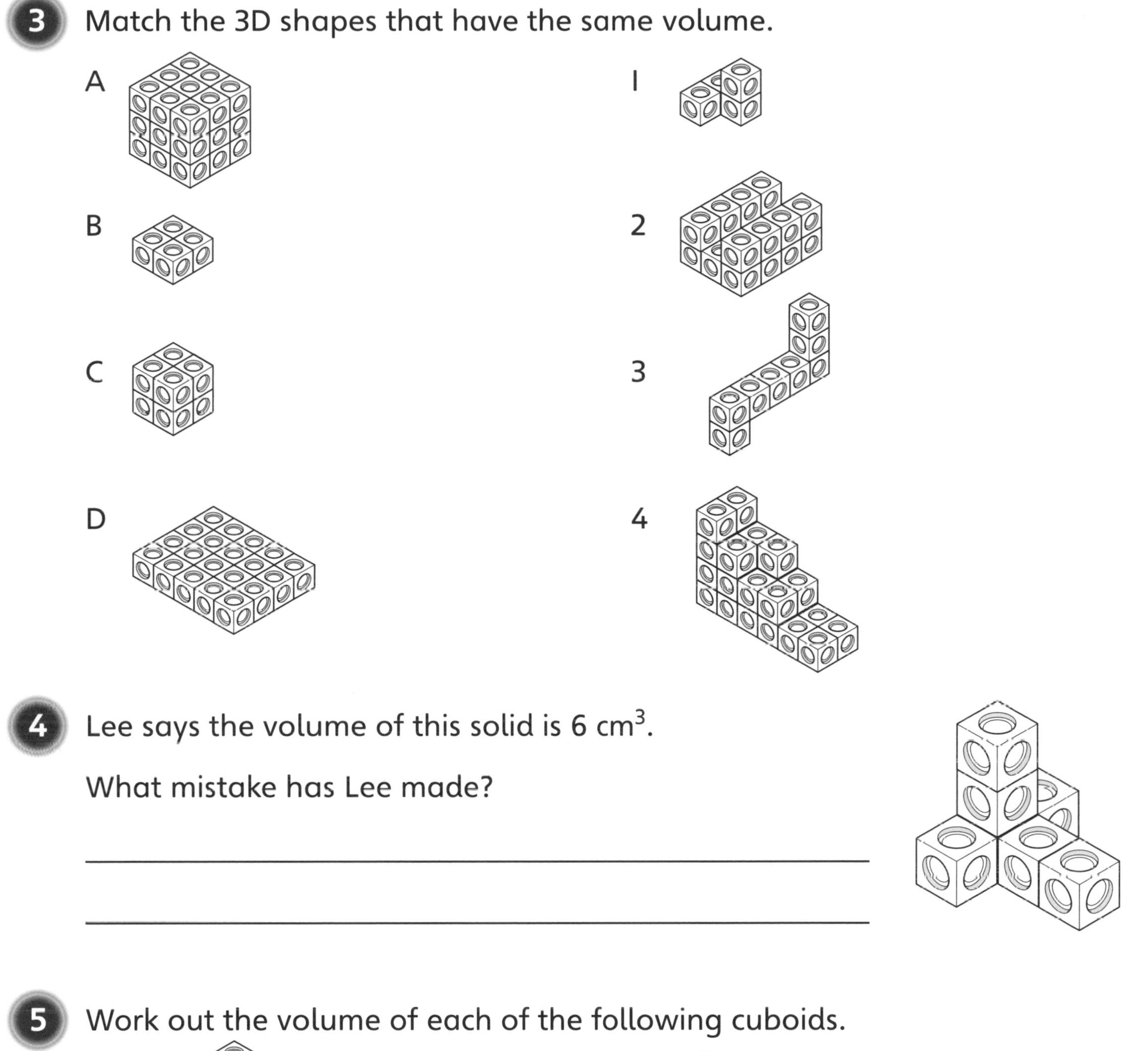

4 Lee says the volume of this solid is 6 cm^3.

What mistake has Lee made?

____

____

5 Work out the volume of each of the following cuboids.

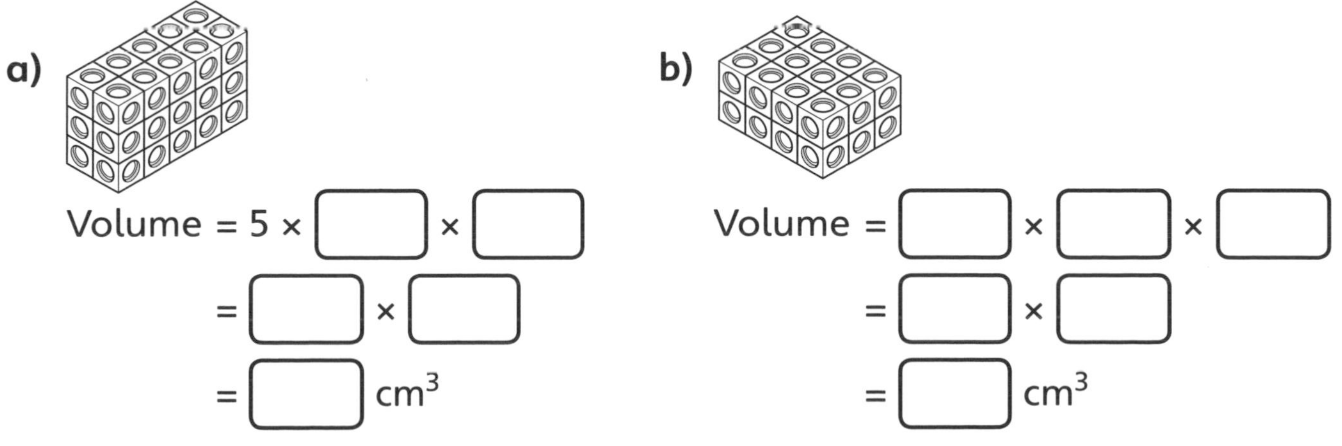

a) Volume = 5 × ☐ × ☐

= ☐ × ☐

= ☐ cm^3

b) Volume = ☐ × ☐ × ☐

= ☐ × ☐

= ☐ cm^3

6 Ella thinks she can make a cube using all the 1 cm^3 blocks from this solid.

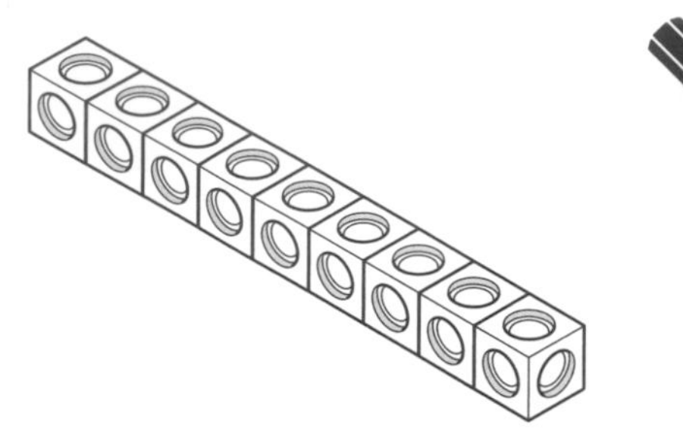

Is Ella correct? Explain your answer.

____

____

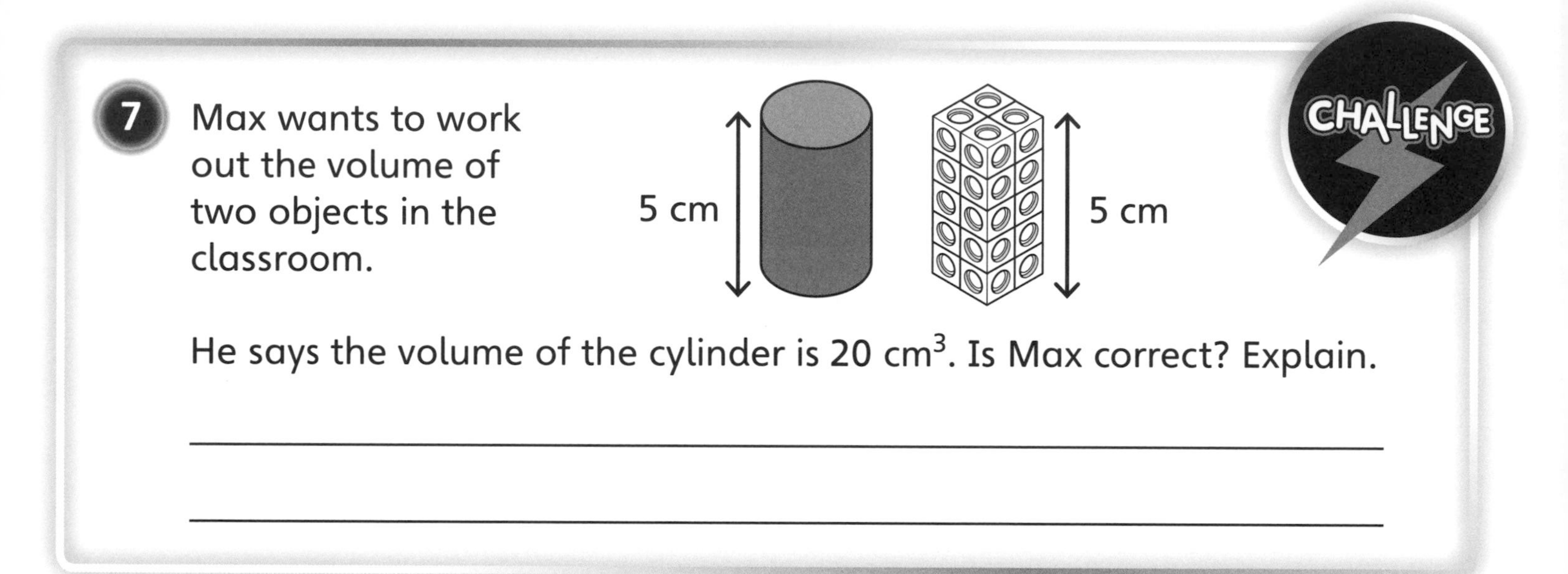

7 Max wants to work out the volume of two objects in the classroom.

He says the volume of the cylinder is 20 cm^3. Is Max correct? Explain.

____

____

Reflect

Can you make a cube using exactly 27 smaller cubes? How do you know?

____

____

____

→ Textbook 6B p200

Volume of a cuboid 2

Find the volume of each of these cuboids.

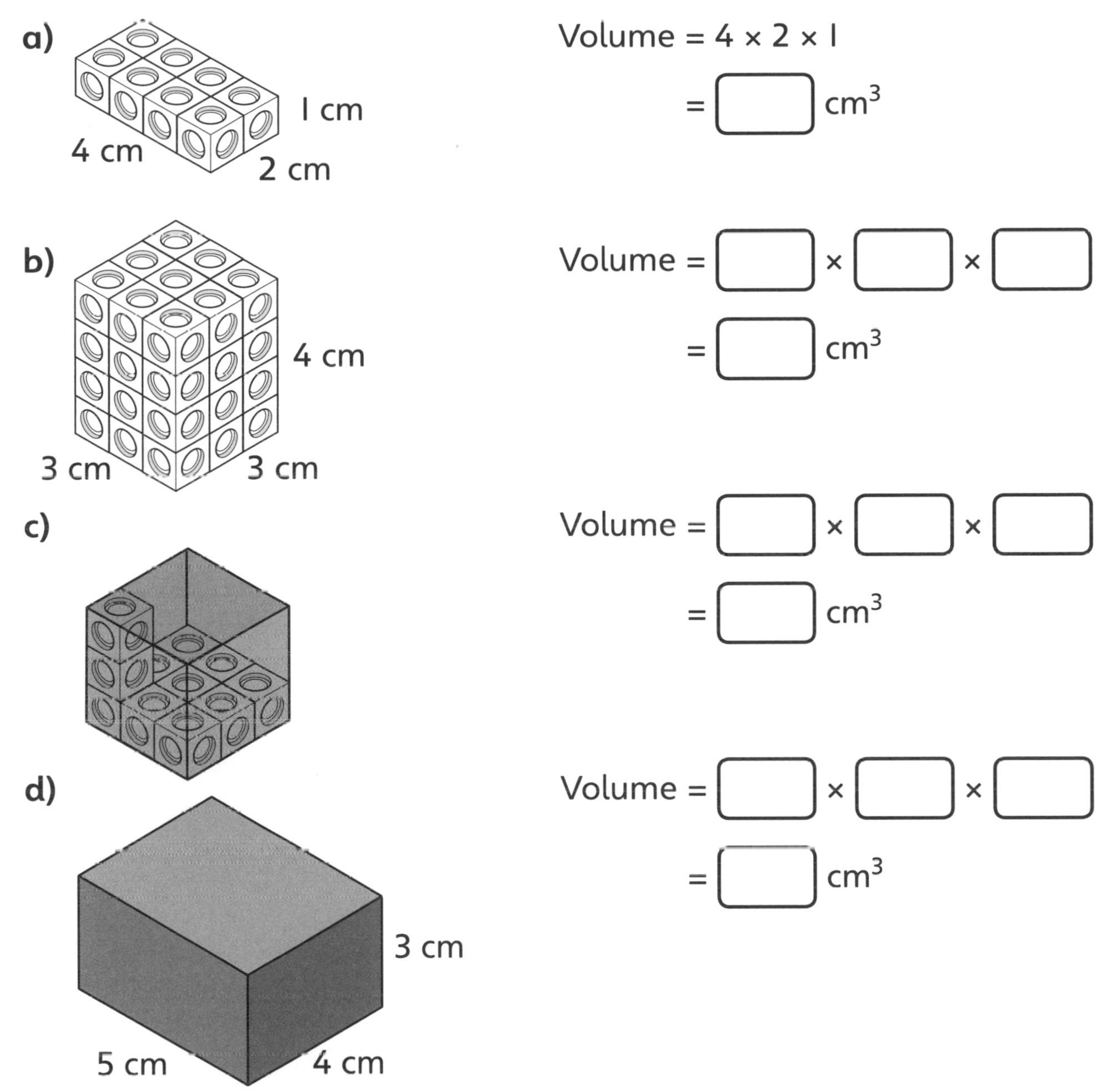

a) Volume = $4 \times 2 \times 1$

= ☐ cm^3

b) Volume = ☐ × ☐ × ☐

= ☐ cm^3

c) Volume = ☐ × ☐ × ☐

= ☐ cm^3

d) Volume = ☐ × ☐ × ☐

= ☐ cm^3

2 Explain two ways you can work out the volume of an $8 \times 7 \times 5$ cuboid.

____

____

____

3 A sculptor carves a hole that is 10 cm long by 11 cm wide by 4 cm deep.

He fills the hole with coloured glass.

What is the volume of the coloured glass?

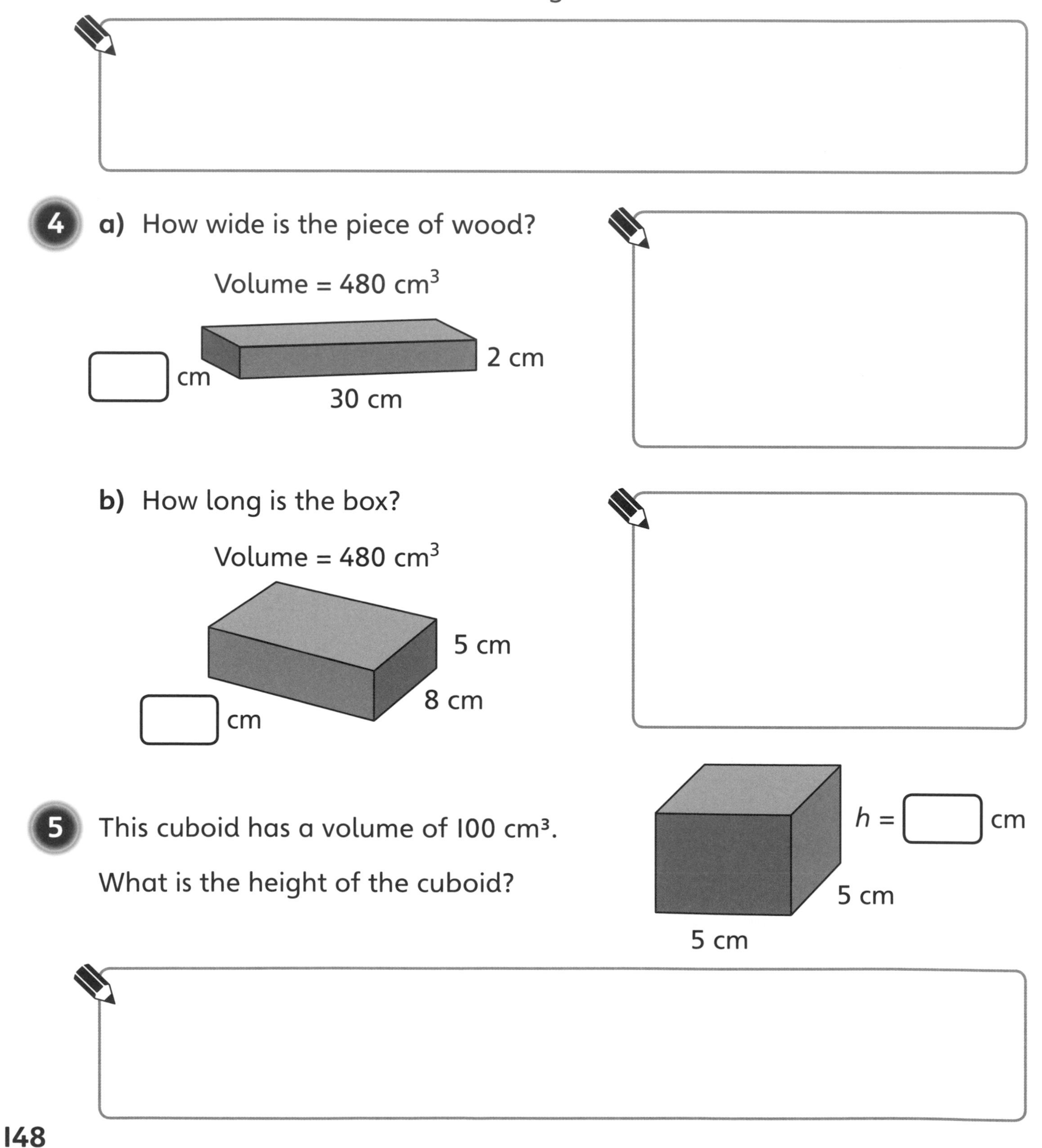

4 **a)** How wide is the piece of wood?

b) How long is the box?

5 This cuboid has a volume of 100 cm³.

What is the height of the cuboid?

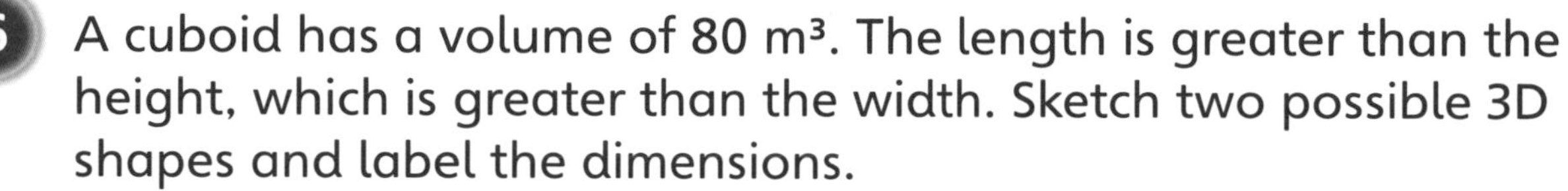

6 A cuboid has a volume of 80 m³. The length is greater than the height, which is greater than the width. Sketch two possible 3D shapes and label the dimensions.

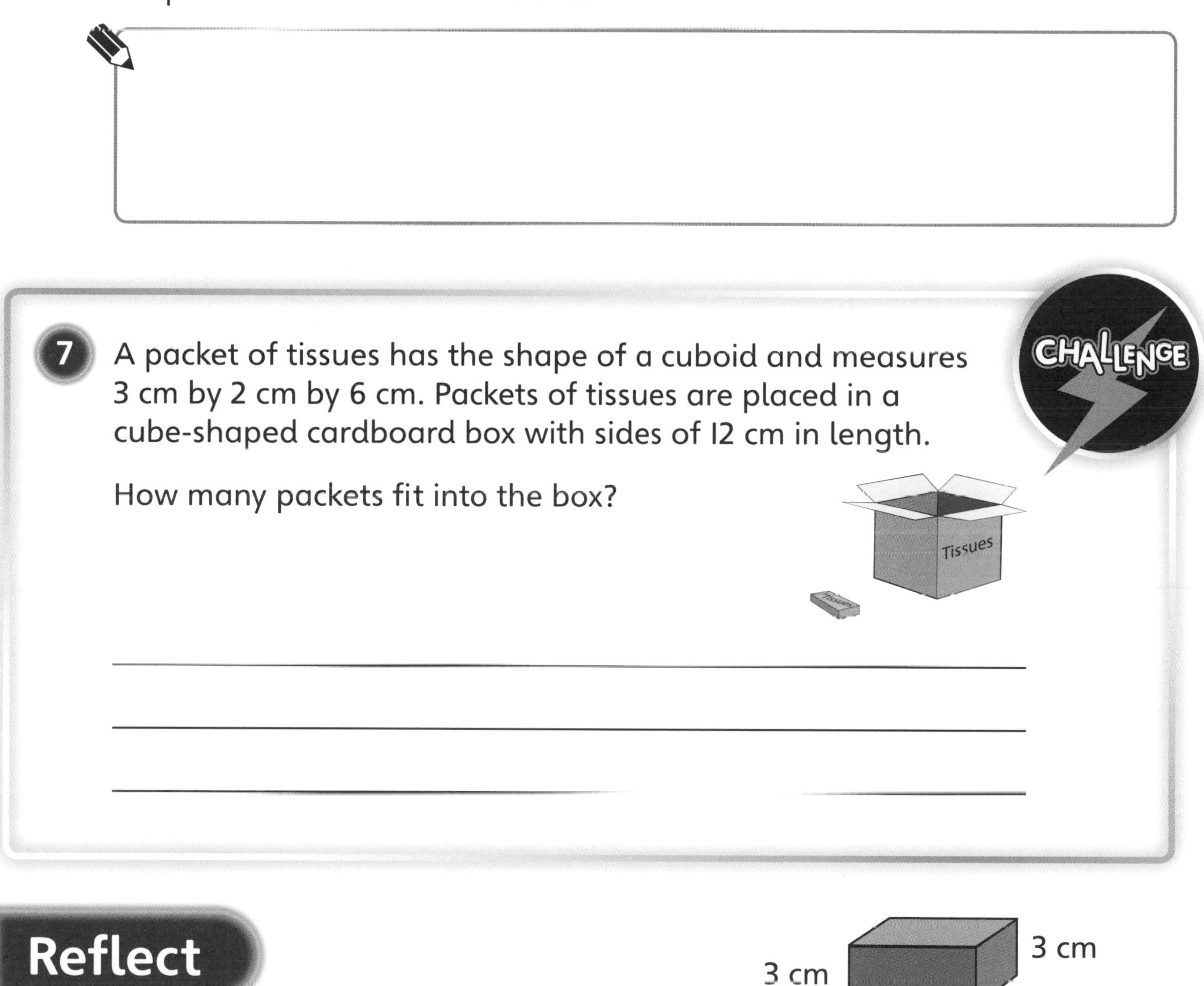

7 A packet of tissues has the shape of a cuboid and measures 3 cm by 2 cm by 6 cm. Packets of tissues are placed in a cube-shaped cardboard box with sides of 12 cm in length.

How many packets fit into the box?

Reflect

Explain how to find the volume of this cuboid.

3 cm
3 cm
1 cm
4 cm

→ Textbook 6B p204

End of unit check

My journal

1 Explain how you would find the area of each shape.

a) I know that the area of this parallelogram

is ________ because ____________________

____ .

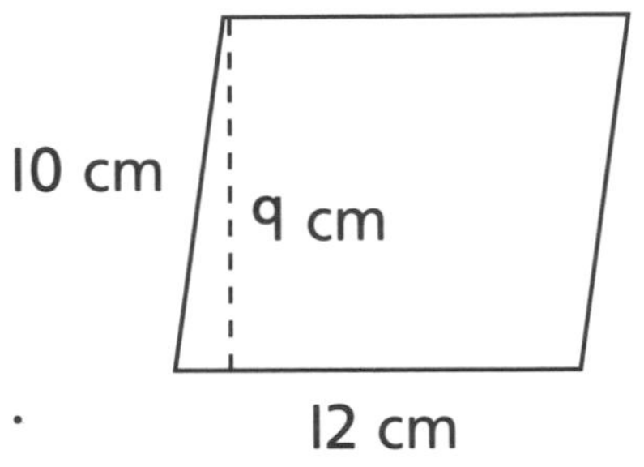

10 cm
9 cm
12 cm

b) I know that the area of this triangle

is ________ because ____________________

____ .

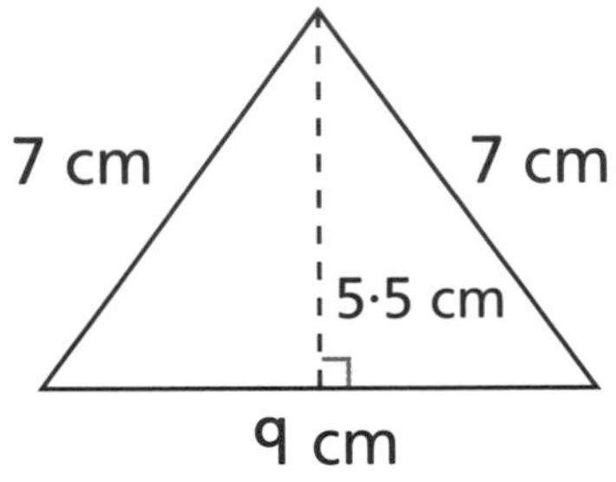

7 cm
7 cm
5·5 cm
9 cm

2 Rectangles with the same area have the same perimeter. True or False? Draw and label examples to explain your answer.

3 Look carefully at the following shapes.

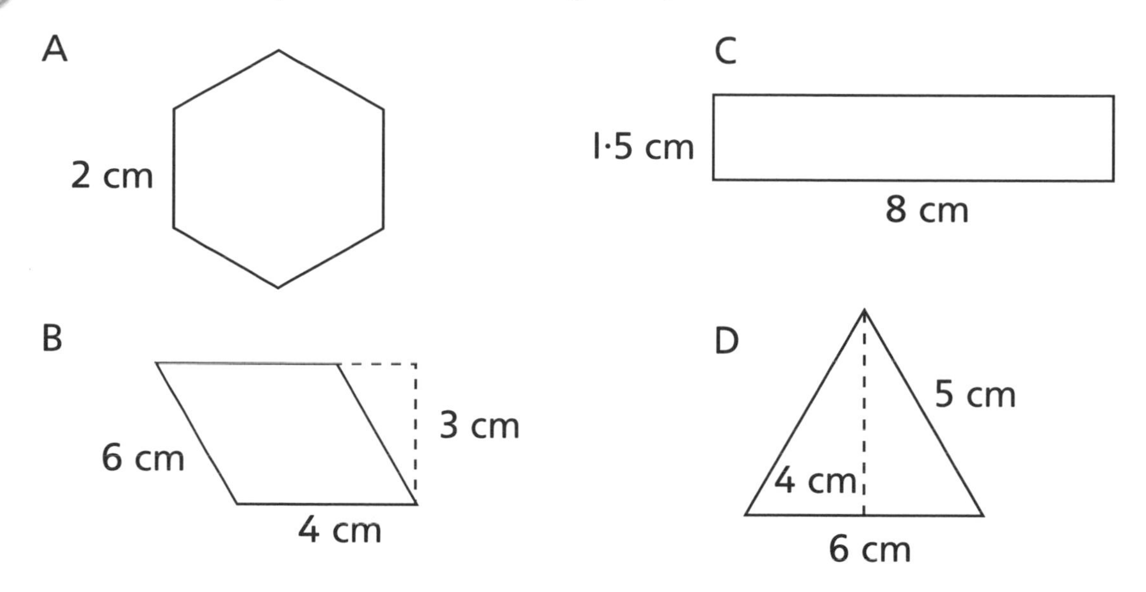

a) Which shape is the odd one out?

Shape ________ is the odd one out.

b) Explain your answer.

____

____

c) Look at the shapes again. Find another shape that is the odd one out and give a different reason.

____

____

____

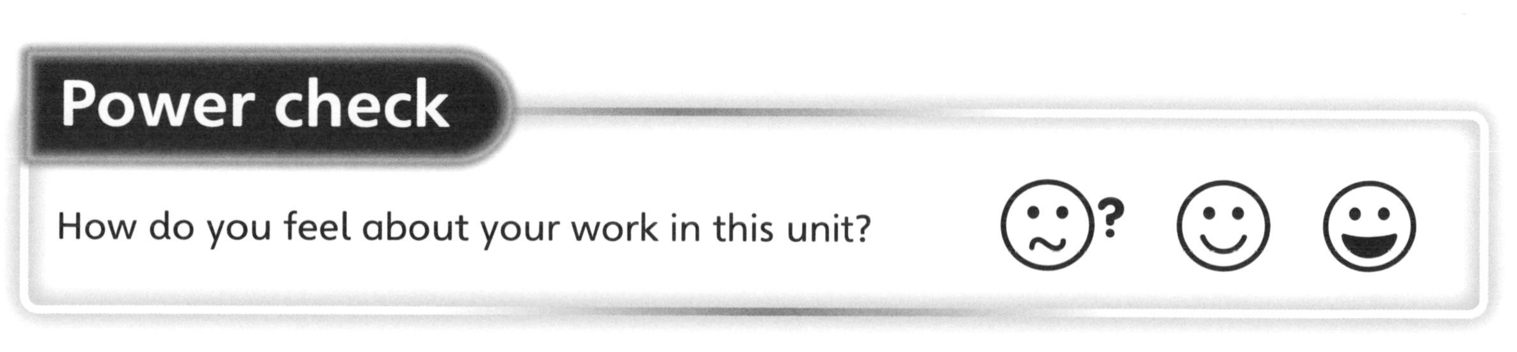

Power puzzle

Show your working for each of these puzzles.

1. A tank measuring 8 cm by 4 cm by 6 cm is $\frac{1}{3}$ filled with water. Amy pours the water into another tank in the shape of a cube with sides 4 cm long. Can she fill the second tank?

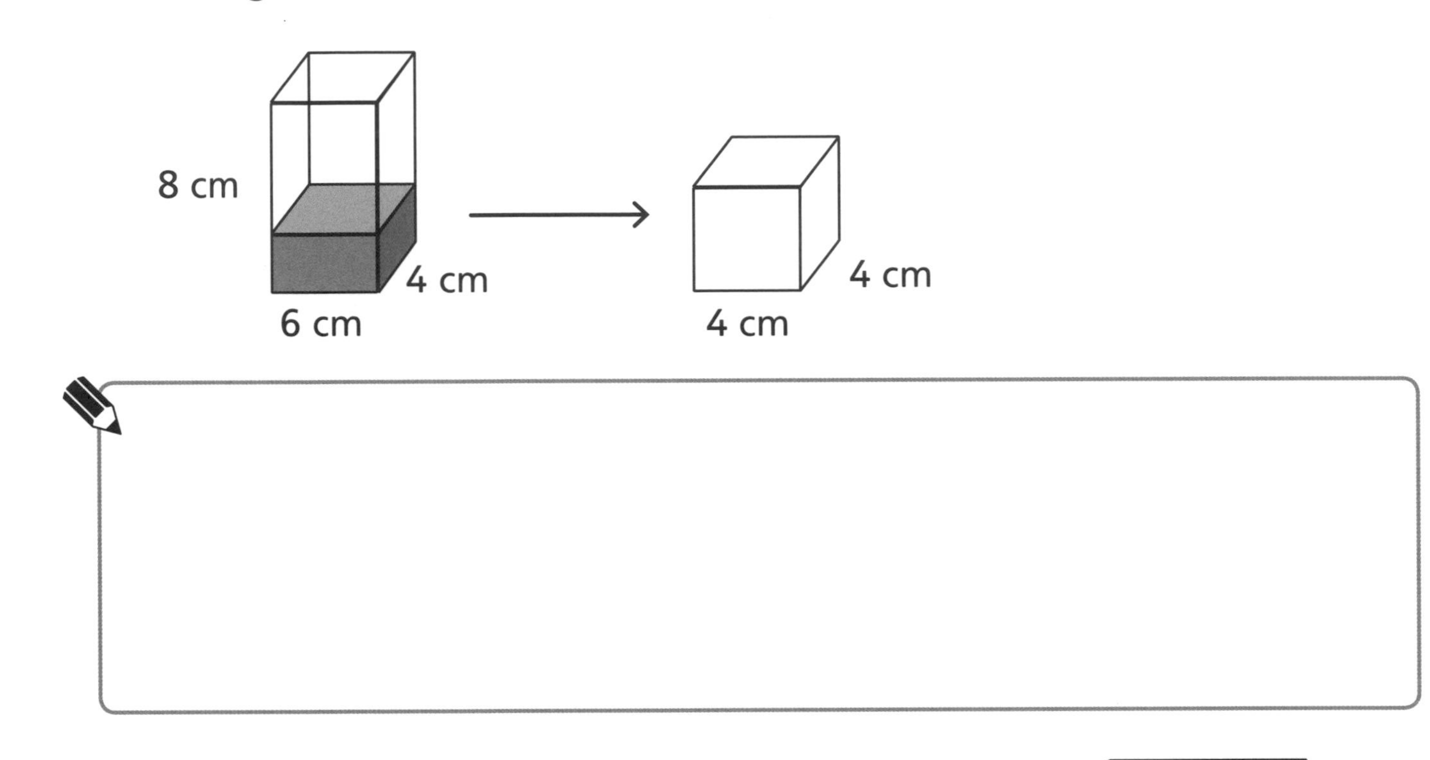

2. Isla puts a cube into a tub of water as shown in the diagram. The water rises to double the height that it was before. What are the dimensions of the cube?

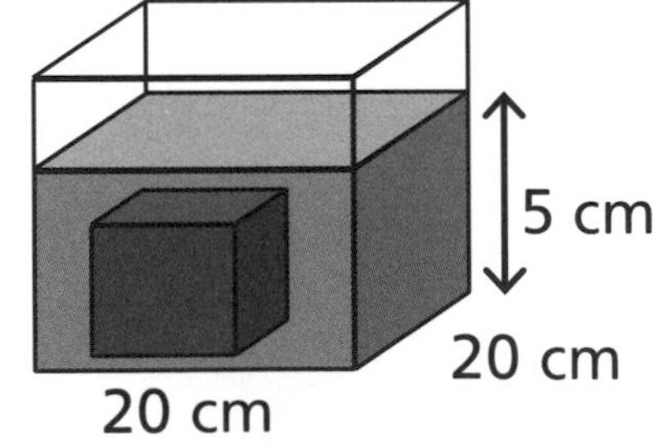

→ Textbook 6B p208

Ratio 1

1 **a)** Sort the fruit into equal groups.

b) Complete the sentences.

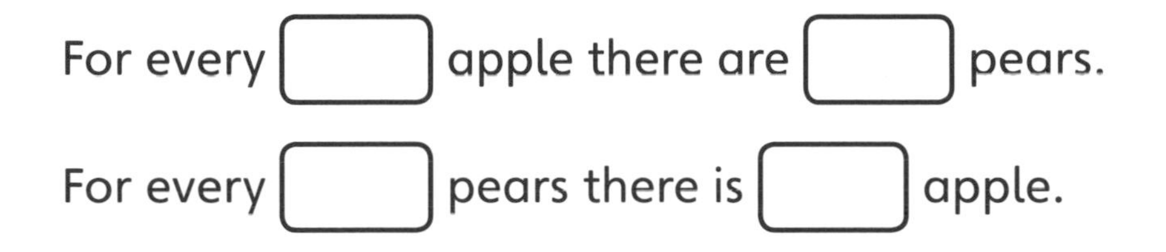

For every ☐ apple there are ☐ pears.

For every ☐ pears there is ☐ apple.

2 Complete the sentences for the pencils and rulers.

a) For every ☐ rulers there are ☐ pencils.

b) For every ☐ pencils there are ☐ rulers.

c) $\frac{☐}{☐}$ of the objects are rulers.

d) $\frac{☐}{☐}$ of the objects are pencils.

3 Draw shapes to represent the following ratio sentences.

a) There are 3 triangles for every 1 circle.

b) There are 2 squares for every 5 circles.

4 **a)** Draw a line to match the correct shape to its corresponding ratio statement.

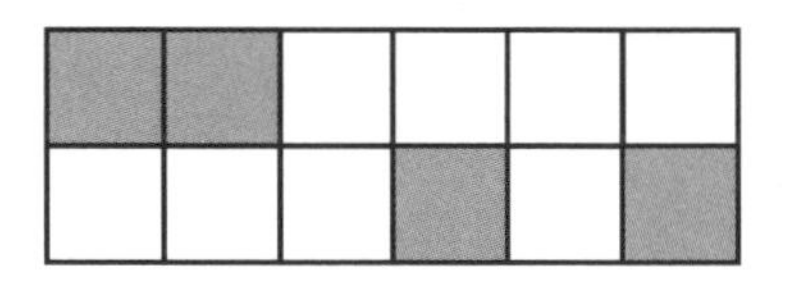

For every 1 grey square there is 1 white square.

For every 1 grey square there are 2 white squares.

For every 2 grey squares there is 1 white square.

b) Shade squares in the rectangle to match the description below.

'For every 1 white square there are 5 grey squares.'

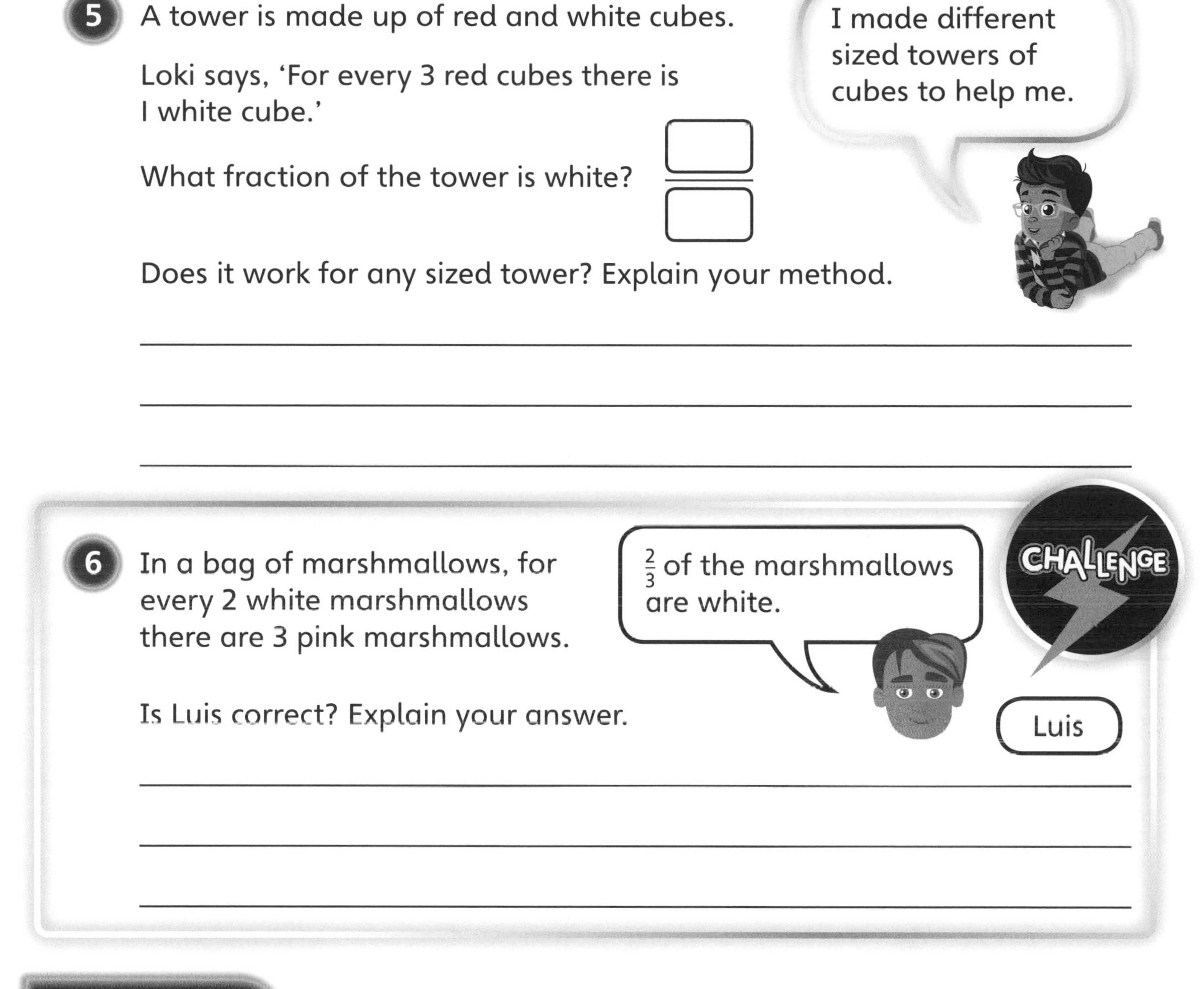

5 A tower is made up of red and white cubes.

Loki says, 'For every 3 red cubes there is 1 white cube.'

What fraction of the tower is white? $\frac{\square}{\square}$

Does it work for any sized tower? Explain your method.

____

____

____

6 In a bag of marshmallows, for every 2 white marshmallows there are 3 pink marshmallows.

Is Luis correct? Explain your answer.

____

____

____

Reflect

What can you see? Write your answer as a ratio sentence.

____

____

____

→ Textbook 6B p212

Ratio 2

At the farm there are 12 chicks and 3 hens.

What is the ratio of chicks to hens?

For every [ ] chicks there is [ ] hen.

Or, the ratio of chicks to hens is [ ] : [ ].

2 Complete the ratios for the jars and tins.

Try to give your answers in their simplest form.

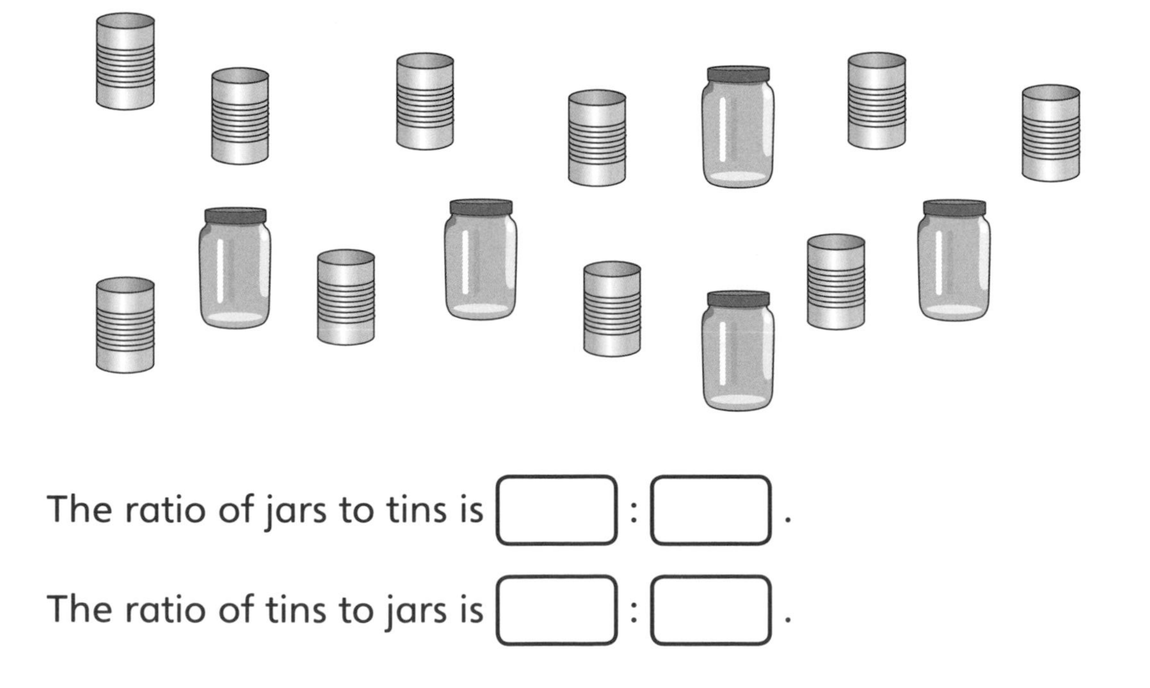

The ratio of jars to tins is [ ] : [ ].

The ratio of tins to jars is [ ] : [ ].

3 What is the ratio of shaded to non-shaded squares in each diagram?

a)

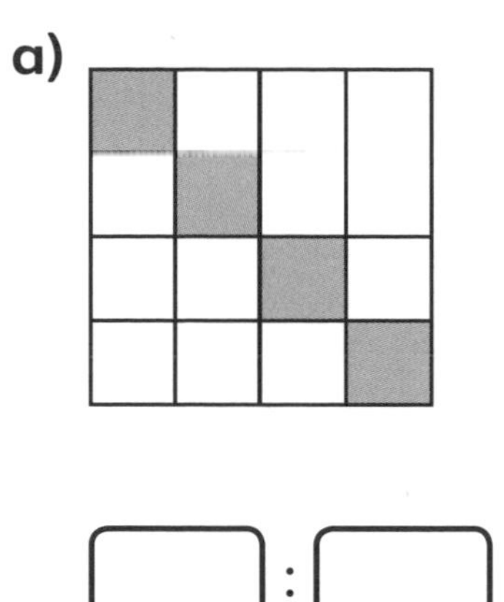

☐ : ☐

b)

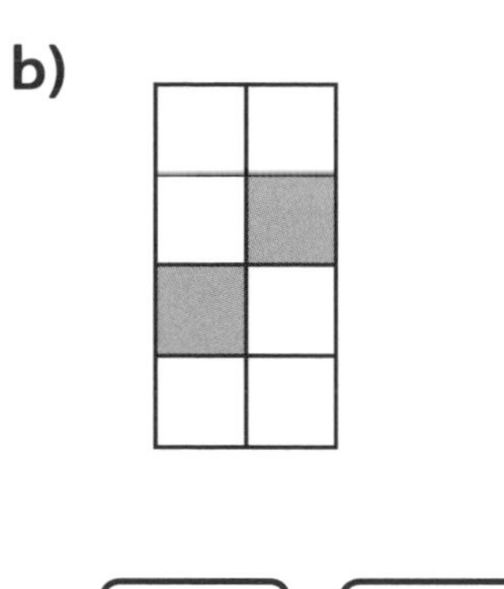

☐ : ☐

c)

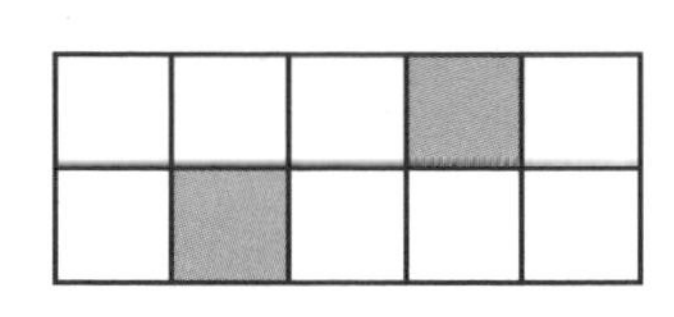

☐ : ☐

In each box, draw triangles and circles to show the ratio.

Draw more than six shapes in each box.

a) The ratio of triangles to circles is 3 : 1.	**c)** The ratio of circles to triangles is 1 : 3.
b) The ratio of triangles to circles is 3 : 2.	**d)** The ratio of triangles to circles is 1 : 4.

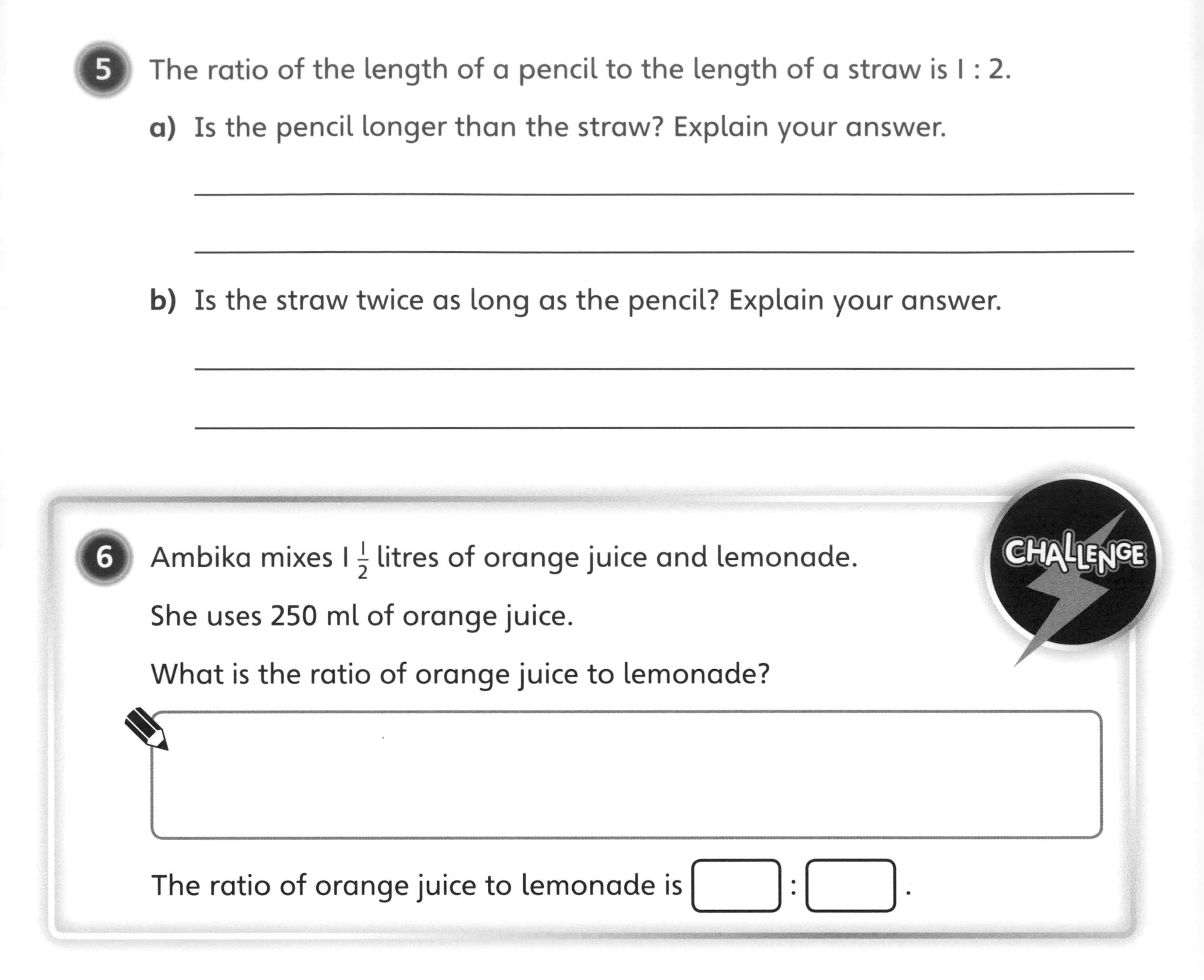

5 The ratio of the length of a pencil to the length of a straw is 1 : 2.

a) Is the pencil longer than the straw? Explain your answer.

____

____

b) Is the straw twice as long as the pencil? Explain your answer.

____

____

6 Ambika mixes $1\frac{1}{2}$ litres of orange juice and lemonade.

She uses 250 ml of orange juice.

What is the ratio of orange juice to lemonade?

The ratio of orange juice to lemonade is ☐ : ☐.

Reflect

'The ratio 2 : 1 is the same as the ratio 1 : 2.' Do you agree? Explain your answer.

→ Textbook 6B p216

Ratio 3

1 Lee draws some shapes.

For every 3 squares he draws, he draws 4 circles.

Here is part of the diagram Lee has drawn.

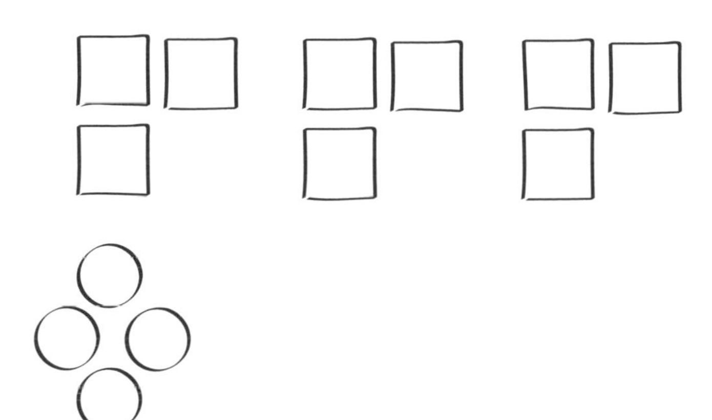

a) Complete Lee's diagram.

b) How many circles does Lee draw in total? ☐

2 A jar contains strawberry sweets and lime sweets.

For every 2 strawberry sweets, there are 3 lime sweets.

There are 18 lime sweets in the jar.

Use the table to help you work out how many strawberry sweets are in the jar.

There are ☐ strawberry sweets in the jar.

Strawberry	Lime
2	3
4	6

3 A box contains some buttons.

For every 2 white buttons there are 5 black buttons.

If there are 12 white buttons in the box, how many black buttons are there?

There are [ ] black buttons in the box.

4 In a fish tank, for every 1 clown fish there are 4 box fish.

If the tank contains 7 clown fish, how many box fish are there?

There are [ ] box fish in the tank.

5 A pattern is made up of squares and rectangles.

For every 2 squares there are 5 rectangles.

Explain why the pattern cannot have 7 squares.

6 There are some cows and sheep in a field.

For every 9 cows there are 5 sheep.

There are 36 cows in the field.

How many more cows than sheep are in the field?

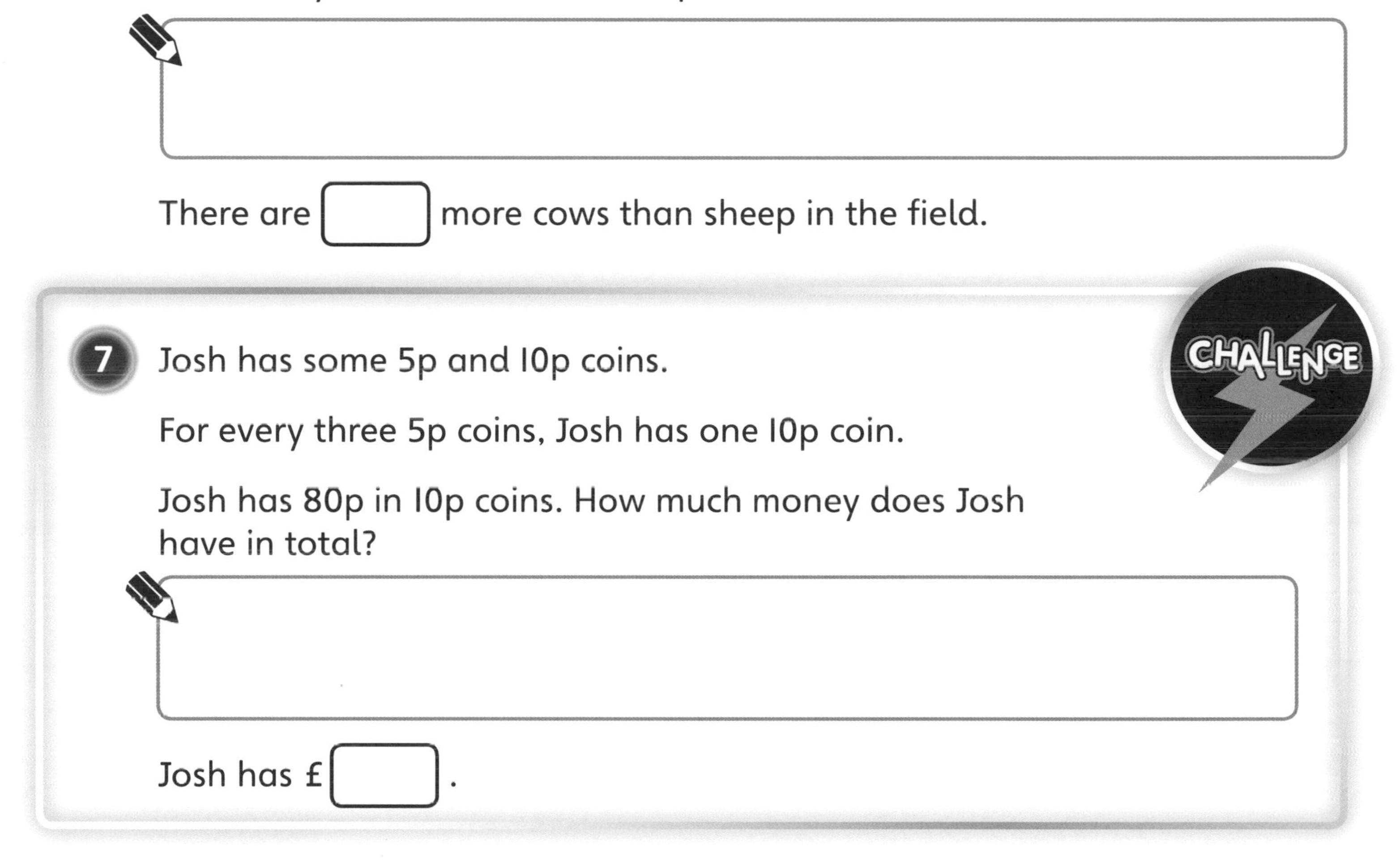

There are [ ] more cows than sheep in the field.

7 Josh has some 5p and 10p coins.

For every three 5p coins, Josh has one 10p coin.

Josh has 80p in 10p coins. How much money does Josh have in total?

Josh has £[ ].

Reflect

In a bag of balloons, there are 3 red balloons for every 4 blue balloons.

Are there more red or more blue balloons in the bag? How do you know?

→ Textbook 6B p220

Ratio 4

There are 20 slices of cake.

For every 1 slice of carrot cake there are 4 slices of lemon cake.

How many slices of each cake are there?

Complete the bar model to help you work out the answer.

Carrot

Lemon

20

There are ☐ slices of carrot cake and ☐ slices of lemon cake.

2 Mr Lopez counts 63 balls in the PE cupboard.

For every 2 footballs there are 5 tennis balls.

How many of each ball are there?

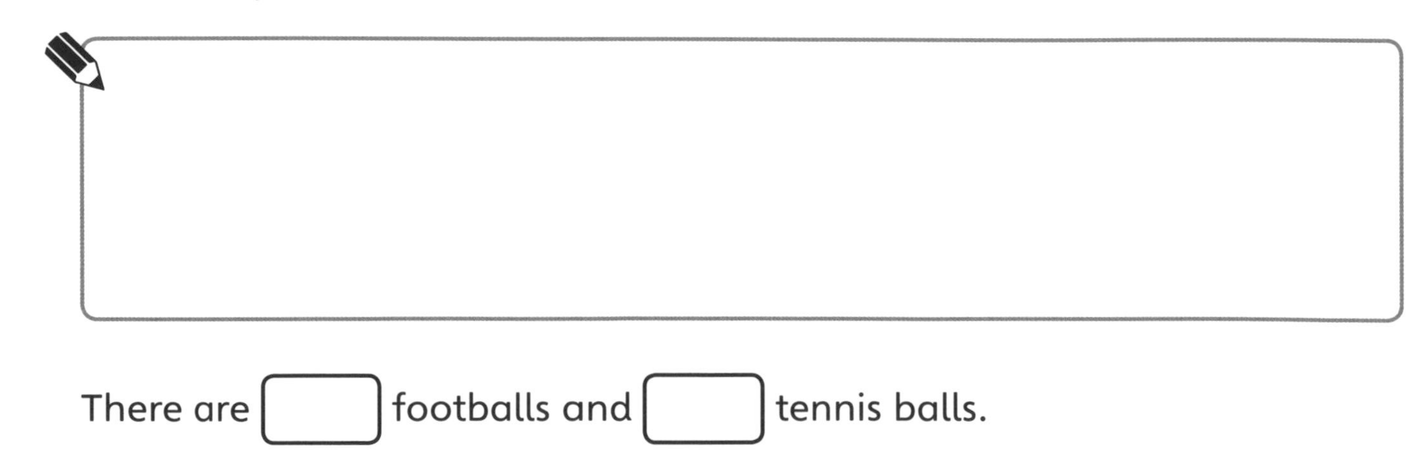

There are ☐ footballs and ☐ tennis balls.

3 Shade in the rectangle to show 3 red squares for every 5 blue squares.

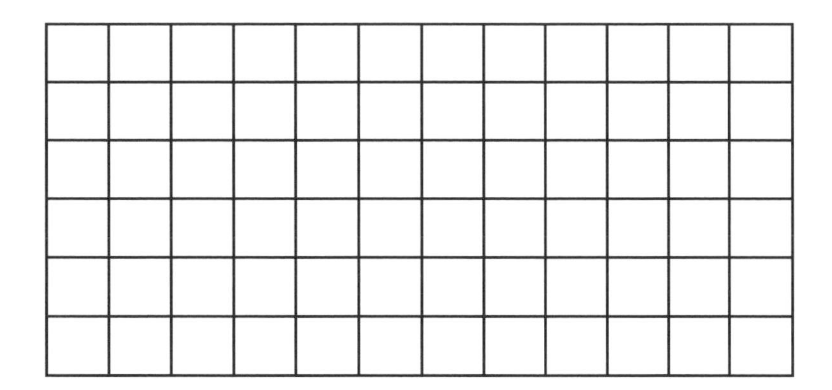

Explain your method.

___

___

___

4 There are 40 socks in a drawer.

The ratio of grey to white socks is 3 : 2.

a) How many grey socks are there?

There are ☐ grey socks in the drawer.

b) How many pairs of white socks can be made?

☐ pairs of white socks can be made.

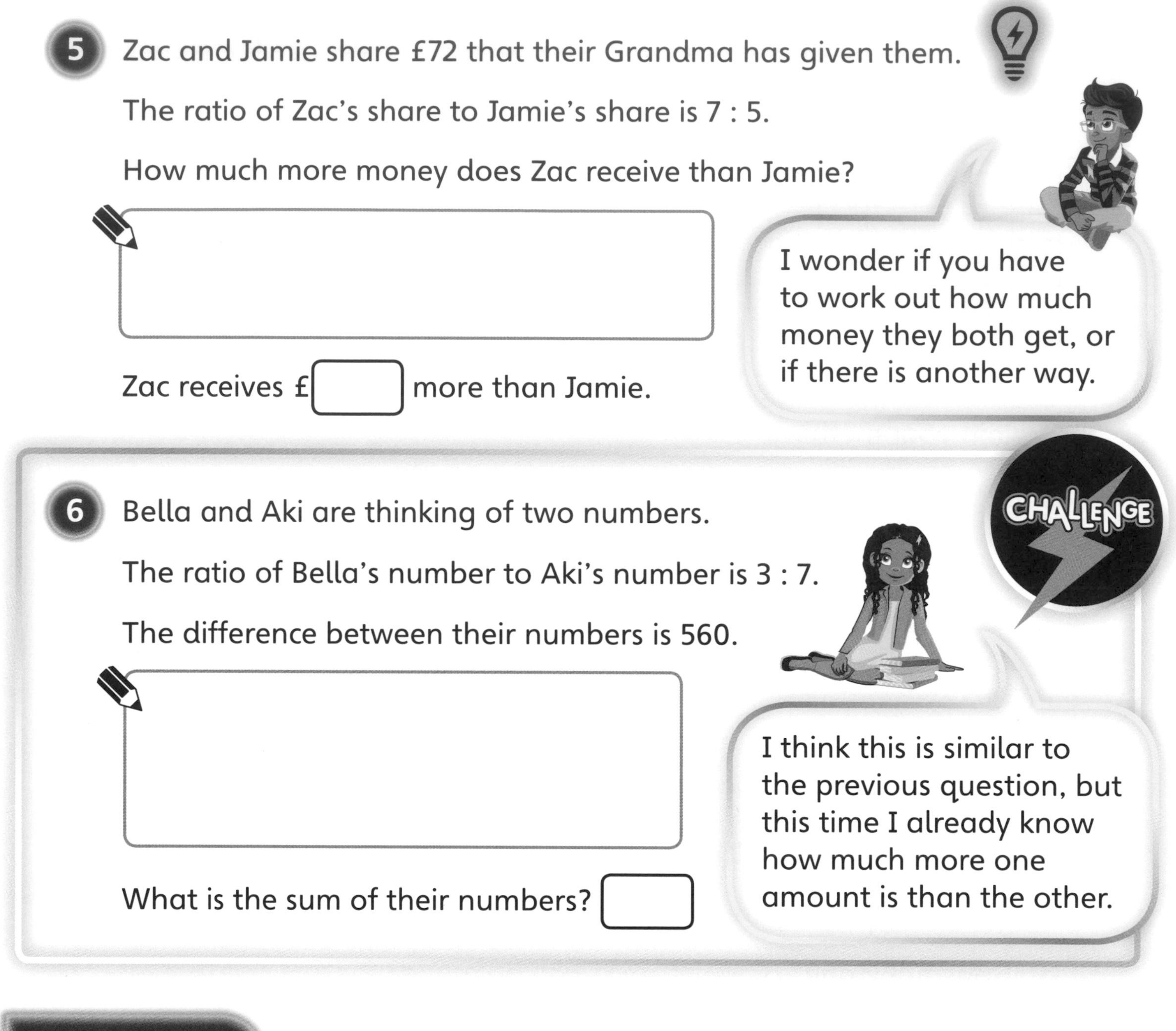

5 Zac and Jamie share £72 that their Grandma has given them.

The ratio of Zac's share to Jamie's share is 7 : 5.

How much more money does Zac receive than Jamie?

Zac receives £☐ more than Jamie.

6 Bella and Aki are thinking of two numbers.

The ratio of Bella's number to Aki's number is 3 : 7.

The difference between their numbers is 560.

What is the sum of their numbers? ☐

Reflect

Explain the method you would use to share 60 into the ratio 2 : 3.

→ Textbook 6B p224

Scale drawings

1 The diagram shows a plan of an office space.

Board room

Stock cupboard

Canteen

Meeting room

On the plan, 1 cm represents 2 m in real life.

a) Complete the scale.

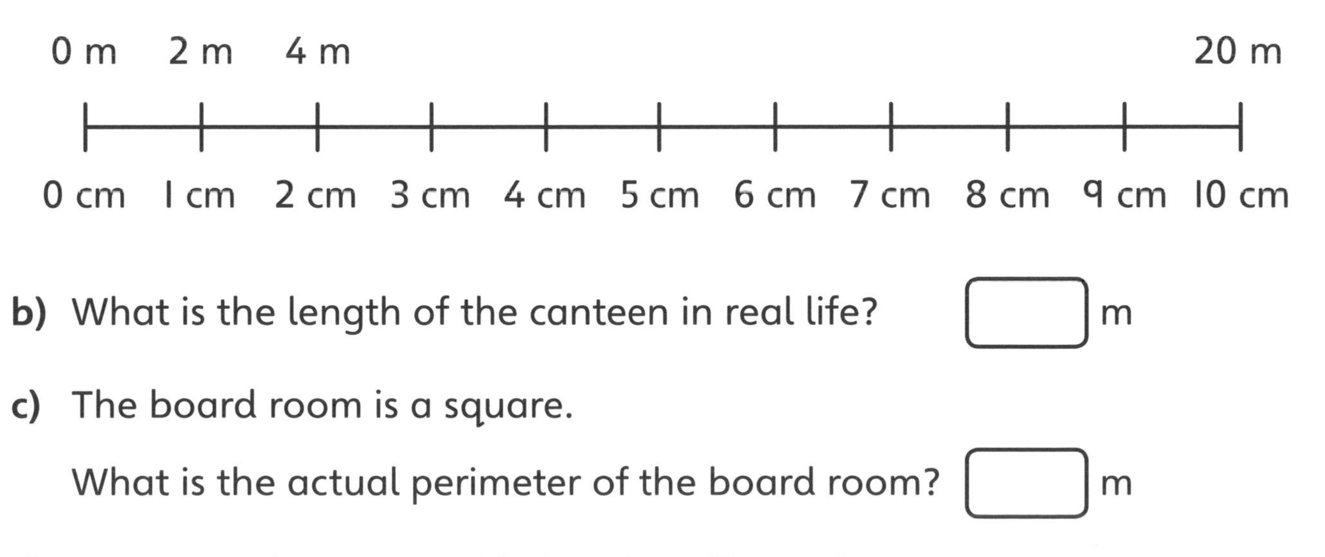

b) What is the length of the canteen in real life? ☐ m

c) The board room is a square.

What is the actual perimeter of the board room? ☐ m

d) A rectangular rug is added to the office. It is 2 metres × 5 metres.

Draw and label the rug on the grid.

2 Kate draws a plan of her classroom to scale. She uses the scale 2 cm : 1 m.

a) What does the scale mean?

Every [ ] cm on the plan represents [ ] m in real life.

b) Complete the scale.

0 m 1 m 2 m 3 m 4 m 5 m 6 m 7 m 8 m 9 m 10 m

0 cm

c) What is the perimeter of the carpet area in real life?
Show all your working.

Carpet area

The perimeter is [ ] m.

3 Lexi and Jen are cycling from Wakefield to York.

1 cm : 5 km

They work out a route on the map that is 11 cm long. The scale on the map is 1 cm : 5 km.

What is the actual length of their route?

Length of route = [ ] km

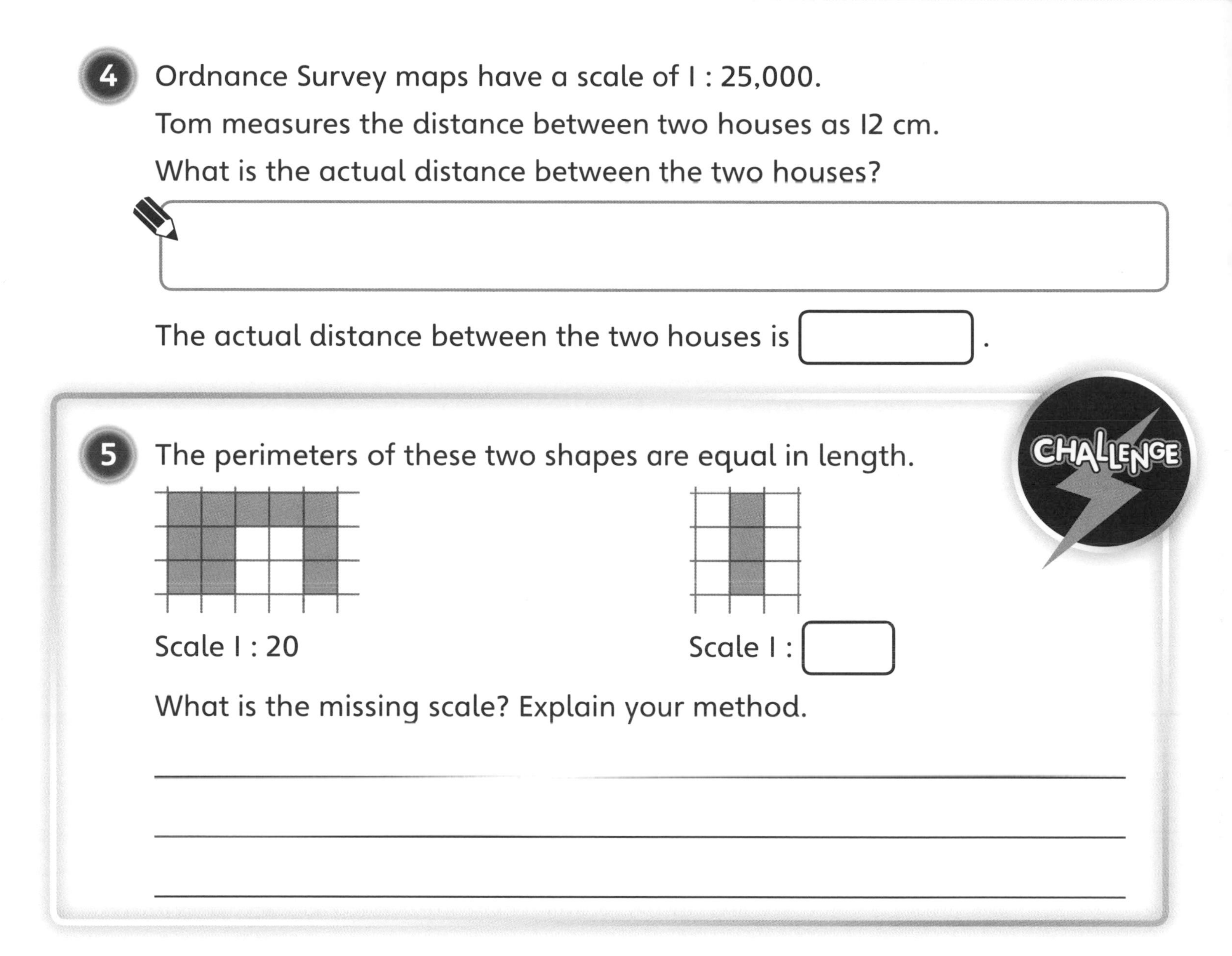

4 Ordnance Survey maps have a scale of 1 : 25,000.

Tom measures the distance between two houses as 12 cm.

What is the actual distance between the two houses?

The actual distance between the two houses is [ ].

5 The perimeters of these two shapes are equal in length.

CHALLENGE

Scale 1 : 20

Scale 1 : [ ]

What is the missing scale? Explain your method.

Reflect

What is the same about these scales? What is different?

1 : 200 1 cm : 2 m

→ Textbook 6B p228

Scale factors

1 Zac draws a line 9 cm long.

a) Mo draws a line 18 cm long.

How many times longer is Mo's line than Zac's?

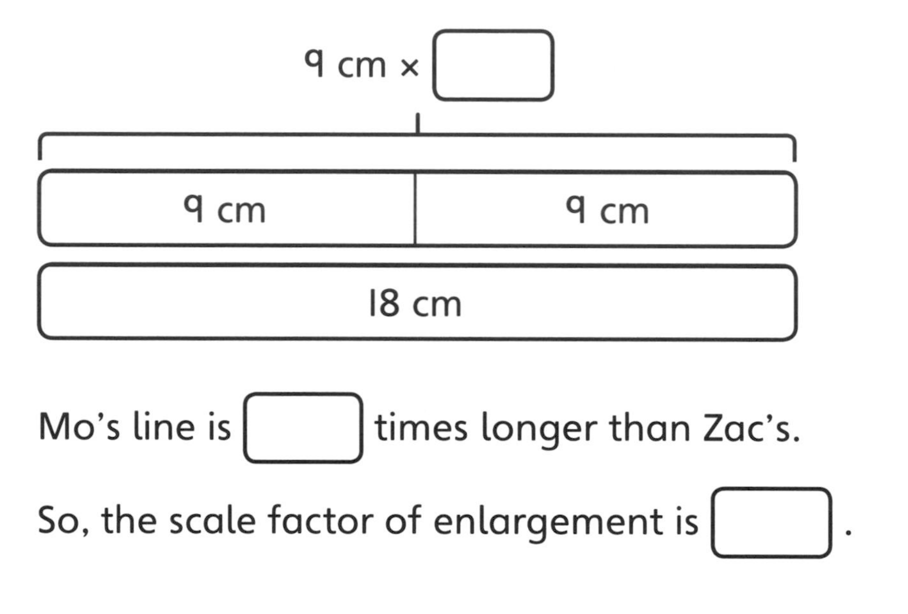

Mo's line is ☐ times longer than Zac's.

So, the scale factor of enlargement is ☐.

b) Olivia draws a line 45 cm long.

How many times longer is Olivia's line than Zac's?

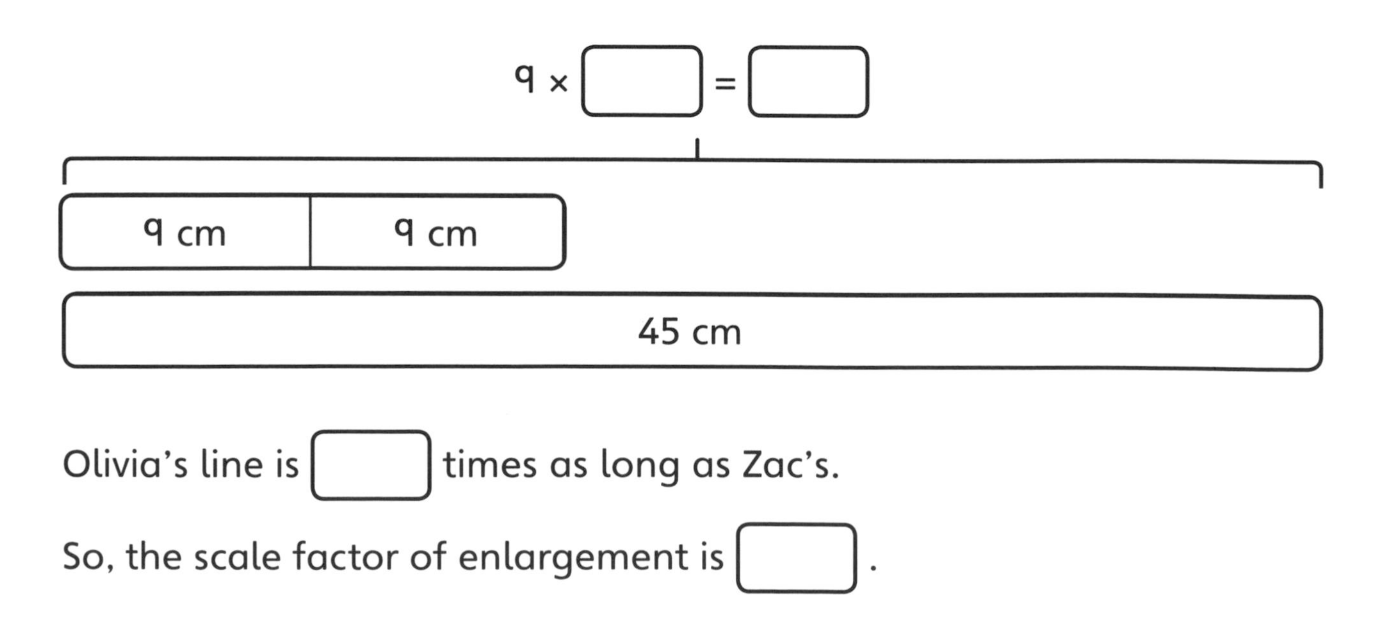

Olivia's line is ☐ times as long as Zac's.

So, the scale factor of enlargement is ☐.

2 The rectangle has been enlarged by a scale factor of 2.

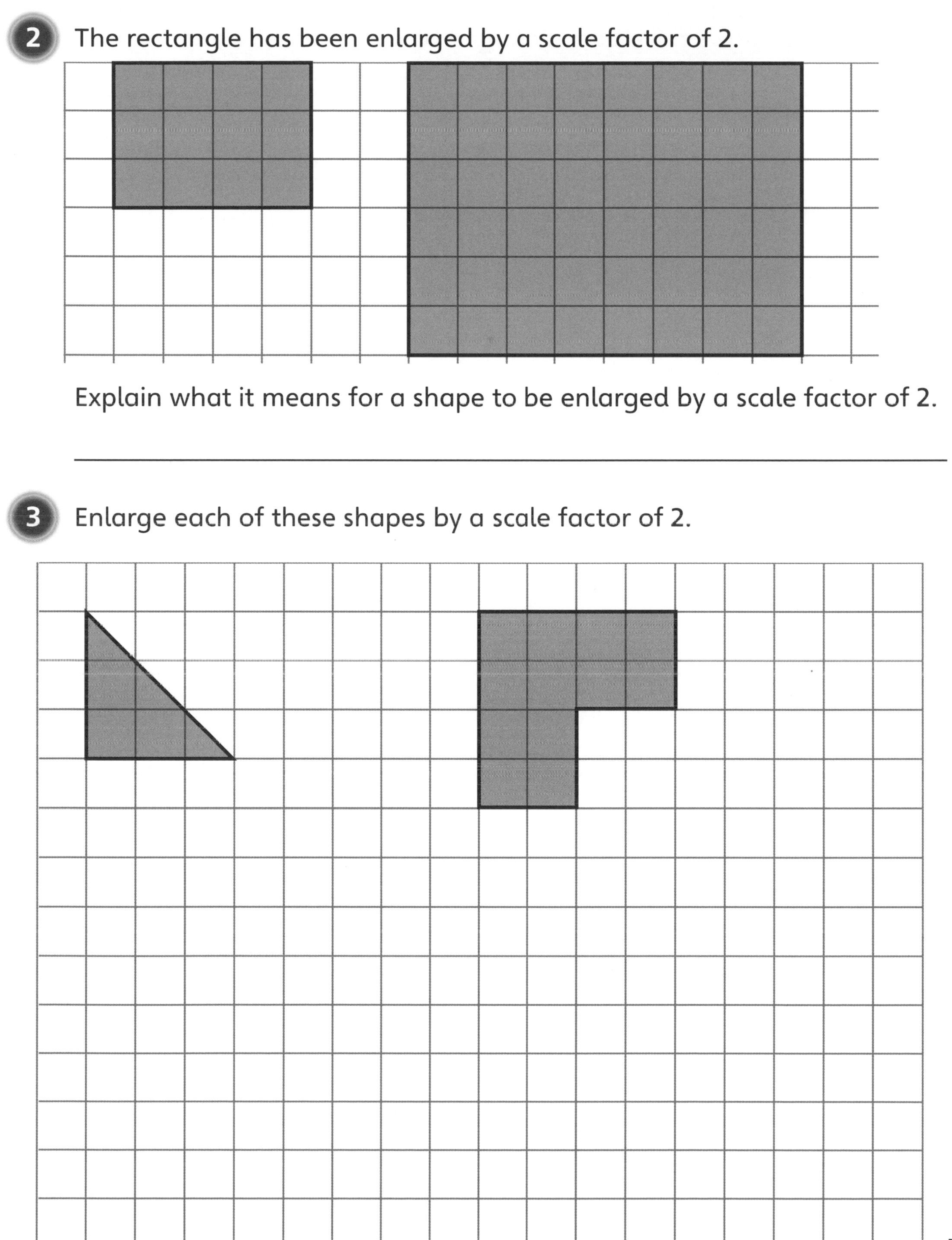

Explain what it means for a shape to be enlarged by a scale factor of 2.

____

3 Enlarge each of these shapes by a scale factor of 2.

4 Some rectangles have been enlarged by different scale factors. The table shows what happens to the length of the rectangles. Complete the table.

Rectangle	Original length	Scale factor of enlargement	New length
A	6 cm	4	
B		5	60 cm
C	18 cm	$\frac{1}{2}$	
D	18 cm	$1\frac{1}{2}$	
E	5 cm		5 m

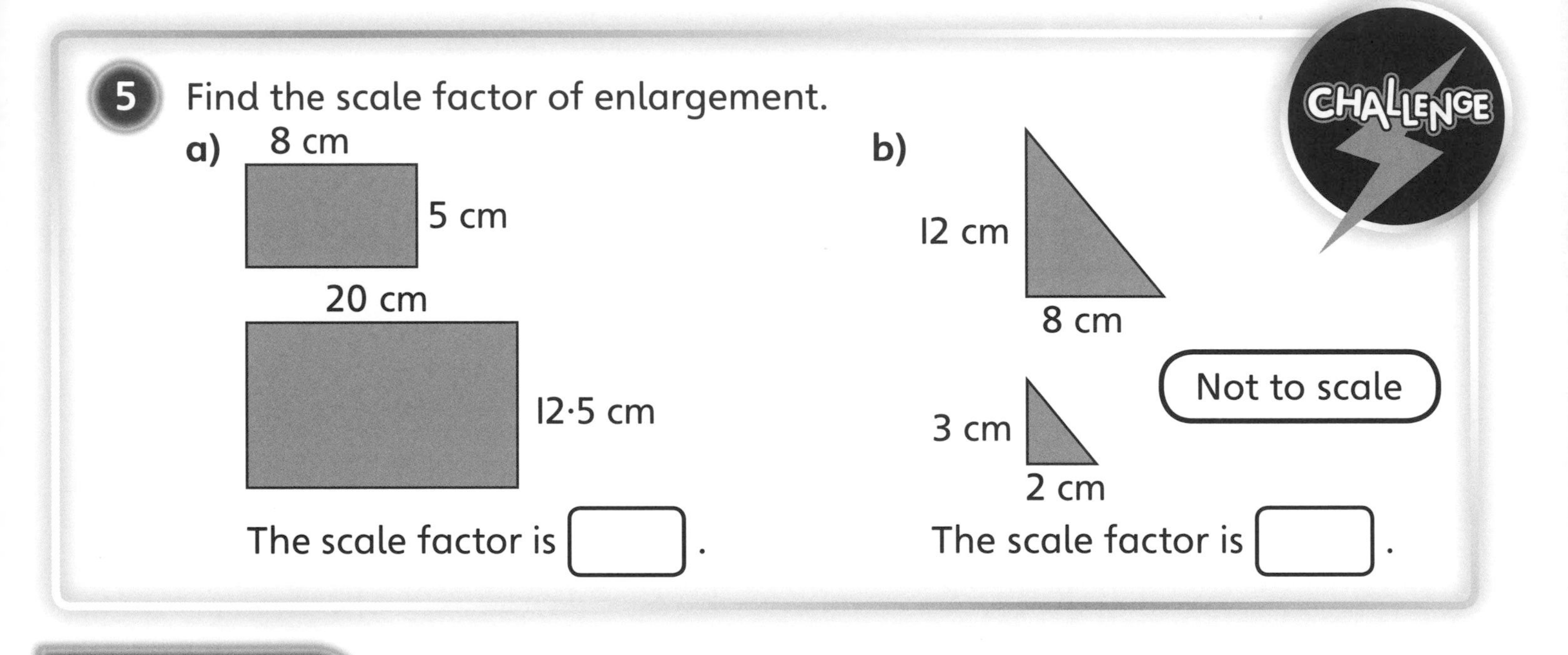

5 Find the scale factor of enlargement.

a) The scale factor is ☐.

b) The scale factor is ☐.

Reflect

Explain what it means for a shape to be enlarged by a scale factor of $\frac{1}{2}$.

→ Textbook 6B p232

Similar shapes

Are these shapes similar?

If so, what is the scale factor of enlargement? Explain your answer.

a)

b)

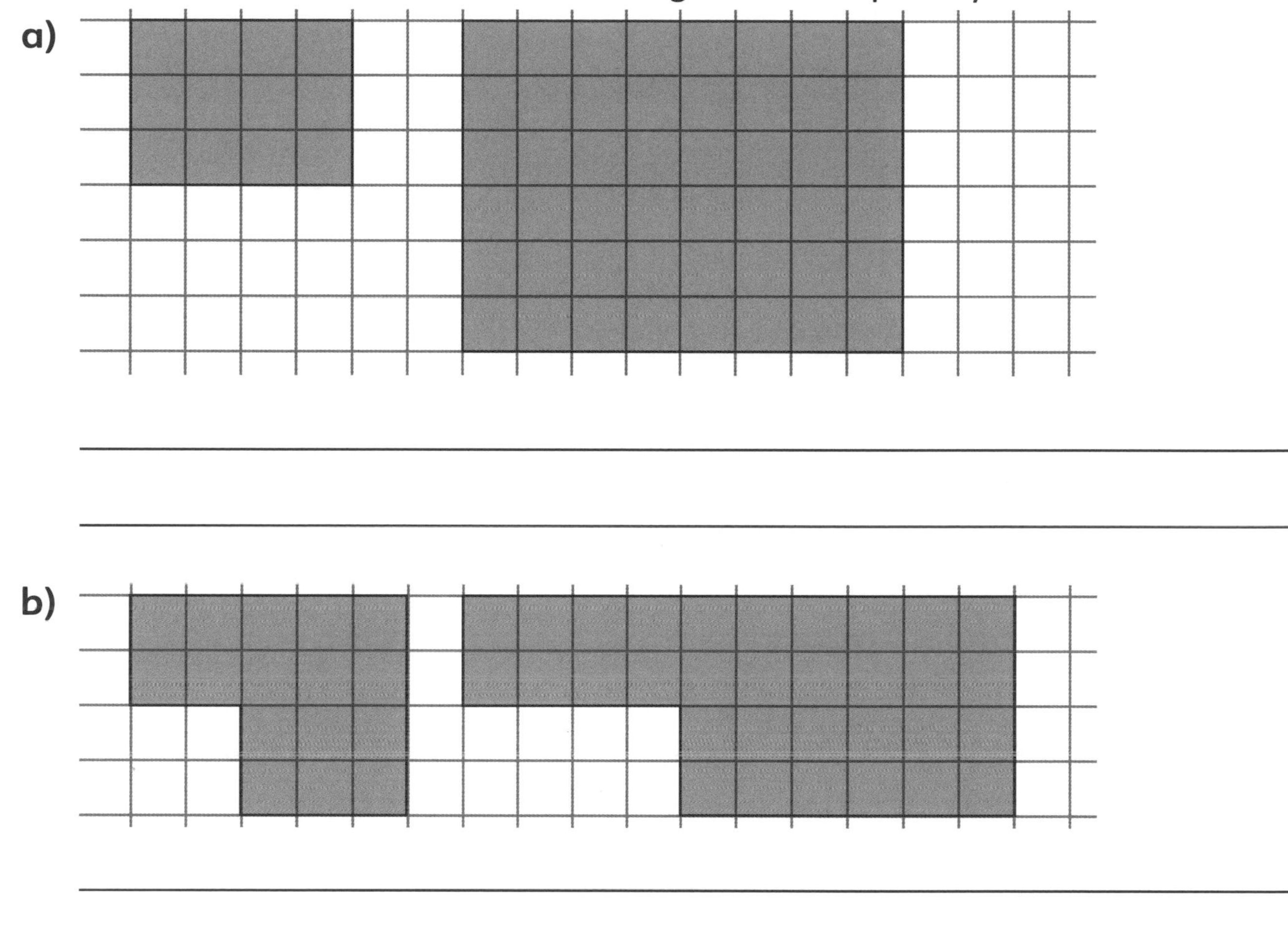

2 Draw two triangles that are similar.

3 These pairs of shapes are similar.

For each pair of shapes, find the scale factor of enlargement and then find the missing side.

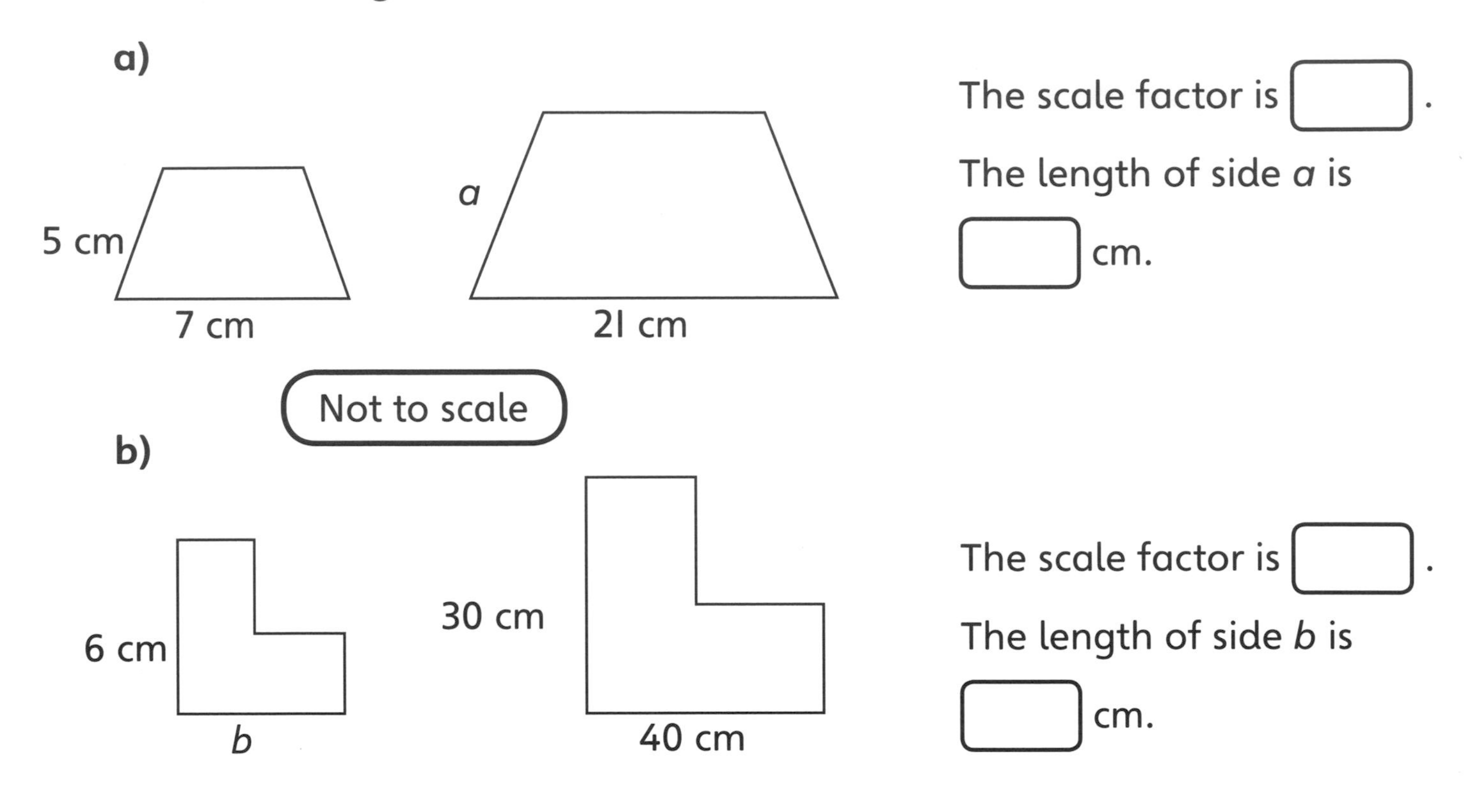

a) The scale factor is ☐.

The length of side a is ☐ cm.

b) The scale factor is ☐.

The length of side b is ☐ cm.

4 These shapes are all similar. Find the missing sides.

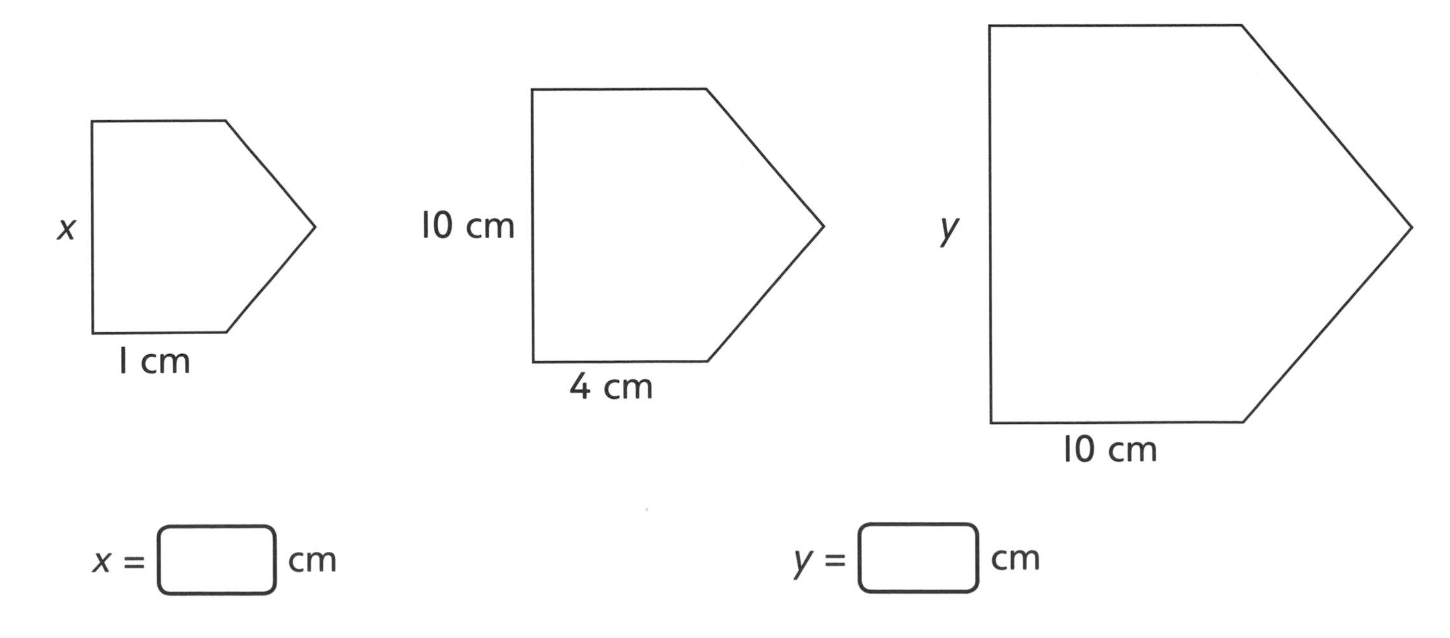

$x =$ ☐ cm

$y =$ ☐ cm

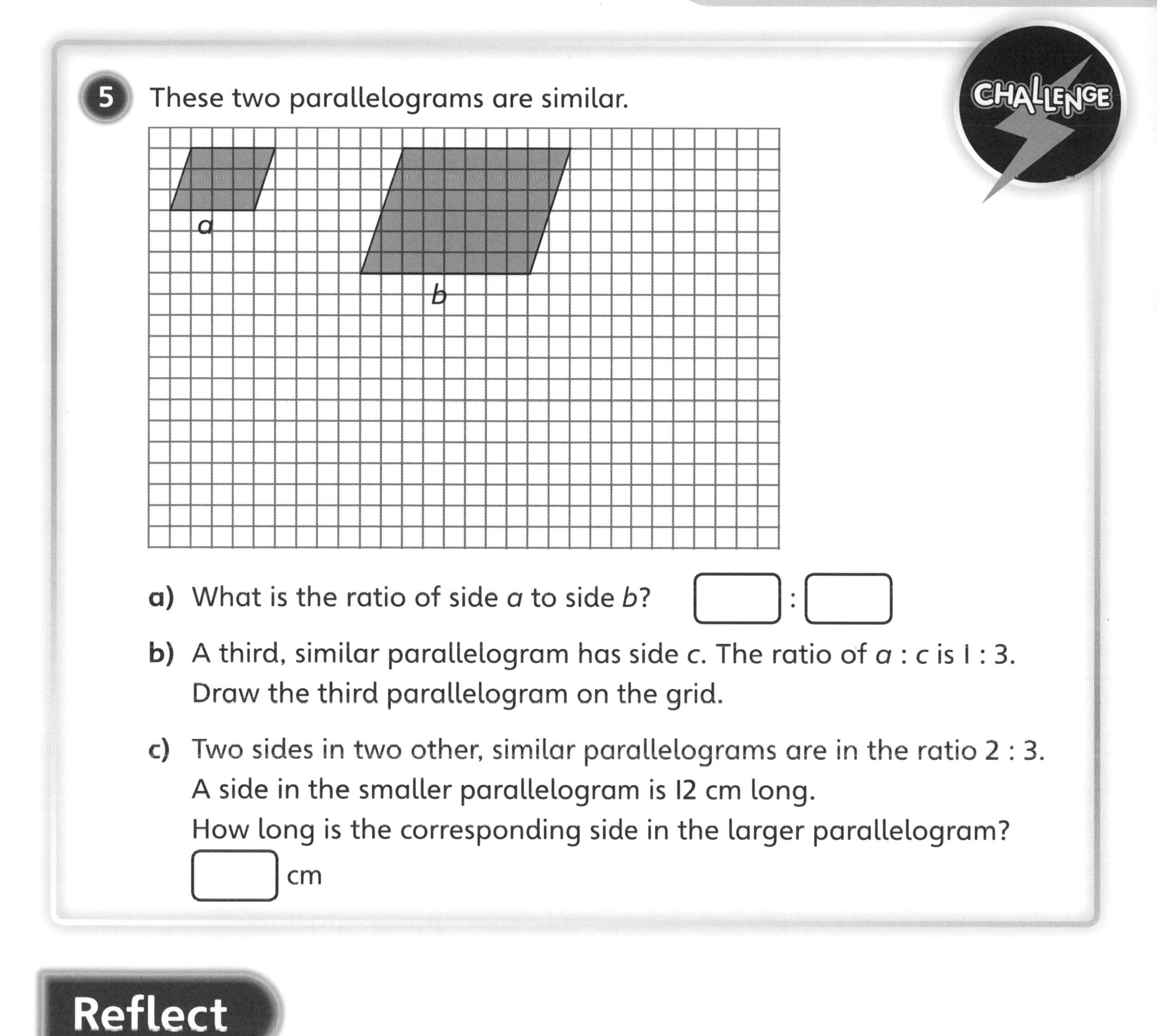

5 These two parallelograms are similar.

a) What is the ratio of side *a* to side *b*? ☐ : ☐

b) A third, similar parallelogram has side *c*. The ratio of *a* : *c* is 1 : 3.
Draw the third parallelogram on the grid.

c) Two sides in two other, similar parallelograms are in the ratio 2 : 3.
A side in the smaller parallelogram is 12 cm long.
How long is the corresponding side in the larger parallelogram?
☐ cm

Reflect

Two sides in two similar shapes are in the ratio 1 : 4. What else do you know?

→ Textbook 6B p236

Problem solving – ratio and proportion 1

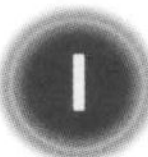

5 pencils cost 60p.

How much do 7 pencils cost?

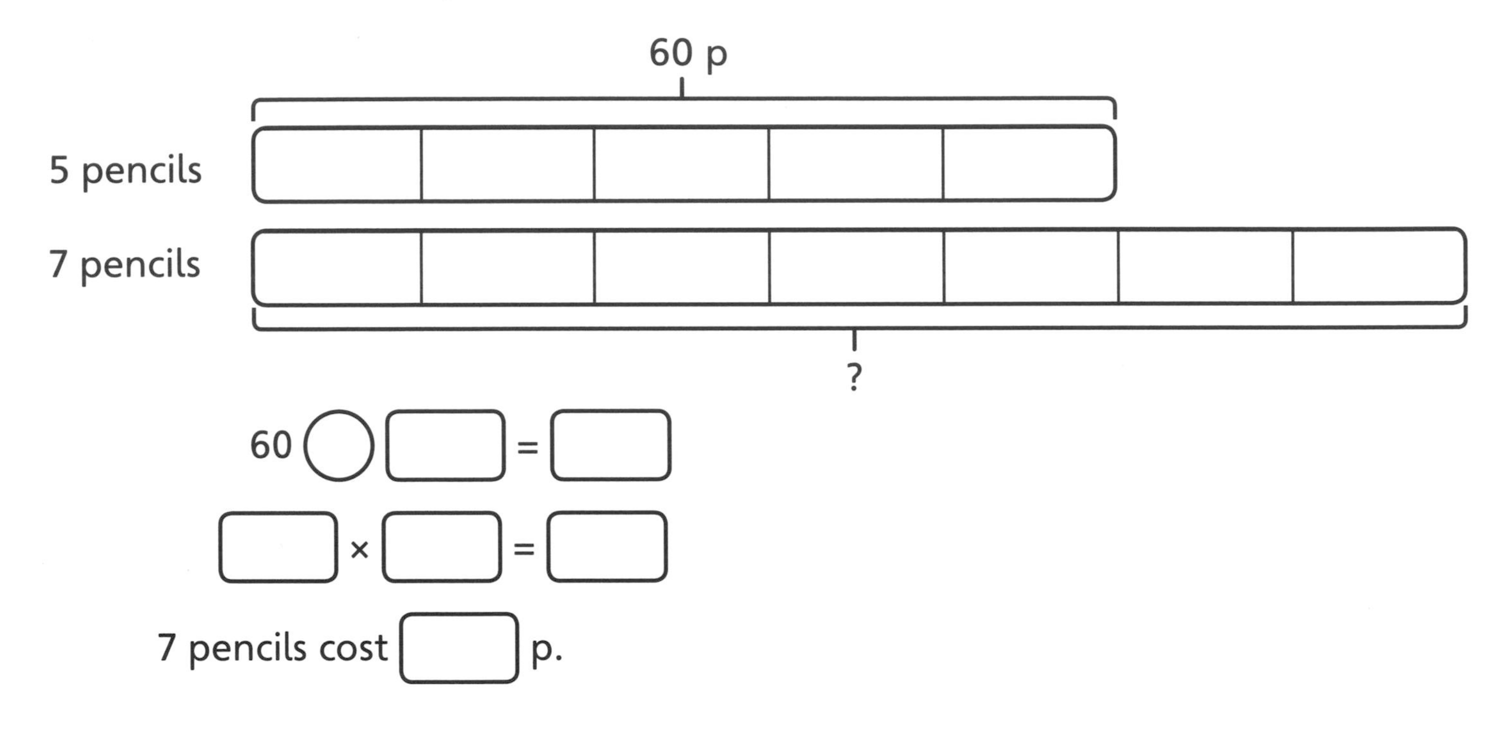

60 ◯ ☐ = ☐

☐ × ☐ = ☐

7 pencils cost ☐ p.

2 Eight identical, square paving slabs are laid to make a patio.

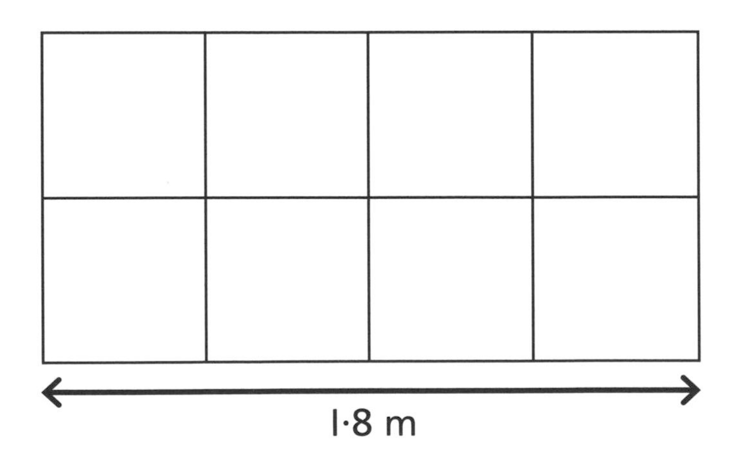

The length of the patio is 1·8 m.

What is the perimeter of the patio?

The perimeter of the patio is ☐ m.

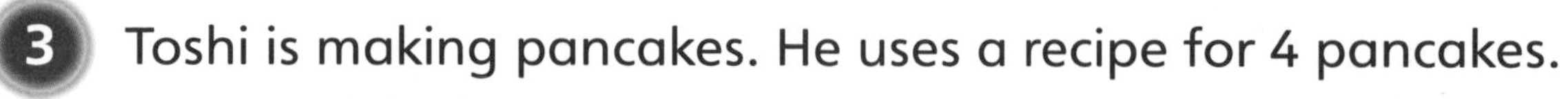

3 Toshi is making pancakes. He uses a recipe for 4 pancakes.

Pancake Recipe

Makes 4 pancakes

100 g flour

2 eggs

300 ml milk

1 tbsp oil

Pancake Recipe

Makes 12 pancakes

☐ g flour

☐ eggs

☐ ml milk

☐ tbsp oil

a) Complete the recipe for 12 pancakes.

b) Toshi wants to make 10 pancakes. How much flour does he need?

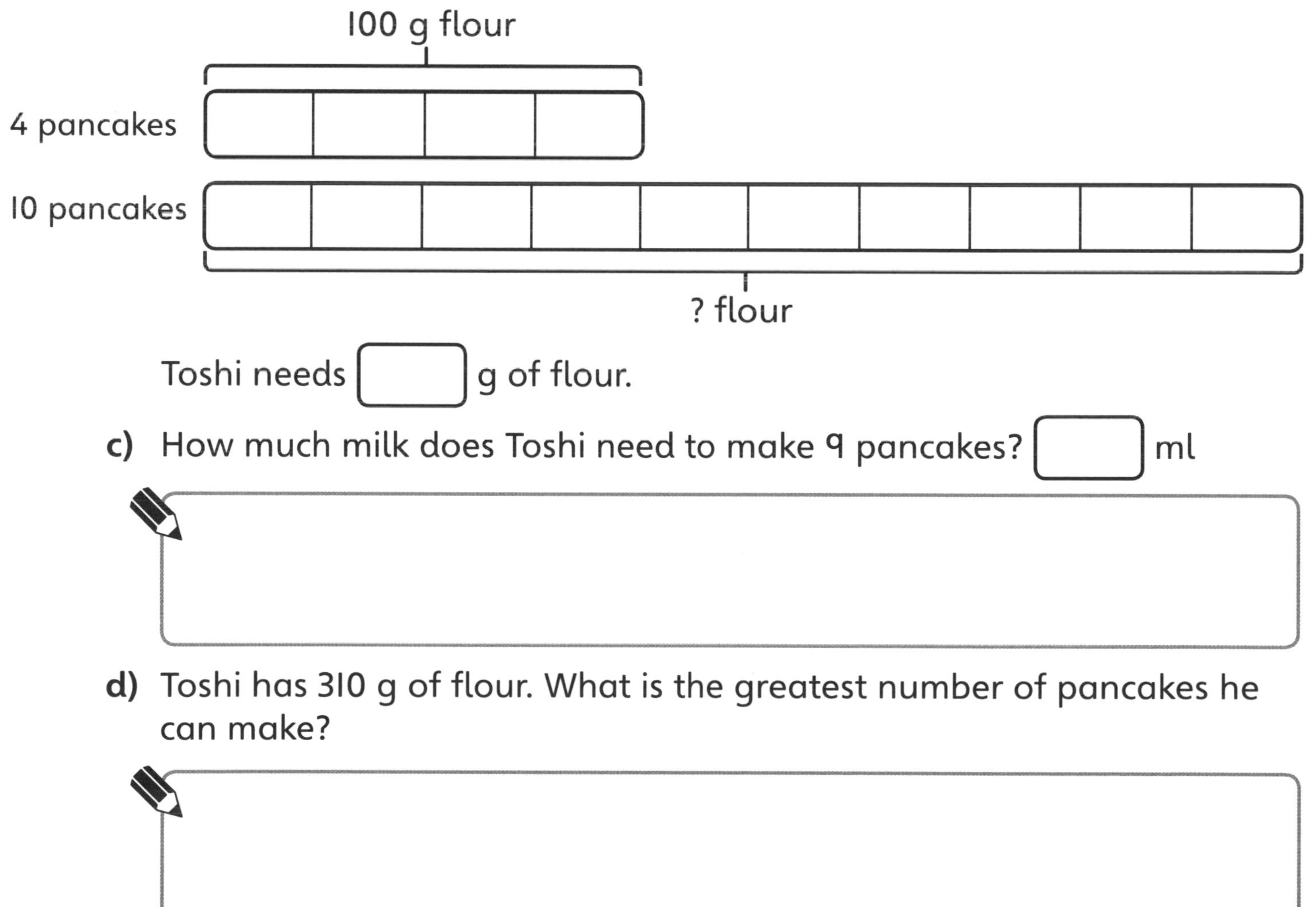

Toshi needs ☐ g of flour.

c) How much milk does Toshi need to make 9 pancakes? ☐ ml

d) Toshi has 310 g of flour. What is the greatest number of pancakes he can make?

Toshi can make ☐ pancakes.

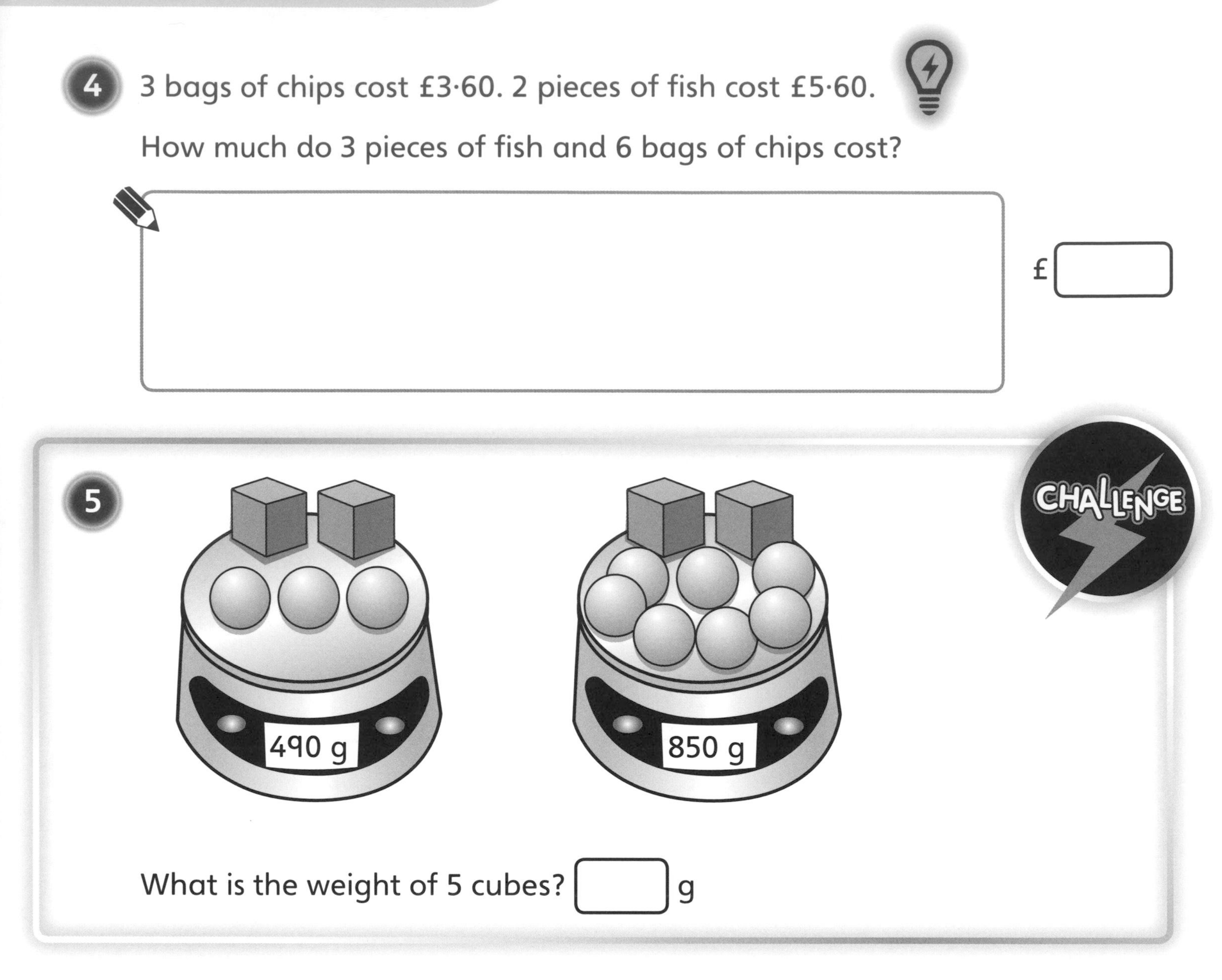

4 3 bags of chips cost £3·60. 2 pieces of fish cost £5·60.

How much do 3 pieces of fish and 6 bags of chips cost?

£ ☐

5 What is the weight of 5 cubes? ☐ g

Reflect

6 identical chocolates weigh 120 g.

Explain two ways you can work out the weight of 9 chocolates.

→ Textbook 6B p240

Problem solving – ratio and proportion 2

A florist is making a bouquet of flowers.

For every 4 roses in the bouquet there are 3 lilies.

There are 16 roses. How many lilies are there?

Choose the method you want to use.

There are ☐ lilies.

2 A bag contains a mix of mint and strawberry sweets.

The ratio of mint to strawberry sweets is 4 : 1.

a) How many times more mint sweets are there than strawberry sweets?

Explain how you know.

____

____

b) There are 32 mint sweets in the bag.

How many strawberry sweets are in the bag? 

3 Reena and Richard share a chocolate bar.

For every 3 squares of chocolate Reena eats, Richard eats 2 squares.

Richard eats 16 squares of chocolate.

How many squares of chocolate are there in the whole bar? ☐

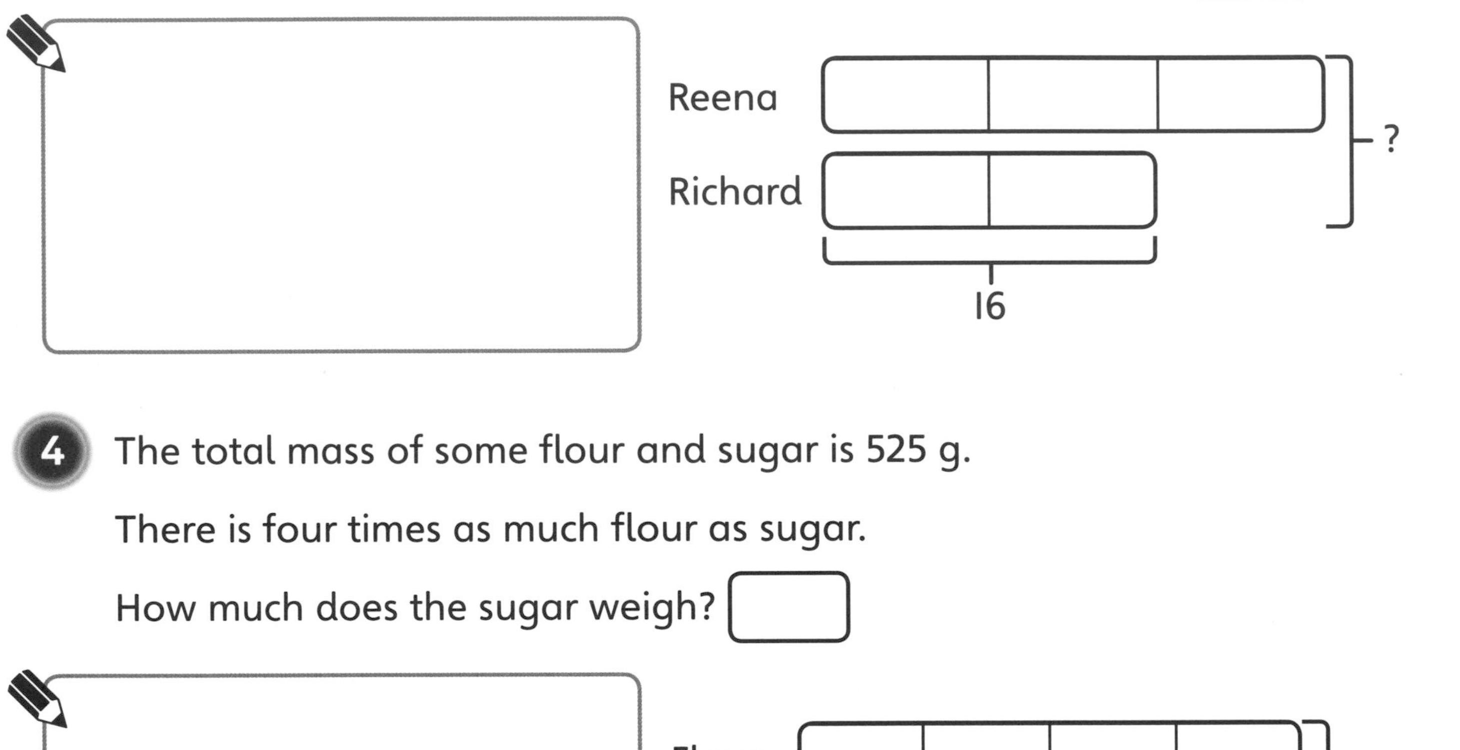

4 The total mass of some flour and sugar is 525 g.

There is four times as much flour as sugar.

How much does the sugar weigh? ☐

Flour
Sugar
525 g
?

5 In a box of toy bricks, there are 4 red bricks for every 2 blue and 1 yellow.

There are 5 yellow bricks. How many bricks are there altogether? ☐

6 In a bag of marbles, there are 4 blue marbles for every 1 green marble.

There are 15 more blue marbles than green marbles.

How many blue marbles are there? ☐

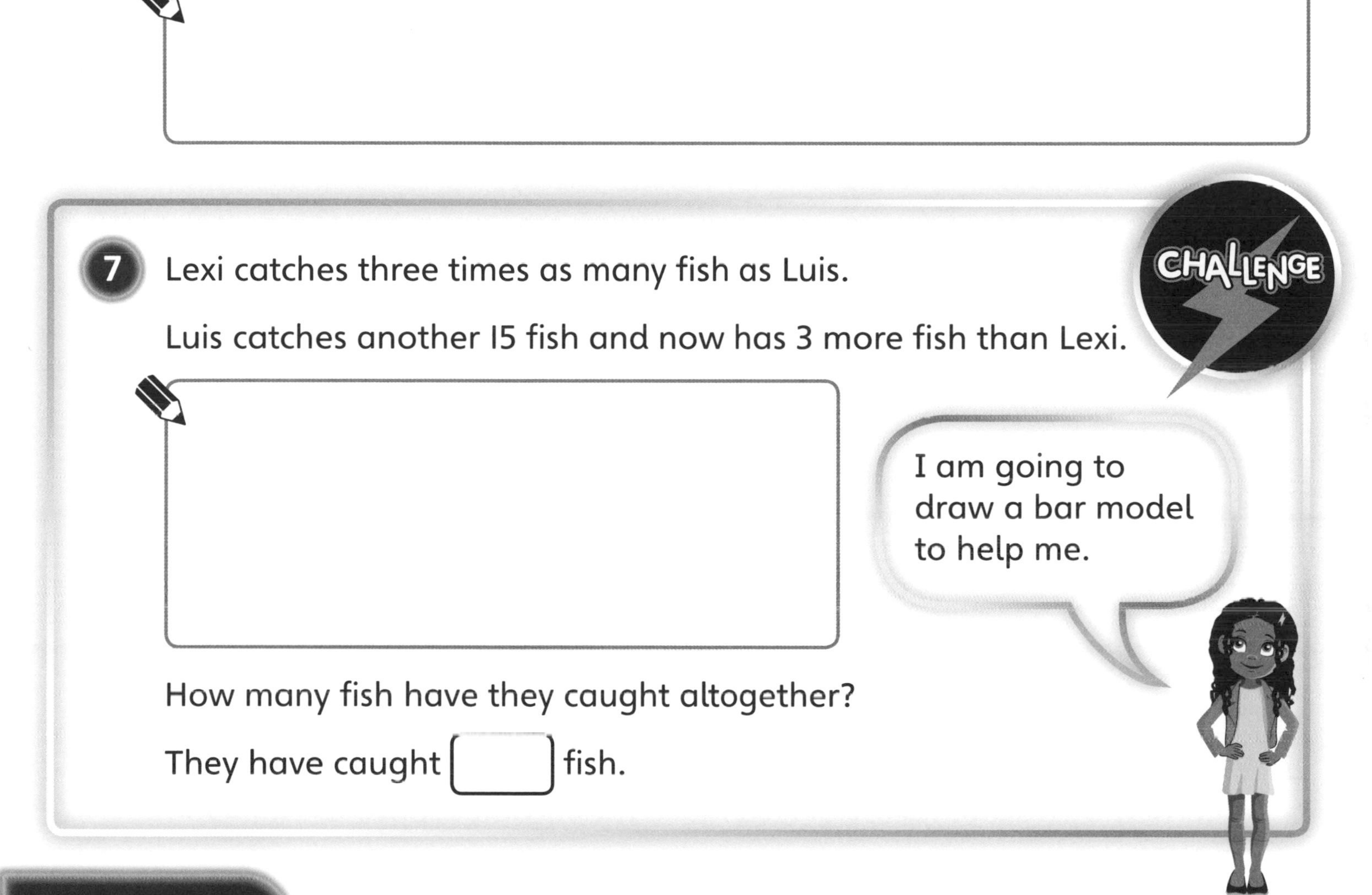

7 Lexi catches three times as many fish as Luis.

Luis catches another 15 fish and now has 3 more fish than Lexi.

How many fish have they caught altogether?

They have caught ☐ fish.

Reflect

Do you find it helpful to use a bar model to solve these types of questions?

→ Textbook 6B p244

End of unit check

My journal

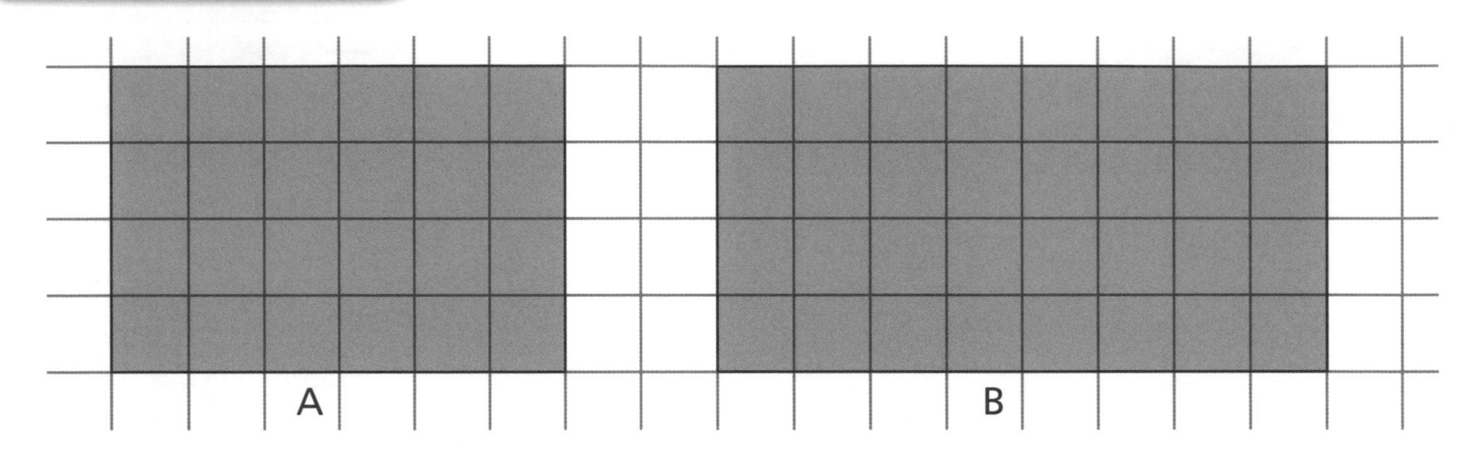

a) Andy says, 'When shape A is enlarged by a scale factor of 2, you get shape B.'

Is Andy correct? Explain your answer.

____

____

____

b) What is the ratio of the sides in two shapes, if the first shape has been enlarged by a scale factor of 2 to make the second shape? Explain your answer.

____

____

Power check

How do you feel about your work in this unit?

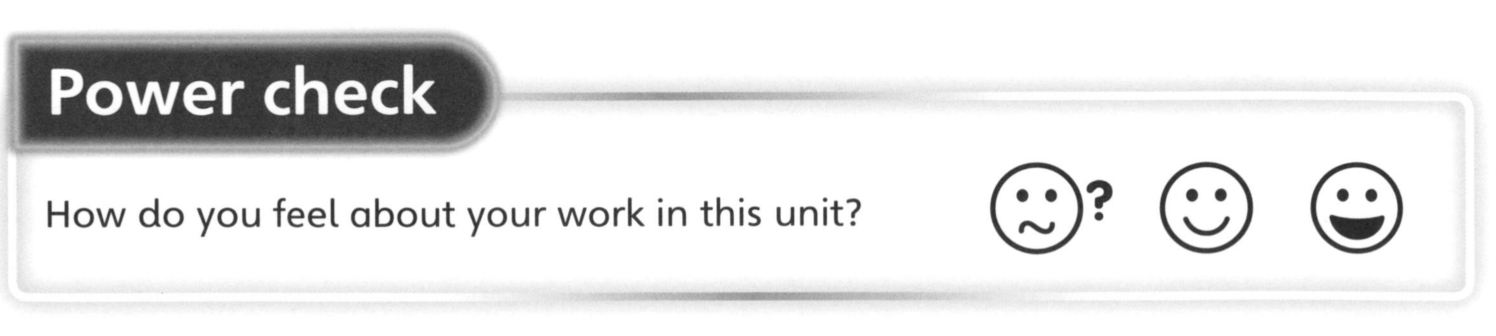

Power play

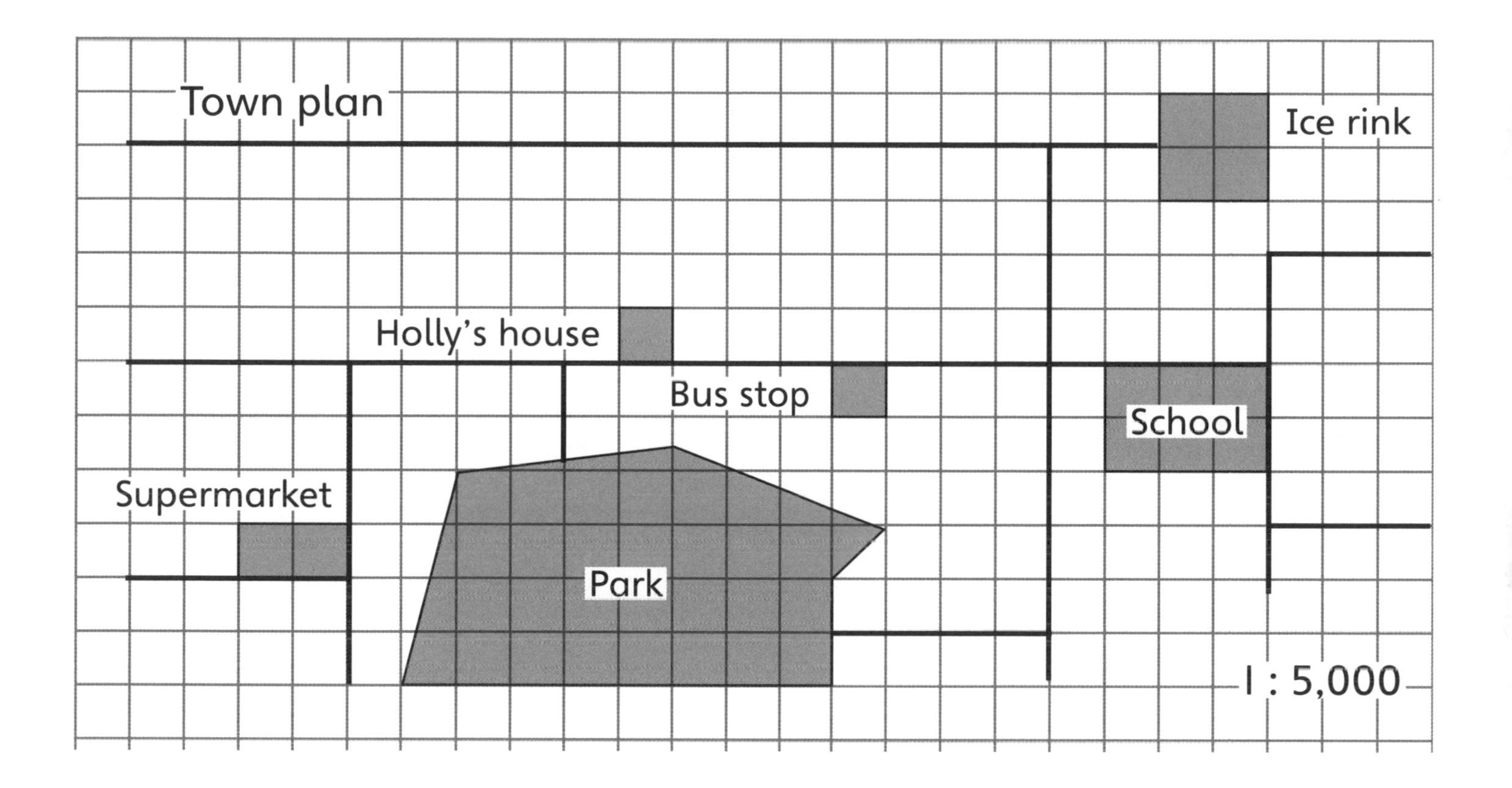

a) What does 1 cm on the plan represent in real life? How do you know?

____

b) Find the shortest distance between Holly's house and the bus stop.

Explain your method.

____

____

c) Holly walks 350 m, the shortest distance from her house to the swimming pool.

Show two different locations on the plan where the swimming pool could be.

My power points

Put a tick against the topics you have learnt about. Show how confident you are with each one by giving it a number on a scale of 1 to 3.

1 = not at all confident;
2 = getting there;
3 = very confident

Unit 7

I have learnt how to ...

- Multiply by 10, 100 and 1,000
- Write decimals as fractions
- Convert fractions to decimals
- Multiply decimals
- Divide decimals

Unit 8

I have learnt how to ...

- Find percentages
- Find missing values
- Convert fractions to percentages
- Find equivalent fractions, decimals and percentages

Unit 9

I have learnt how to ...

- Find a rule in algebra
- Use a rule in algebra
- Use and write formulae
- Solve equations

Unit 10

I have learnt how to ...

- Use metric measurements for length, weight and capacity
- Convert metric measurements
- Solve problems with metric measurements
- Understand miles and kilometres
- Recognise imperial measurements

Unit 11

I have learnt how to ...

- Find and draw shapes with the same area
- Explore different areas for the same perimeter
- Find the area of a parallelogram
- Find the area of a triangle
- Find the volume of a cuboid

Unit 12

I have learnt how to ...

- Understand ratios
- Solve problems about ratios
- Find the scale of a drawing
- Solve proportion problems

Keep up the good work!

Notes